Everyday Mathematics®

The University of Chicago School Mathematics Project

Assessment Handbook

Grade 3

McGraw Hill Education

Chicago, IL • Columbus, OH • New York, NY

The University of Chicago School Mathematics Project (UCSMP)

Max Bell, Director, UCSMP Elementary Materials Component; Director, *Everyday Mathematics* First Edition
James McBride, Director, *Everyday Mathematics* Second Edition
Andy Isaacs, Director, *Everyday Mathematics* Third Edition
Amy Dillard, Associate Director, *Everyday Mathematics* Third Edition
Rachel Malpass McCall, Associate Director, *Everyday Mathematics* Common Core State Standards Edition

Authors

Jean Bell, William M. Carroll, Amy Dillard, Kathleen Pitvorec

Common Core State Standards Edition

Sarah R. Burns, Mary Ellen Dairyko, Rachel Malpass McCall, Cheryl G. Moran, Lila K. Schwartz

Technical Art
Diana Barrie

Teacher in Residence
Soundarya Radhakrishnan

Contributors

Amy Brich, Nina Dordek, Crescencio Toriz, Lindsay Youngblood, Sharon Draznin, Nancy Hanvey, Laurie Leff, Denise Porter, Herb Price, Joyce Timmons, Lisa Winters

Acknowledgments

We gratefully acknowledge the work of the following classroom teachers who provided input
and suggestions as we designed this handbook: Huong Banh, Fran Moore, Jenny Waters, and Lana Winnet.

Photo Credits

Cover (l)Stockdisc/PunchStock/Getty Images, (r bkgd)Tim Flach/Stone+/Getty Images; **Back Cover Spine** Stockdisc/PunchStock/Getty Images.

Permissions

The quotes on pages 4, 5, 8, and 35 are reprinted with permission from *Knowing What Students Know: The Science and Design of Educational Assessment* © 2001 by the National Academy of Sciences, courtesy of the National Academies Press, Washington, D.C.

everyday**math**.com

 Education

Send all inquiries to:
McGraw-Hill Education
STEM Learning Solutions Center
P.O. Box 812960
Chicago, IL 60681

ISBN: 978-0-07-657701-9
MHID: 0-07-657701-5

Printed in the United States of America.

4 5 6 7 8 9 QDB 17 16 15 14 13 12

McGraw-Hill is committed to providing instructional materials
in Science, Technology, Engineering, and Mathematics (STEM)
that give all students a solid foundation, one that prepares them
for college and careers in the 21st century.

The **McGraw-Hill** Companies

Contents

Philosophy of Assessment in *Everyday Mathematics*®

Introduction

Too often, school assessment tends to provide only scattered snapshots of student achievement rather than continuous records of growth. In *Everyday Mathematics,* assessment is like a motion picture, revealing the development of each child's mathematical understanding over time while also giving the teacher useful feedback about the instructional needs of individual children and the class.

For assessment to be useful to teachers, children, parents, and others, the *Everyday Mathematics* authors believe that...

◆ Teachers need to have a variety of assessment tools and techniques to choose from so children can demonstrate what they know in a variety of ways and teachers can have reliable information from multiple sources.

◆ Children should be included in the assessment process. Self assessment and reflection are skills children will develop over time if they are encouraged.

◆ Assessment and instruction should be closely aligned. Assessment should assist teachers in making instructional decisions concerning individual children and the class.

◆ Assessment should focus on all important outcomes, not only on outcomes that are easy to measure.

◆ A good assessment program makes instruction easier.

◆ The best assessment plans are developed by teachers working collaboratively within their schools and districts.

Everyday Mathematics offers many opportunities for assessing children's knowledge and skills. This handbook describes the *Everyday Mathematics* assessment resources and serves as a guide for navigating through those resources and helping you design and implement a balanced classroom assessment plan.

Balanced Assessment

When planning a balanced assessment, begin by asking several basic questions:

◆ *What are the purposes of assessment?*

◆ *What are the contexts for assessment?*

◆ *What are the sources of evidence for assessment?*

◆ *What content is assessed?*

What Are the Purposes of Assessment?

The purposes of assessment serve three main functions: to support learning, to measure achievement, and to evaluate programs. Each purpose is integral to achieving a balanced assessment plan.

Formative assessment supports learning by providing information about children's current knowledge and abilities so you can plan future instruction more effectively. Formative assessment encourages children to identify their areas of weakness or strength so they can focus their efforts more precisely.

Summative assessment measures student growth and achievement. A summative assessment might be designed, for example, to determine whether children have learned certain material by the end of a fixed period of study.

Program evaluation means judging how well a program is working. A school district, for example, may want to identify schools with especially strong mathematics programs so their successes can be replicated in other schools with weaker programs. Program evaluation makes this possible.

Assessment tools and techniques often serve more than one purpose. Assessments built into a curriculum might give teachers information they can use to plan future instruction more effectively or prepare progress reports. District administrators might use this information to allocate professional development resources.

Purposes of Assessment

Formative Assessment	Summative Assessment	Program Evaluation
◆ Used to plan instruction ◆ Helps students to reflect on their progress	◆ Used to measure student growth and achievement ◆ Helps determine if students have learned content	◆ Used to evaluate overall success of the math program

What Are the Contexts for Assessment?

Assessment occurs in a variety of contexts.

- ◆ **Ongoing assessment** involves gathering information from children's everyday work. These assessments can take place at the same time as regular classroom instruction.
- ◆ **Periodic assessment** consists of formal assessments that are built in to a curriculum, such as an end-of-unit Progress Check.
- ◆ **External assessment** is independent of the curriculum. An example of an external assessment is a standardized test.

Everyday Mathematics supports all three contexts for assessment, and it provides tools and materials for ongoing and periodic assessments that you can use to create a balanced assessment plan.

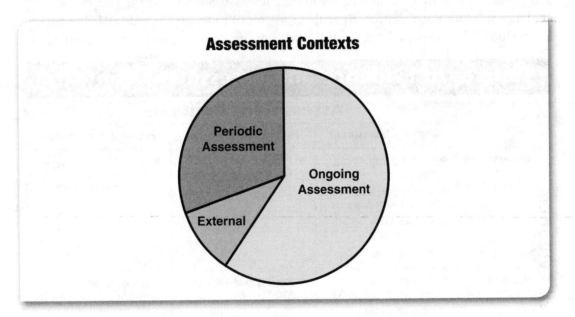

The sizes of the sections of the circle in the figure above are meant to be suggestive, but the exact proportions of ongoing, periodic, and external assessments will vary depending on your grade level, the time of year, state and district mandates, and many other factors.

For all *Everyday Mathematics* assessments, provide children with tools that may be helpful in completing the assessment. Such tools include, but are not limited to, number lines, number grids, scratch paper, base-10 blocks, coins and bills, counters, blank situation diagrams, Pattern Blocks, and Pattern-Block Templates.

What Are the Sources of Evidence for Assessment?

> *Assessment is a process of reasoning from evidence.*
>
> (Pellegrino, Chudowsky, and Glaser 2001, 36)

The evidence for assessing what children know is indirect because we cannot know exactly what they are thinking. Evidence about children's knowledge and capabilities comes from observing children while they are actively engaged and from analyzing the products of their work. Whatever conclusions we may make about children's thinking must be based on **observations** or **products.**

The table below shows the different contexts for assessment and the sources of evidence used for each context. Specific assessment tasks in *Everyday Mathematics* are included. Use this table as a guide in designing your balanced assessment plan.

Sources of Evidence and Assessment Contexts

		Assessment Contexts		
		Ongoing Assessment	**Periodic Assessment**	**External Assessment**
Sources of Evidence	**Observation**	◆ Informing Instruction notes ◆ Recognizing Student Achievement notes for • Mental Math and Reflexes ◆ "Kid watching"	◆ Progress Check Oral/Slate Assessments	◆ Classroom observations by resource teachers or other outside experts
	Product	◆ Recognizing Student Achievement notes for • Journal pages • Exit Slips • Games record sheets • Math Boxes ◆ Writing/Reasoning prompts ◆ Portfolio opportunities	◆ Beginning-of-Year, Mid-Year, and End-of-Year assessments ◆ Progress Check Written Assessments ◆ Student Self Assessments ◆ Open Response problems	◆ Standardized tests mandated by the school district or the state

Each context for assessment (ongoing, periodic, or external) can yield evidence through observations or products.

- ◆ Observing children as they are doing their daily work can provide a great deal of information about their understandings, skills, and dispositions; this kind of ongoing observational assessment may be considered "kid watching."
- ◆ A written assessment that is included as part of a curriculum is an example of a periodic product assessment.
- ◆ A classroom visit by an outside expert who will observe particular children is an example of an external assessment using observational evidence.

What Content Is Assessed?

> *Assessment does not exist in isolation, but must be closely aligned with the goals of curriculum and instruction.*
>
> (Pellegrino, Chudowsky, and Glaser 2001, 36)

In recent years, national organizations and most states have issued detailed sets of learning goals and standards, which provide useful guidance about what content is important to learn and, therefore, important to assess. Aligning assessment, curriculum, and instruction with standards and goals increases coherence in the system and produces better outcomes. To help teachers understand the structure of *Everyday Mathematics* and therefore better understand what to assess, the authors developed Program Goals, which are organized by content strand and carefully articulated across the grades. Below are the six content strands and their related Program Goals.

Everyday Mathematics Program Goals

Number and Numeration
- Understand the meanings, uses, and representations of numbers
- Understand equivalent names for numbers
- Understand common numerical relations

Operations and Computation
- Compute accurately
- Make reasonable estimates
- Understand meanings of operations

Data and Chance
- Select and create appropriate graphical representations of collected or given data
- Analyze and interpret data
- Understand and apply basic concepts of probability

Measurement and Reference Frames
- Understand the systems and processes of measurement; use appropriate techniques, tools, units, and formulas in making measurements
- Use and understand reference frames

Geometry
- Investigate characteristics and properties of two- and three-dimensional geometric shapes
- Apply transformations and symmetry in geometric situations

Patterns, Functions, and Algebra
- Understand patterns and functions
- Use algebraic notation to represent and analyze situations and structures

Program Goals are threads that weave the curriculum together across grades. "Compute accurately," for example, is a Program Goal. Children in *Everyday Mathematics* are expected to compute accurately. The expectations for a student achieving this goal in Grade 2 are obviously different from what is expected from a child in Grade 6. For this reason, the Program Goals are further refined through Grade-Level Goals.

Grade-Level Goals are guideposts along trajectories of learning that span multiple years. They are the big ideas at each grade level; they do not capture all of the content covered. The Grade-Level Goals describe how *Everyday Mathematics* builds mastery over time—first through informal exposure, later through more formal instruction, and finally through application. Because the Grade-Level Goals are cumulative, it is essential for students to experience the complete curriculum at each grade level. The example below shows the development of Grade-Level Goals for models for the operations.

Grade K	Identify join and take-away situations.
Grade 1	Identify change-to-more, change-to-less, comparison, and parts-and-total situations.
Grade 2	Identify and describe change, comparison, and parts-and-total situations; use repeated addition, arrays, and skip counting to model multiplication; use equal sharing and equal grouping to model division.
Grade 3	Recognize and describe change, comparison, and parts-and-total situations; use repeated addition, arrays, and skip counting to model multiplication; use equal sharing and equal grouping to model division.
Grade 4	Use repeated addition, skip counting, arrays, area, and scaling to model multiplication and division.
Grade 5	Use repeated addition, arrays, area, and scaling to model multiplication and division; use ratios expressed as words, fractions, percents, and with colons; solve problems involving ratios of parts of a set to the whole set.
Grade 6	Use ratios and scaling to model size changes and to solve size-change problems; represent ratios as fractions, percents, and decimals, and using a colon; model and solve problems involving part-to-whole and part-to-part ratios; model rate and ratio number stories with proportions; use and explain cross multiplication and other strategies to solve proportions.

All assessment opportunities in *Everyday Mathematics* are linked to specific Grade-Level Goals. The curriculum is designed so that the vast majority of students will reach the Grade-Level Goals for a given grade upon completion of that grade and as a result will be well prepared to succeed in higher levels of mathematics. The complete list of Program Goals and Grade-Level Goals begins on page 37 of this handbook.

Creating a Balanced Assessment Plan

In *Everyday Mathematics,* assessment is primarily designed to help you

◆ learn about children's current knowledge and abilities so you can plan future instruction more effectively—formative assessment; and

◆ measure children's progress toward and achievement of Grade-Level Goals—summative assessment.

Although there is no one right assessment plan for all classrooms, all assessment plans should provide a balance of assessment sources from different contexts. See the chart on page 4 of this handbook for specific assessment tasks in Everyday Mathematics that support the different sources and contexts.

Planning Tips

Do not try to use all the assessment resources at once. Instead, devise a manageable, balanced plan. Choose those tools and techniques that best match your teaching style and your children's needs.

Consider the following guidelines:

◆ Start small.
◆ Incorporate assessment into your daily class routine.
◆ Set up an easy and efficient record-keeping system.
◆ Personalize and adapt the plan as the year progresses.

Your assessment plan should be designed to answer these questions:

◆ How is the class doing?
◆ How are individual children doing?
◆ How do I need to adjust instruction to meet children's needs?
◆ How can I communicate to children, parents, and others about the progress being made?

The following sections of this handbook provide further details about the tools and techniques you can use to develop a balanced assessment plan. Using these tools, you can support children's learning, improve your instruction, measure children's growth and achievement, and make the most of your experience with *Everyday Mathematics.*

Ongoing Assessment

> *No single test score can be considered a definitive measure of a student's competence. Multiple measures enhance the validity and fairness of the inferences drawn by giving students various ways and opportunities to demonstrate their competence.*
>
> (Pellegrino, Chudowsky, and Glaser 2001, 253)

An integral part of a balanced assessment plan involves gathering information from children's everyday work. Opportunities for collecting ongoing assessment in the form of observations and products are highlighted in *Everyday Mathematics* through Informing Instruction and Recognizing Student Achievement notes.

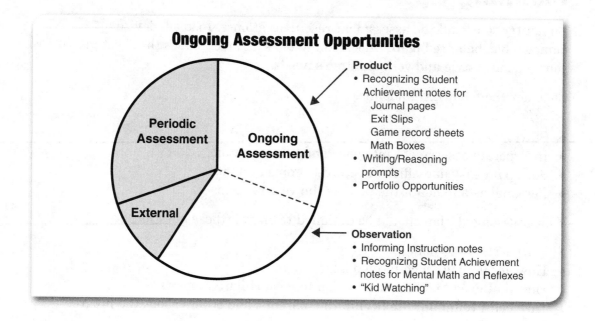

Ongoing Assessment— Informing Instruction

Informing Instruction notes are designed to help you anticipate and recognize common errors and misconceptions in children's thinking and alert you to multiple solution strategies or unique insights that children may offer. These notes suggest how to use observations of children's work to effectively adapt instruction.

 Sample 1 Informing Instruction

 Ongoing Assessment: Informing Instruction

Watch for children who have difficulty remembering the meanings of *perimeter* and *area*. Point out that *perimeter* contains the word *rim*.

 Sample 2 Informing Instruction

 Ongoing Assessment: Informing Instruction

Watch for children who insert the word *and* after *thousand* when reading a whole number. A number like 4,009 should be read as "four thousand nine," not "four thousand and nine." Proper use of *and* is especially important when reading decimals. See Lesson 5-9.

Ongoing Assessment— Recognizing Student Achievement

Each lesson in *Everyday Mathematics* contains a Recognizing Student Achievement note. These notes highlight specific tasks that teachers can use for assessment to monitor children's progress toward Grade-Level Goals.

These tasks include:

◆ Journal pages (written problems—sometimes including explanations)
◆ Mental Math and Reflexes (oral or slate)
◆ Exit Slips (explanations of strategies and understanding)
◆ *Everyday Mathematics* Games (record sheets or follow-up sheets)
◆ Math Boxes (written practice problems)

Each Recognizing Student Achievement note identifies the task to gather information from, the concept or skill to be assessed, and the expectations for a child who is *making adequate progress* toward meeting the specific Grade-Level Goal.

Sample 1 **Recognizing Student Achievement**
Math Journal 1

Ongoing Assessment: Recognizing Student Achievement

Journal page 128 Problem 3

Use journal **page 128, Problem 3** to assess children's progress toward drawing line segments. Children are making adequate progress if they are able to draw at least four line segments for Problem 3. Some children may be able to draw more line segments. Others may be able to complete Problem 4.

[Geometry Goal 1]

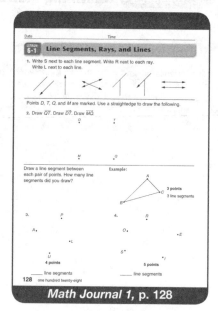

Math Journal 1, p. 128

Sample 2 **Recognizing Student Achievement**
Mental Math and Reflexes

 Ongoing Assessment: Mental Math
Recognizing Student Achievement and Reflexes ★

Use **Mental Math and Reflexes** to assess children's progress toward making ballpark estimates and recording number models.

Children are making adequate progress if they are able to make ballpark estimates and record number models for the ●○○ problems. Some children may be able to complete the ●●○ and ●●● problems.

[Operations and Computation Goal 5]

Mental Math and Reflexes ★

Children make ballpark estimates and record number models on half sheets of paper. *Suggestions:*
Sample answers:

●○○ 99 + 49 100 + 50 = 150   ●●○ 249 − 103 250 − 100 = 150   ●●● 338 + 79 340 + 80 = 420
   76 + 24 75 + 25 = 100   421 − 296 420 − 300 = 120   347 − 258 350 − 260 = 90
   49 − 21 50 − 20 = 30   584 + 121 580 + 120 = 700   537 + 186 540 + 190 = 730

 Sample 3 **Recognizing Student Achievement**
Exit Slip

 Ongoing Assessment: Exit Slip
Recognizing Student Achievement

Use an **Exit Slip** (*Math Masters*, page 398) to assess children's ability to write number models. Children are making adequate progress if they are able to write a number model for this story: *Two alligators each laid a clutch of eggs. One clutch had 60 eggs; the other had 33 eggs. How many eggs were there in all?* Some children might include a unit box or a parts-and-total diagram.

[Patterns, Functions, and Algebra Goal 2]

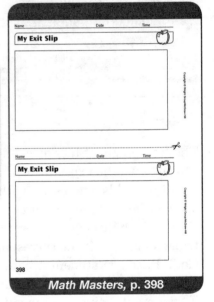

Math Masters, p. 398

Sample 4 **Recognizing Student Achievement**
Game Record Sheet

 Ongoing Assessment:
Recognizing Student Achievement

Math Masters
page 451

Use *Math Masters,* page 451 to assess children's progress toward writing equivalent names for numbers. Children are making adequate progress if they write a number sentence using at least two of the five faceup cards and the target card as the sum or difference. Some children may write number sentences using more than two cards or more than one operation.

[Number and Numeration Goal 4]

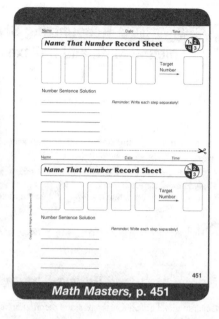

Math Masters, p. 451

 Sample 5 **Recognizing Student Achievement**
Math Boxes

 Ongoing Assessment:
Recognizing Student Achievement

Math Boxes
Problem 3

Use **Math Boxes, Problem 3** to assess children's progress toward writing whole numbers. Children are making adequate progress if they are able to write the numbers that are 10 more and less than the given 3-digit number. Some children may be able to write numbers that are 10 more and less than the given 4- and 5-digit numbers.

[Number and Numeration Goal 1]

3. Write the numbers that are 10 less and 10 more than each given number.

	10 less	10 more
368	_____	_____
789	_____	_____
1,999	_____	_____
40,870	_____	_____

SRB
7, 18, 19

The Recognizing Student Achievement tasks were chosen with the expectation that the majority of children will be successful with them. Children who are *making adequate progress* as defined by a Recognizing Student Achievement task are on a trajectory to meet the corresponding Grade-Level Goal. Based on student progress toward Grade-Level Goals, you may choose to use Readiness activities or Enrichment activities to modify your instructional plan to meet an individual child's needs. See the chart on the next page for how to understand and use the results of the Recognizing Student Achievement tasks.

Using the Results of Recognizing Student Achievement Tasks

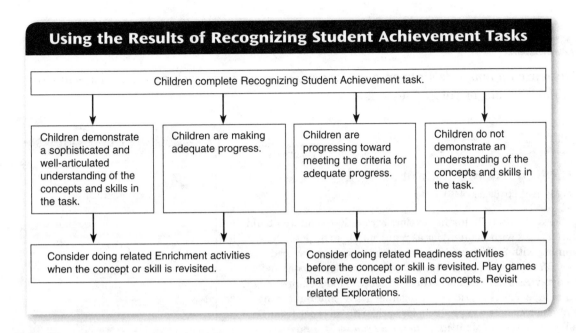

| Children complete Recognizing Student Achievement task. |

Children demonstrate a sophisticated and well-articulated understanding of the concepts and skills in the task.

Children are making adequate progress.

Children are progressing toward meeting the criteria for adequate progress.

Children do not demonstrate an understanding of the concepts and skills in the task.

Consider doing related Enrichment activities when the concept or skill is revisited.

Consider doing related Readiness activities before the concept or skill is revisited. Play games that review related skills and concepts. Revisit related Explorations.

 **Sample** **Recognizing Student Achievement**

The following example illustrates how to implement further Enrichment or Readiness for a given Recognizing Student Achievement task.

Ongoing Assessment:
Recognizing Student Achievement

Journal
Page 81 ★

Use **journal page 81** to assess whether children are making progress toward using arrays and multiples of equal groups to demonstrate the meaning of multiplication. Children are making adequate progress if they are able to draw arrays and find the answer for Problems 1, 2, and 3. Some children may be able to fill in the diagrams and write the number models that match.

[Operations and Computation Goal 6]

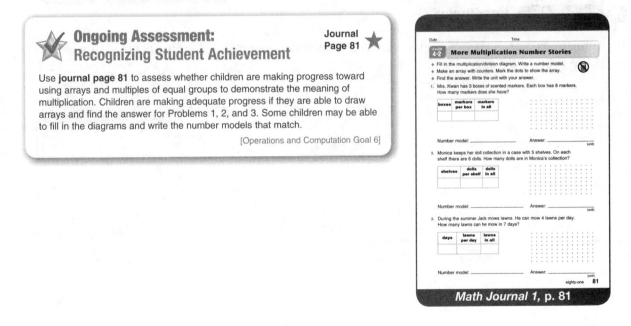

Math Journal 1, p. 81

Sample **Enrichment**

If children are *making adequate progress,* consider using the Enrichment activities in this lesson, if applicable, or related lessons.

ENRICHMENT

SMALL-GROUP ACTIVITY

15–30 Min

▶ **Exploring Square Numbers**
(*Math Masters,* pp. 89 and 416)

Algebraic Thinking To further explore arrays, have children build square arrays with counters for as many numbers as possible, beginning with 2. They record their arrays on centimeter grid paper (*Math Masters,* page 416) and write a number model under each array. As children build arrays for larger products, they might need to tape sheets of grid paper together. Have children arrange the number models and products for each array in order from smallest to largest. Ask: *What patterns do you see?* Sample answer: The differences between consecutive products are odd numbers, and they increase by 2.

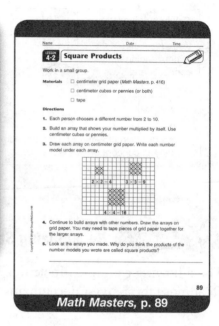

Math Masters, p. 89

 **Sample** **Readiness**

If children are *not making adequate progress,* consider using the Readiness activities before teaching related lessons.

READINESS

INDEPENDENT ACTIVITY

5–15 Min

▶ **Making Equal Groups on a Number Line**
(*Math Masters,* p. 93)

To provide experience with equal-grouping situations using a number-line model, have children solve equal-grouping problems by marking and counting hops on a number line.

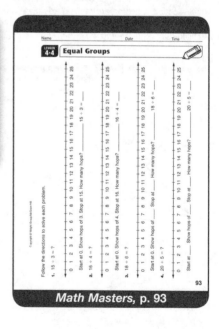

Math Masters, p. 93

Writing/Reasoning Prompts for Math Boxes

Every unit contains suggestions for prompts to use with Math Boxes problems. Use these prompts in a number of ways: (1) Collect children's responses to these prompts on Exit Slips. (2) Request that children keep a math notebook where they record their answers to Math Message problems, Exit Slip prompts, and Writing/Reasoning prompts for Math Boxes problems. (3) Have children record responses on Math Log or Exit Slip masters and then add them to their portfolio collections.

 **Sample 1** Writing/Reasoning Prompt

 Writing/Reasoning Have children write an answer to the following: *Explain your strategy for Problem 4.* Sample answer: I counted up $0.12 from $7.88 to get to $8.00. From $8.00 to $10.00 is $2.00. The change is $2.00 + $0.12 or $2.12.

4. You spent $7.88 at the store. You gave the cashier a $10 bill. How much change should you receive?

_____

 **Sample 2** Writing/Reasoning Prompt

 Writing/Reasoning Have children write an answer to the following: *Explain how you found the length of the fence in Problem 6.* Sample answer: I added all of the sides.

6. How long is the fence around the flowers?

_____ feet

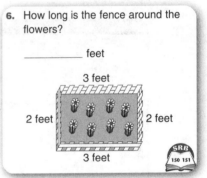

Portfolios

Portfolios are a versatile tool for student assessment. They help children reflect on their mathematical growth and help you understand and document that growth. Portfolios are part of a balanced assessment plan in that they:

◆ emphasize progress over time;

◆ involve students more directly in the assessment process as they participate in selecting work and explaining what the work demonstrates; and

◆ document strengths and weaknesses in a child's mathematical development

is the symbol used to indicate opportunities to collect children's work for portfolios. Several portfolio opportunities are highlighted in each unit but in addition to highlighted opportunities, you and your children can choose from the variety of work in daily lessons to add to children's portfolios.

Consider asking children to write about their selected works. Two optional masters, Good Work! and My Work, are provided for this.

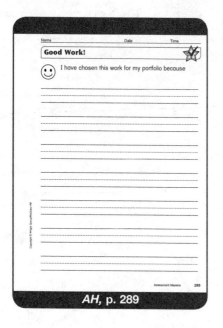

AH, p. 289

AH, p. 290

See pages 283–291 in this book for additional masters that you might ask children to complete periodically and incorporate into their portfolios.
For example:

◆ Math Log A   ◆ About My Math Class A
◆ Math Log B   ◆ About My Math Class B
◆ Math Log C

You may also ask parents to complete a Parent Reflections page (*Assessment Handbook,* page 282) for inclusion in children's portfolios.

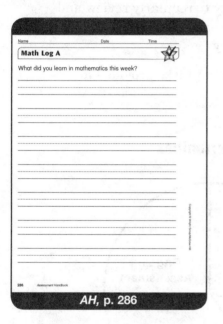

AH, p. 286

AH, p. 288

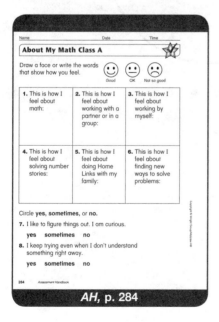

AH, p. 284

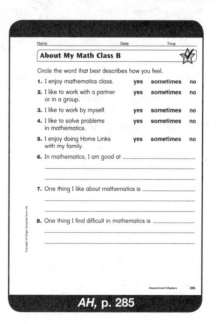

AH, p. 285

Periodic Assessment

Periodic assessments are another key component of a balanced assessment plan. Progress Check lessons and Beginning-of-Year, Mid-Year, and End-of-Year assessments require children to complete a variety of tasks, including short answer questions, open response problems, and reflection questions. These tasks provide you and your children with the opportunity to regularly review and reflect upon their progress—in areas that were recently introduced as well as in areas that involve long-term retention and mastery.

The figure below lists the various periodic assessment tasks provided in *Everyday Mathematics*.

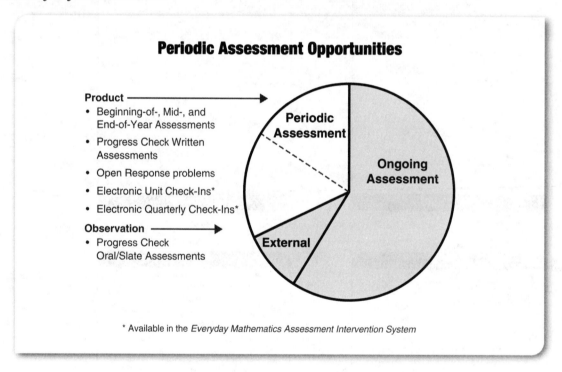

Periodic Assessment Opportunities

Product
- Beginning-of-, Mid-, and End-of-Year Assessments
- Progress Check Written Assessments
- Open Response problems
- Electronic Unit Check-Ins*
- Electronic Quarterly Check-Ins*

Observation
- Progress Check Oral/Slate Assessments

Periodic Assessment

Ongoing Assessment

External

* Available in the *Everyday Mathematics Assessment Intervention System*

Progress Check Written Assessments

Each Progress Check lesson includes a Written Assessment incorporating tasks that address content from lessons in the current and previous units. The Grade-Level Goals addressed in the Written Assessment are listed at the beginning of the lesson. These assessments provide information for evaluating student progress and planning for future instruction.

Written Assessments are one way children demonstrate what they know. Maximize opportunities for children to show the breadth of their knowledge on these assessments by adapting questions as appropriate. Beginning on page 51 in the unit-specific section of this handbook, there are suggested modifications for the Written Assessments that will allow you to tailor questions and get a more accurate picture of what children know.

Experts in assessment distinguish between summative and formative purposes of assessment. Summative assessment measures student growth and achievement so you can determine whether children have learned certain material. Formative assessment provides information about children's current knowledge and abilities so you can plan future instruction more effectively.

Accordingly, all *Everyday Mathematics* Progress Check written assessments include two parts:

◆ Part A is designed for summative purposes. The questions provide teachers with information on how children are progressing toward Grade-Level Goals. The questions can be used in the same way as Recognizing Student Achievement notes. Children *making adequate progress* toward Grade-Level Goals should do fairly well on this section.

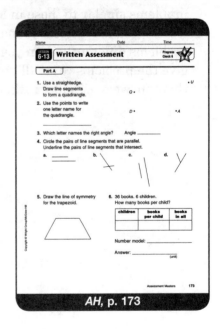

AH, p. 173

◆ Part B is designed for formative purposes. The questions can be used to establish baselines for documenting student growth over time. The questions also assist teachers in their long-term planning in the same way as Informing Instruction notes help teachers in planning lessons.

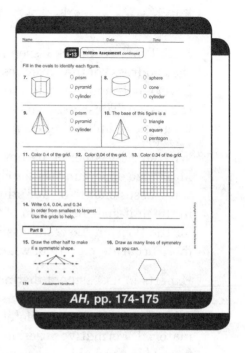

AH, pp. 174–175

Oral and Slate Assessment

Each Progress Check lesson features an Oral and Slate Assessment that includes problems similar to those in Mental Math and Reflexes, which appears in each lesson. You may choose to manage the collection of information from these problems differently than you do with the daily practice. For example, you may give the problems to small groups of children at a time or have children record their answers on paper rather than on slates.

Student Self Assessment

Each Progress Check lesson includes a Self Assessment master that children complete. These Self Assessments are part of a balanced assessment plan as they allow the following:

◆ children to reflect on their progress, strengths, and weaknesses;

◆ teachers to gain insights into how children perceive their progress; and

◆ teachers and children to plan how to address weaknesses.

The Self Assessment engages children in evaluating their competency with the concepts and skills addressed in the unit. For each skill or concept, children check a box to indicate one of the following:

◆ I can do this by myself. I can explain how to do this.

◆ I can do this by myself.

◆ I can do this with help.

If children feel as though they need help or do not understand, consider talking with them about how they may learn more about the concept or skill. Look to related Readiness activities in Part 3 of lessons and to games for ideas about further developing children's understanding.

AH, p. 172

Open Response Tasks

Each Progress Check lesson includes an Open Response task linked to one or more Grade-Level Goals emphasized in the unit. These Open Response assessment tasks can provide additional balance in an assessment plan as they allow children to:

◆ become more aware of their problem-solving processes as they communicate their understanding, for example, through words, pictures, or diagrams;

◆ apply a variety of strategies to solve the longer tasks;

◆ further demonstrate their knowledge and understanding through application of skills and concepts in meaningful contexts; and

◆ be successful on a variety of levels.

AH, p. 176

The Open Response tasks have been selected with the following points in mind:

◆ The problem context makes sense to children.
◆ The skill level of the problem is appropriate for children.
◆ The problem involves mathematics in which children have a foundation.
◆ The mathematics of the problem is important to the grade level. The problem addresses one or more Grade-Level Goals for the grade.
◆ The problem has connections to the real world that children have experience with.
◆ The problem may not be a multistep problem, but the solution strategy involves several steps.
◆ The problem may have more than one correct solution.

In the unit-specific section of this handbook that begins on page 51, each Open Response task has suggested implementation strategies, a sample task-specific rubric, and annotated children's samples demonstrating the expectations described in the rubric. The unit-specific section also includes suggestions for adapting the Open Response task to meet the needs of a diverse group of children.

The sample rubrics are on a 4-point scale. The top two scores (4 points and 3 points) are designated for student work that demonstrates success with the task. The bottom two scores (2 points and 1 point) are designated for student work that does not demonstrate success with the task; 0 points are reserved for situations where children have made no effort to understand or solve the problem.

In general, the sample rubrics focus on assessing the following items:

◆ whether the mathematics children use is correct;
◆ whether the solution strategy makes sense, is reasonable, addresses the problem, and may lead to a successful solution;
◆ whether the explanation of the strategy is clear and easy to follow; and
◆ whether the solution is correct (or correct except for minor errors).

Writing Directions Rubric

4	Uses mathematical language, including Word Box vocabulary, to describe the main components of the figure. Refers to all sides being one inch. Explains the steps clearly and makes connections between the steps. The instructions might need some clarification, but they could result in drawing the figure.
3	Uses mathematical language, including Word Box vocabulary, to describe some main components of the figure. Might refer to all sides being one inch. Explains some steps and makes some connections between the steps. The instructions might need some clarification or steps added, but they make sense in the context of the problem.
2	There is evidence of some understanding of the task. Attempts to use Word Box vocabulary to describe some components of the figure, but there might be no connections between the components. The instructions make some sense in the context of the problem, but there might be errors.
1	Shows little evidence of understanding the task. Might attempt to use Word Box vocabulary to describe some components of the figure, but the instructions might demonstrate conceptual errors.
0	Does not attempt to solve the problem.

You may want to work with other teachers from your grade level to apply the *Everyday Mathematics* rubric to your children's work or to create rubrics for scoring these tasks. Consider the expectations of standardized tests in your area when creating or applying a rubric and modify this sample rubric as appropriate. For more child involvement, consider having children participate in developing a list of expectations for a Level-4 paper.

Beginning-of-Year, Mid-Year, and End-of-Year Assessments

To provide a snapshot of how children are progressing toward a broader range of Grade-Level Goals, the program includes three assessments at each grade level—Beginning-of-Year, Mid-Year, and End-of-Year. These assessments cover important concepts and skills presented throughout the year. The Beginning-of-Year, Mid-Year, and End-of-Year assessments provide additional information that you may wish to include in developing your balanced assessment plan.

In order to be successful with these assessments, some children, especially children in Grades 1 and 2, may benefit from having problems read aloud to them. Consider administering these assessments over two or more days. And, as with all *Everyday Mathematics* assessments, provide children with tools that may be helpful in completing the assessment. In some cases, problems suggest tools that can be used, but in other cases simply having access to manipulatives, such as counters or a number line, is enough to provide children access to the content.

External Assessment

Outside tests, which are one example of external assessment, are generally tests given at the school, district, or state level, or are nationally standardized tests. Most teachers are familiar with the standardized tests that have multiple-choice responses. The frustrating aspect of this type of test is that it analyzes a narrow range of mathematical thinking and does not assess the depth and breadth of the mathematical knowledge that should be attained in a well-implemented *Everyday Mathematics* classroom.

Everyday Mathematics can help your children function more effectively in testing environments. For example, some Math Boxes problems have been tailored to help prepare children for the formats of an outside test. Even without such preparation, *Everyday Mathematics* students generally do just as well on the computation sections of standardized tests. However, they do much better on concepts and problem-solving sections than children in traditional programs.

More recently, some district and state tests have included performance assessments or open-ended components. *Everyday Mathematics* presents varied mathematics tasks that prepare children for these testing situations: problems requiring children to explain their thinking, writing prompts designed to help children explore content more deeply, and richer Open Response tasks that may require an entire class period for children to solve. If you have a choice in your district, encourage the use of these performance-based or open-ended assessments. They better depict the depth of your children's understandings, as well as their abilities to communicate mathematically, solve problems, and reason.

Performance-based assessments developed at the school or district level probably provide the best opportunities to gather information about student achievement in local classrooms. Teams of teachers and administrators can develop assessments and rubrics that enhance the learning process rather than focus on narrow thinking used only in a small portion of mathematical activities. At some grade levels, these assessments can be used exclusively. When standardized testing is mandatory at a certain grade level, performance-based assessments can provide a better picture of the mathematical education occurring in the classroom than other types of standardized tests.

Record Keeping

If you teach *Everyday Mathematics* as intended and use the techniques described in this book, you will soon have a vast amount of information about children's mathematical skills and understanding. This section of the handbook offers several tools to help you organize and record this information.

Class Checklists and Individual Profiles of Progress

Each lesson in *Everyday Mathematics* identifies a suggested ongoing assessment opportunity in the form of a Recognizing Student Achievement note. These notes highlight specific tasks from which teachers can collect student performance data to monitor and document children's progress toward meeting specific Grade-Level Goals. Each unit in *Everyday Mathematics* contains a Progress Check lesson with suggested periodic assessment tasks. A wealth of assessment information can be collected from these and other sources.

To help you keep track of children's progress in areas that are important to your school and district, checklists for individuals and for the class are provided beginning on page 236 of this handbook. There are Class Checklists for each unit and for each quarter. There are Individual Profiles of Progress for each unit. These checklists provide an organizational system for recording the information you collect to assess student progress on Grade-Level Goals.

The unit checklists include places to record information gathered from the Recognizing Student Achievement notes and from the Progress Check lesson in the unit. The checklists identify the related Grade-Level Goal for each Recognizing Student Achievement task. There is an additional column in which you can add your comments or other notes. To simplify data entry, these checklists are organized according to lesson number.

The quarterly checklists include places to record information gathered throughout the quarter from the Recognizing Student Achievement tasks. To simplify the process of aggregating data in meaningful ways, these checklists are organized according to mathematical strand.

You may prefer using the Class Checklists (on the right) to gather and organize information, transferring selected information to the Individual Profiles of Progress sheet for each child's portfolio or for use during parent conferences.

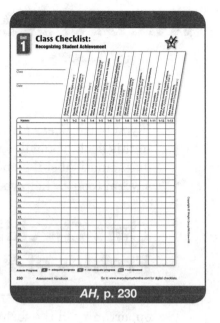

AH, p. 230

Checklist Flow Chart

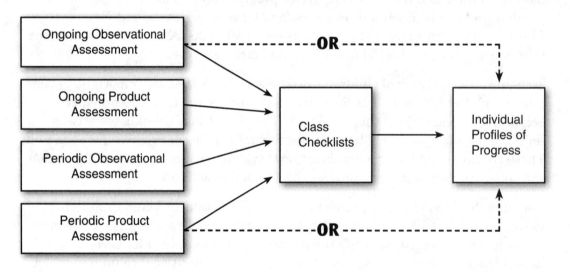

The Individual Profiles of Progress, Class Checklists, and Quarterly Checklists can be found in the *Assessment Masters* beginning on page 228 of this handbook. Blank checklists have been provided as well. Assessment checklists are also available online at www.everydaymathonline.com.

Options for Recording Data on Checklists

There are several different record-keeping schemes for checklists. Two such schemes are described below.

Option 1

Because Recognizing Student Achievement suggestions include descriptions of the expectations for *making adequate progress,* consider recording this information on a checklist using the following:

A	Child is making adequate progress toward Grade-Level Goal.
N	Child is not making adequate progress toward Grade-Level Goal.

or

✓	Child is making adequate progress toward Grade-Level Goal.
–	Child is not making adequate progress toward Grade-Level Goal.

Option 2

As the teacher, you can decide how you define what is *making adequate progress* and what is not. For example, if you use a 4-point rubric like the sample below, you may decide to define 3 or 4 points as *making adequate progress* and 1 or 2 points as *not making adequate progress.*

4 points	Child is making adequate progress. Child solves the problem correctly and demonstrates a sophisticated and well-articulated understanding of the concept or skill being assessed.
3 points	Child is making adequate progress. Child solves the problem correctly with only minor errors and demonstrates a developmentally appropriate understanding of the concept or skill being assessed.
2 points	Child is not making adequate progress. Child appears to understand some components of the problem and attempts to solve the problem. Child demonstrates an understanding of the concept or skill being assessed that is marginally short of what is expected.
1 point	Child is not making adequate progress. Child appears to not understand the problem but makes some attempt to solve it. Child demonstrates an understanding of the concept or skill being assessed that is significantly short of what is expected.
0 points	Child does not attempt to solve the problem.

Assessment Management Spreadsheets

Introduction

The digital *Everyday Mathematics Assessment Management Spreadsheets* are designed to help you track and record information about children's progress towards the *Everyday Mathematics* Grade-Level Goals and the Common Core State Standards. This application contains digital versions of all of the Class Checklists and Individual Profiles of Progress located at the back of this book and can be found at www.everydaymathonline.com.

Everyday Mathematics: Common Core State Standards Edition was designed so the vast majority of children will be successful in mastering the Common Core State Standards and the *Everyday Mathematics* Grade-Level Goals for a given grade upon completion of that grade. Each assessment task provides a snapshot of a child's progress toward the corresponding Grade-Level Goal(s). Taken together, these snapshots form a moving picture that can help you assess whether a child is on a trajectory, or path, to meet the Grade-Level Goal.

Record Keeping

You can use the digital *Everyday Mathematics Assessment Management Spreadsheets* to enter children's performance information for the following assessment types:

◆ Ongoing Assessment: Recognizing Student Achievement
◆ Progress Check: Oral and Slate
◆ Progress Check: Written Assessment Parts A and B
◆ Progress Check: Open Response
◆ Beginning-of-Year Assessment
◆ Mid-Year Assessment
◆ End-of-Year Assessment

You can also easily complement the assessments provided in *Everyday Mathematics* by adding children's performance data from tasks you design or from the many other tasks in the *Everyday Mathematics* curriculum.

Grading Assistance

While grading is not the primary goal of the *Everyday Mathematics Assessment Management Spreadsheets,* the tool can assist you in assigning grades and creating report cards. You can use it to record children's progress on many types of assessment tasks, including those that you create, so your evidence for assessment is based on multiple sources. These records of children's performance, combined with the careful observations you make about your children's work, will help you assign fair and accurate grades.

Using the Digital *Assessment Management Spreadsheets*

The digital *Assessment Management Spreadsheets* include many features for supporting your balanced assessment plan. *For example:*

◆ All the suggested *Everyday Mathematics* assessment tasks are built into the system. Selecting a unit number will bring you to a screen that mirrors the Class Checklist masters, which list all the assessment tasks in a given unit.

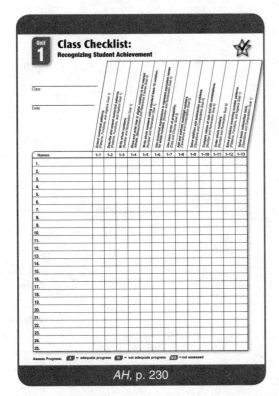

AH, p. 230

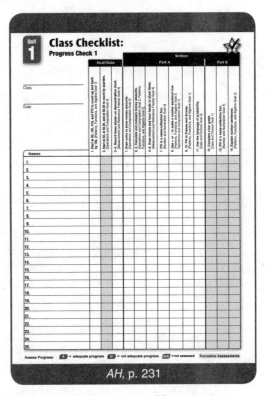

AH, p. 231

Digital versions of these checklists for all units are available through the Assessment Management Spreadsheets, *found at www.everydaymathonline.com.*

◆ A digital version of the Individual Profile of Progress can be automatically generated from the digital class checklists. You can add text comments for individual children on the digital Individual Profile of Progress.

◆ Teacher-created tasks can be added to the digital spreadsheets.

◆ In addition to classifying children's performance as "making adequate progress" or "not making adequate progress," there is a 0- to 4-point (detailed) scoring option. The detailed scoring option can be used for all assessments or just for open-response items. You can determine the level of specificity that best suits your assessment needs.

For assistance with the *Assessment Management Spreadsheets* and specific feature instructions, click the Help link at the top of any screen within the tool.

Frequently Asked Questions

1. **Do the Grade-Level Goals summarize all the concepts and skills that are covered each year?**

   No; Although the Grade-Level Goals reflect the core of the curriculum at each grade level, they are not comprehensive. They do not capture all the content that is addressed each year. Nor are they a list of activities that are completed each year. Some grade-level content supports future Grade-Level Goals that are not articulated at the given grade level.

2. **With all these Grade-Level Goals, how will I know when I'm simply exposing children to a concept or skill?**

   The *Everyday Mathematics* curriculum aims for student proficiency with concepts and skills through repeated exposures over several years. The *Teacher's Lesson Guide* alerts teachers to content that is being introduced for the first time through Links to the Future notes. These notes provide specific references to future Grade-Level Goals and help teachers understand introductory activities at their grade levels in the context of the entire K–6 curriculum.

   All the content in *Everyday Mathematics* is important, whether it's being experienced for the first or the fifth time. The *Everyday Mathematics* curriculum is similar to an intricately woven rug, with many threads that appear and reappear to form complex patterns. Different children will progress at different rates, so multiple exposures to important content are critical for accommodating individual differences. The program was created so it is consistent with how children learn mathematics. It builds understanding over a period of time, first through informal exposure and later through more formal and directed instruction. For children to succeed, they need the opportunity to experience all that the curriculum has to offer in every grade.

3. **There are a lot of lessons in my grade-level materials. Do I have to finish all of them? For example, I teach second grade. Automaticity with multiplication facts is not a Grade-Level Goal until third grade. Can't I just skip all of the second-grade lessons that cover multiplication facts?**

Everyday Mathematics was created to be consistent with how children actually learn mathematics, building understanding over time, first through informal exposure and later through more formal instruction. Because the Grade-Level Goals are cumulative, it is essential for children to experience the complete curriculum at each grade level. Children in *Second Grade Everyday Mathematics,* for example, participate in many hands-on activities designed to develop an understanding of multiplication. This makes it possible for children to achieve multiplication goals in third grade.

4. **Do I need to keep track of progress on Program Goals?**

Program Goals are the threads that weave the content together across grade levels and form the skeleton of the curriculum. The Program Goals are further refined through the Grade-Level Goals. *Everyday Mathematics* provides a variety of tools you can use to assess student progress on the Grade-Level Goals throughout the year. Because every Grade-Level Goal is related to a Program Goal, you are gathering information at this less-specific level as well. This allows great flexibility in reporting to parents. Depending on how your district requires you to aggregate data, you can look broadly at strands, more closely at Program Goals, or specifically at Grade-Level Goals using the suggested assessments in *Everyday Mathematics.*

5. **What do the authors mean by "adequate progress"?**

Children who are making adequate progress as defined by a Recognizing Student Achievement note are on a trajectory to meet the Grade-Level Goal. Such children have successfully accomplished what is expected up to that point in the curriculum. If children continue to progress as expected, then they will demonstrate proficiency with the Grade-Level Goal upon completion of the year.

The performance expectations described in the Recognizing Student Achievement notes for any given Grade-Level Goal progress developmentally throughout the year. The level of performance that is expected in October is not the same as what is expected in April. The term *adequate progress* describes the level of competency that the majority of children can be expected to have at a particular time. The authors of *Everyday Mathematics* chose the Recognizing Student Achievement tasks with the expectation that the majority of children would be successful with them, which is in line with the expectation that the vast majority of children will successfully reach the Grade-Level Goals for their grade level.

6. **Do children have to complete all the Recognizing Student Achievement tasks before I can know whether they are making adequate progress?**

Each lesson in *Everyday Mathematics* contains a Recognizing Student Achievement note. These notes highlight specific tasks from which teachers can collect student performance data to monitor and document children's progress toward meeting specific Grade-Level Goals. Each Recognizing Student Achievement note addresses part of a Grade-Level Goal. The suggested assessment tasks build a complete picture over time for each Grade-Level Goal. If children perform well on one or two Recognizing Student Achievement tasks for a goal, that may not provide enough information about the goal in its entirety. Teachers are the experts in their classrooms. If you choose to not do some of the Recognizing Student Achievement tasks, consider collecting similar information from tasks you designate to assemble a complete picture for each Grade-Level Goal.

7. **Can I use only Math Boxes to collect assessment information? They seem to have all the skills in them.**

Everyday Mathematics includes a variety of assessment tasks to ensure that all children have sufficient opportunities to demonstrate what they know. Some children best demonstrate their knowledge through pencil-and-paper tasks, some through performance tasks, and some through explanations and demonstrations. The assessment tasks in the program have been chosen to accommodate a range of learners. Using only one tool might limit what you are able to learn about your children.

8. **I understand that *Everyday Mathematics* provides a Recognizing Student Achievement task for every lesson. May I choose my own instead of or in addition to the ones designated by the curriculum? If I don't think the results of a particular Recognizing Student Achievement task accurately reflect what a child knows, what should I do?**

The Recognizing Student Achievement tasks and Progress Check questions occur at carefully chosen points, based on the opportunities for distributed practice that occur throughout the program. Assessment tasks were also designed to vary the ways in which children are assessed for each Grade-Level Goal.

The *Everyday Mathematics* authors respect teachers as professionals and expect that teachers will use their professional judgment when assessing children. If a particular Recognizing Student Achievement task does not adequately assess student achievement, the teacher may choose to disregard it. The *Everyday Mathematics* authors also anticipate that children's performances on tasks that are not identified in Recognizing Student Achievement notes will often provide useful information regarding their progress toward a particular Grade-Level Goal. Teachers should feel free to link such tasks to appropriate Grade-Level Goals and include them in their assessment stories.

9. **I understand the different record-keeping options that were presented in this handbook. My district, however, evaluates children by assigning traditional letter grades. How should I evaluate student performance?**

Because local assessment systems are based on local norms and values, it would be impossible to design a system that would apply universally. But the authors of *Everyday Mathematics* recognize that many teachers are required by their districts to give traditional grades. And although it is impossible to design a single grading system that will work for everyone, there are some broad principles to follow:

◆ Grades should be fair and based on evidence that can be documented.
◆ Evidence for grading should come from multiple sources.
◆ Grades should be based on content that is important. They should not be based only on the content that is most easily assessed.
◆ The grading system should be aligned with both state and local standards and with the curriculum.

10. **Suppose a child makes adequate progress on the majority of Recognizing Student Achievement tasks and Progress Check questions for a given Grade-Level Goal throughout the year. At the end of the year how likely is it that the child will have achieved the Grade-Level Goal?**

The Recognizing Student Achievement and Progress Check tasks supply a great deal of data on which teachers can base inferences about children's achievement of Grade-Level Goals. In the case of a consistent pattern of adequate progress on assessment tasks for a given Grade-Level Goal, one can reasonably conclude that the child has in fact achieved the given goal. As with any assessment, however, inferences based on positive performance are more straightforward than those based on negative performance. That is, if a child performs well, the most straightforward conclusion is that the child has probably mastered the material; whereas if a child performs poorly, there are many possible explanations, only one of which is a lack of mastery.

Teachers should also recognize that inferences about what children know should always be considered provisional because the inferences are fallible, based as they are on incomplete information, and because children are constantly growing and changing.

According to *Knowing What Students Know*:

> *... by its very nature, assessment is imprecise to some degree. Assessment results are estimates, based on samples of knowledge and performance drawn from the much larger universe of everything a person knows and can do.... Assessment is a process of reasoning from evidence. Because one cannot directly perceive students' mental processes, one must rely on less direct methods to make judgments about what they know.*
>
> (Pellegrino, Chudowsky, and Glaser 2001, 36)
>
> *An assessment is a tool designed to observe students' behavior and produce data that can be used to draw reasonable inferences about what students know.*
>
> (Pellegrino, Chudowsky, and Glaser 2001, 42)

11. What about a child who normally performs well in class but does poorly on the electronic Quarterly Check-Ins?

Electronic Quarterly Check-Ins are just one piece of the *Everyday Mathematics* assessment story; they are not meant to stand alone and do not provide a complete picture of a child's progress towards any one goal. Because they can be administered and scored electronically, they provide teachers wth some relatively easy data collection. However, because the Quarterly Check-Ins were written in multiple-choice format, they are limited in the information they can provide about what a child knows.

The pencil-and-paper Mid-Year and End-of-Year Assessments are the "best" assessments we offer in *Everyday Mathematics*. They are more comprehensive in their coverage of what children should be responsible for knowing at the time they are given. Children are able to show what they know in a variety of ways, and teachers can gather more information about a child by reviewing the work produced during one of these assessments.

We recommend that teachers administer all electronic and paper-and-pencil assessments. However, teachers worried about over-testing may choose to skip the review portion of the Quarter 2 Check-In, as the questions related to those goals are assessed in a more comprehensive manner on the Mid-Year Assessment.

Recommended Reading

Black, Paul, and Dylan Wiliam. "Assessment and Classroom Learning." *Assessment in Education* (March, 1998): 7–74.

———. "Inside the Black Box: Raising Standards Through Classroom Assessment." *Phi Delta Kappan* 80, no. 2 (October, 1998): 139–149.

Bryant, Brian R., and Teddy Maddox. "Using Alternative Assessment Techniques to Plan and Evaluate Mathematics." *LD Forum 21,* no. 2 (winter, 1996): 24–33.

Eisner, Elliot W. "The Uses and Limits of Performance Assessment." *Phi Delta Kappan* 80, no. 9 (May, 1999): 658–661.

Kulm, Gerald. *Mathematics Assessment: What Works in the Classroom.* San Francisco: Jossey-Bass Publishers, 1994.

National Council of Teachers of Mathematics (NCTM). *Curriculum and Evaluation Standards for School Mathematics.* Reston, Va.: NCTM, 1989.

———. *Assessment Standards for School Mathematics.* Reston, Va.: NCTM, 1995.

———. *Principles and Standards for School Mathematics.* Reston, Va.: NCTM, 2000.

National Research Council. Committee on the Foundations of Assessment. Pellegrino, James W., Naomi Chudowsky, and Robert Glaser, eds. *Knowing What Students Know: The Science and Design of Educational Assessment.* Washington, D.C.: National Academy Press, 2001.

National Research Council, Mathematical Sciences Education Board. *Measuring What Counts: A Conceptual Guide for Mathematics Assessment.* Washington, D.C.: National Academy Press, 1993.

Pearson, Bethyl, and Cathy Berghoff. "London Bridge Is Not Falling Down: It's Supporting Alternative Assessment." *TESOL Journal* 5, no. 4 (summer, 1996): 28–31.

Shepard, Lorrie A. "Using Assessment to Improve Learning." *Educational Leadership* 52, no. 5 (February, 1995): 38–43.

Stenmark, Jean Kerr, ed. *Mathematics Assessment: Myths, Models, Good Questions, and Practical Suggestions.* Reston, Va.: National Council of Teachers of Mathematics, 1991.

Stiggens, Richard J. *Student-Centered Classroom Assessment.* Englewood Cliffs, N.J.: Prentice-Hall, 1997.

Webb, N. L., and A. F. Coxford, eds. *Assessment in the Mathematics Classroom: 1993 Yearbook.* Reston, Va.: National Council of Teachers of Mathematics, 1993.

http://everydaymath.uchicago.edu/

Everyday Mathematics GOALS

The following tables list the Grade-Level Goals organized by Content Strand and Program Goal.

Everyday Mathematics®

Content Strand: NUMBER AND NUMERATION

Program Goal: Understand the Meanings, Uses, and Representations of Numbers

Content	Kindergarten	First Grade	Second Grade	Third Grade	Fourth Grade	Fifth Grade	Sixth Grade
Rote counting	**Goal 1.** Count on by 1s to 100; count on by 2s, 5s, and 10s and count back by 1s with number grids, number lines, and calculators.	**Goal 1.** Count on by 1s, 2s, 5s, and 10s past 100 and count back by 1s from any number less than 100 with and without number grids, number lines, and calculators.	**Goal 1.** Count on by 1s, 2s, 5s, 10s, 25s, and 100s past 1,000 and back by 1s, 10s, and 100s from any number less than 1,000 with and without number grids, number lines, and calculators.				
Rational counting	**Goal 2.** Count 20 or more objects; estimate the number of objects in a collection.	**Goal 2.** Count collections of objects accurately and reliably; estimate the number of objects in a collection.					
Place value and notation	**Goal 3.** Model numbers with manipulatives; use manipulatives to exchange 1s for 10s and 10s for 100s; recognize that digits can be used and combined to read and write numbers; read numbers up to 30.	**Goal 3.** Read, write, and model with manipulatives whole numbers up to 1,000; identify places in such numbers and the values of the digits in those places.	**Goal 2.** Read, write, and model with manipulatives whole numbers up to 10,000; identify places in such numbers and the values of the digits in those places; read and write money amounts in dollars-and-cents notation.	**Goal 1.** Read and write whole numbers up to 1,000,000; read, write, and model with manipulatives decimals through hundredths; identify places in such numbers and the values of the digits in those places; translate between whole numbers and decimals represented in words, in base-10 notation, and with manipulatives.	**Goal 1.** Read and write whole numbers up to 1,000,000,000 and decimals through thousandths; identify places in such numbers and the values of the digits in those places; translate between whole numbers and decimals represented in words and in base-10 notation.	**Goal 1.** Read and write whole numbers and decimals; identify places in such numbers and the values of the digits in those places; use expanded notation to represent whole numbers and decimals.	**Goal 1.** Read and write whole numbers and decimals; identify places in such numbers and the values of the digits in those places; use expanded notation, number-and-word notation, exponential notation, and scientific notation to represent whole numbers and decimals.

Everyday Mathematics

Content Strand: NUMBER AND NUMERATION *cont.*

Program Goal: Understand the Meanings, Uses, and Representations of Numbers *cont.*

Content	Kindergarten	First Grade	Second Grade	Third Grade	Fourth Grade	Fifth Grade	Sixth Grade
Meanings and uses of fractions	**Goal 4.** Use manipulatives to model half of a region or a collection; describe the model.	**Goal 4.** Use manipulatives and drawings to model halves, thirds, and fourths as equal parts of a region or a collection; describe the model.	**Goal 3.** Use manipulatives and drawings to model fractions as equal parts of a region or a collection; describe the models and name the fractions.	**Goal 2.** Read, write, and model fractions; solve problems involving fractional parts of a region or a collection; describe strategies used.	**Goal 2.** Read, write, and model fractions; solve problems involving fractional parts of a region or a collection; describe and explain strategies used; given a fractional part of a region or a collection, identify the unit whole.	**Goal 2.** Solve problems involving percents and discounts; describe and explain strategies used; identify the unit whole in situations involving fractions.	**Goal 2.** Solve problems involving percents and discounts; explain strategies used; identify the unit whole in situations involving fractions, decimals, and percents.
Number theory		**Goal 5.** Use manipulatives to identify and model odd and even numbers.	**Goal 4.** Recognize numbers as odd or even.	**Goal 3.** Find multiples of 2, 5, and 10.	**Goal 3.** Find multiples of whole numbers less than 10; identify prime and composite numbers; find whole-number factors of numbers.	**Goal 3.** Identify prime and composite numbers; factor numbers; find prime factorizations.	**Goal 3.** Use GCFs, LCMs, and divisibility rules to manipulate fractions.

Program Goal: Understand Equivalent Names for Numbers

Content	Kindergarten	First Grade	Second Grade	Third Grade	Fourth Grade	Fifth Grade	Sixth Grade
Equivalent names for whole numbers	**Goal 5.** Use manipulatives, drawings, and numerical expressions involving addition and subtraction of 1-digit numbers to give equivalent names for whole numbers up to 20.	**Goal 6.** Use manipulatives, drawings, tally marks, and numerical expressions involving addition and subtraction of 1- or 2-digit numbers to give equivalent names for whole numbers up to 100.	**Goal 5.** Use tally marks, arrays, and numerical expressions involving addition and subtraction to give equivalent names for whole numbers.	**Goal 4.** Use numerical expressions involving one or more of the basic four arithmetic operations to give equivalent names for whole numbers.	**Goal 4.** Use numerical expressions involving one or more of the basic four arithmetic operations and grouping symbols to give equivalent names for whole numbers.	**Goal 4.** Use numerical expressions involving one or more of the basic four arithmetic operations, grouping symbols, and exponents to give equivalent names for whole numbers; convert between base-10, exponential, and repeated-factor notations.	**Goal 4.** Apply the order of operations to numerical expressions to give equivalent names for rational numbers.

Everyday Mathematics

Content Strand: NUMBER AND NUMERATION *cont.*

Program Goal: Understand Equivalent Names for Numbers *cont.*

Content	Kindergarten	First Grade	Second Grade	Third Grade	Fourth Grade	Fifth Grade	Sixth Grade
Equivalent names for fractions, decimals, and percents			**Goal 6.** Use manipulatives and drawings to model equivalent names for $\frac{1}{2}$.	**Goal 5.** Use manipulatives and drawings to find and represent equivalent names for fractions; use manipulatives to generate equivalent fractions.	**Goal 5.** Use numerical expressions to find and represent equivalent names for fractions and decimals; use and explain a multiplication rule to find equivalent fractions; rename fourths, fifths, tenths, and hundredths as decimals and percents.	**Goal 5.** Use numerical expressions to find and represent equivalent names for fractions, decimals, and percents; use and explain multiplication and division rules to find equivalent fractions and fractions in simplest form; convert between fractions and mixed numbers; convert between fractions, decimals, and percents.	**Goal 5.** Find equivalent fractions and fractions in simplest form by applying multiplication and division rules and concepts from number theory; convert between fractions, mixed numbers, decimals, and percents.

Program Goal: Understand Common Numerical Relations

Content	Kindergarten	First Grade	Second Grade	Third Grade	Fourth Grade	Fifth Grade	Sixth Grade
Comparing and ordering numbers	**Goal 6.** Compare and order whole numbers up to 20.	**Goal 7.** Compare and order whole numbers up to 1,000.	**Goal 7.** Compare and order whole numbers up to 10,000; use area models to compare fractions.	**Goal 6.** Compare and order whole numbers up to 1,000,000; use manipulatives to order decimals through hundredths; use area models and benchmark fractions to compare and order fractions.	**Goal 6.** Compare and order whole numbers up to 1,000,000,000 and decimals through thousandths; compare and order integers between −100 and 0; use area models, benchmark fractions, and analyses of numerators and denominators to compare and order fractions.	**Goal 6.** Compare and order rational numbers; use area models, benchmark fractions, and analyses of numerators and denominators to compare and order fractions and mixed numbers; describe strategies used to compare fractions and mixed numbers.	**Goal 6.** Choose and apply strategies for comparing and ordering rational numbers; explain those choices and strategies.

Everyday Mathematics

Content Strand: OPERATIONS AND COMPUTATION

Program Goal: Compute Accurately

Content	Kindergarten	First Grade	Second Grade	Third Grade	Fourth Grade	Fifth Grade	Sixth Grade
Addition and subtraction facts	**Goal 1.** Use manipulatives, number lines, and mental arithmetic to solve problems involving the addition and subtraction of single-digit whole numbers; demonstrate appropriate fluency with addition and subtraction facts within 5.	**Goal 1.** Demonstrate appropriate fluency with addition and subtraction facts through 10 + 10.	**Goal 1.** Demonstrate automaticity with all addition facts through 10 + 10 and fluency with the related subtraction facts.	**Goal 1.** Demonstrate automaticity with all addition and subtraction facts through 10 + 10; use basic facts to compute fact extensions such as 80 + 70.	**Goal 1.** Demonstrate automaticity with addition and subtraction fact extensions.		
Addition and subtraction procedures		**Goal 2.** Use manipulatives, number grids, tally marks, mental arithmetic, and calculators to solve problems involving the addition and subtraction of 1-digit whole numbers with 2-digit whole numbers; calculate and compare the values of combinations of coins.	**Goal 2.** Use manipulatives, number grids, tally marks, mental arithmetic, paper & pencil, and calculators to solve problems involving the addition and subtraction of multidigit whole numbers; describe the strategies used; calculate and compare values of coin and bill combinations.	**Goal 2.** Use manipulatives, mental arithmetic, paper-and-pencil algorithms and models, and calculators to solve problems involving the addition and subtraction of whole numbers and decimals in a money context; describe the strategies used and explain how they work.	**Goal 2.** Use manipulatives, mental arithmetic, paper-and-pencil algorithms and models, and calculators to solve problems involving the addition and subtraction of whole numbers and decimals through hundredths; describe the strategies used and explain how they work.	**Goal 1.** Use manipulatives, mental arithmetic, paper-and-pencil algorithms and models, and calculators to solve problems involving the addition and subtraction of whole numbers, decimals, and signed numbers; describe the strategies used and explain how they work.	**Goal 1.** Use mental arithmetic, paper-and-pencil algorithms and models, and calculators to solve problems involving the addition and subtraction of whole numbers, decimals, and signed numbers; describe the strategies used and explain how they work.

Everyday Mathematics

Program Goal: Compute Accurately *cont.*

Content	Kindergarten	First Grade	Second Grade	Third Grade	Fourth Grade	Fifth Grade	Sixth Grade
Multiplication and division facts				**Goal 3.** Demonstrate automaticity with multiplication facts through 10 × 10.	**Goal 3.** Demonstrate automaticity with multiplication facts through 10 * 10 and proficiency with related division facts; use basic facts to compute fact extensions such as 30 * 60.	**Goal 2.** Demonstrate automaticity with multiplication and division fact extensions.	
Multiplication and division procedures				**Goal 4.** Use arrays, mental arithmetic, paper-and-pencil algorithms and models, and calculators to solve problems involving the multiplication of 2- and 3-digit whole numbers by 1-digit whole numbers; describe the strategies used.	**Goal 4.** Use manipulatives, mental arithmetic, paper-and-pencil algorithms and models, and calculators to solve problems involving the multiplication of multidigit whole numbers by 2-digit whole numbers and the division of multidigit whole numbers by 1-digit whole numbers; describe the strategies used and explain how they work.	**Goal 3.** Use manipulatives, mental arithmetic, paper-and-pencil algorithms and models, and calculators to solve problems involving the multiplication of whole numbers and decimals and the division of multidigit whole numbers and decimals by whole numbers; express remainders as whole numbers or fractions as appropriate; describe the strategies used and explain how they work.	**Goal 2.** Use mental arithmetic, paper-and-pencil algorithms and models, and calculators to solve problems involving the multiplication and division of whole numbers, decimals, and signed numbers; describe the strategies used and explain how they work.

Everyday Mathematics

Content Strand: OPERATIONS AND COMPUTATION *cont.*

Program Goal: Compute Accurately *cont.*

Content	Kindergarten	First Grade	Second Grade	Third Grade	Fourth Grade	Fifth Grade	Sixth Grade
Procedures for addition and subtraction of fractions					**Goal 5.** Use manipulatives, mental arithmetic, and calculators to solve problems involving the addition and subtraction of fractions and mixed numbers; describe the strategies used.	**Goal 4.** Use mental arithmetic, paper-and-pencil algorithms and models, and calculators to solve problems involving the addition and subtraction of fractions and mixed numbers; describe the strategies used and explain how they work.	**Goal 3.** Use mental arithmetic, paper-and-pencil algorithms and models, and calculators to solve problems involving the addition and subtraction of fractions and mixed numbers; describe the strategies used and explain how they work.
Procedures for multiplication and division of fractions						**Goal 5.** Use area models, mental arithmetic, paper-and-pencil algorithms and models, and calculators to solve problems involving the multiplication of fractions and mixed numbers; use visual models, paper-and-pencil methods, and calculators to solve problems involving the division of fractions; describe the strategies used.	**Goal 4.** Use mental arithmetic, paper-and-pencil algorithms and models, and calculators to solve problems involving the multiplication and division of fractions and mixed numbers; describe the strategies used and explain how they work.

Everyday Mathematics

Content Strand: OPERATIONS AND COMPUTATION *cont.*

Program Goal: Make Reasonable Estimates

Content	Kindergarten	First Grade	Second Grade	Third Grade	Fourth Grade	Fifth Grade	Sixth Grade
Computational estimation		**Goal 3.** Estimate reasonableness of answers to basic fact problems (e.g., Will 7 + 8 be more or less than 10?).	**Goal 3.** Make reasonable estimates for whole number addition and subtraction problems; explain how the estimates were obtained.	**Goal 5.** Make reasonable estimates for whole number addition, subtraction, multiplication, and division problems; explain how the estimates were obtained.	**Goal 6.** Make reasonable estimates for whole number and decimal addition and subtraction problems and whole number multiplication and division problems; explain how the estimates were obtained.	**Goal 6.** Make reasonable estimates for whole number and decimal addition, subtraction, multiplication, and division problems and fraction and mixed number addition and subtraction problems; explain how the estimates were obtained.	**Goal 5.** Make reasonable estimates for whole number, decimal, fraction, and mixed number addition, subtraction, multiplication, and division problems; explain how the estimates were obtained.

Program Goal: Understand Meanings of Operations

Content	Kindergarten	First Grade	Second Grade	Third Grade	Fourth Grade	Fifth Grade	Sixth Grade
Models for the operations	**Goal 2.** Identify join and take-away situations.	**Goal 4.** Identify change-to-more, change-to-less, comparison, and parts-and-total situations.	**Goal 4.** Identify and describe change, comparison, and parts-and-total situations; use repeated addition, arrays, and skip counting to model multiplication; use equal sharing and equal grouping to model division.	**Goal 6.** Recognize and describe change, comparison, and parts-and-total situations; use repeated addition, arrays, and skip counting to model multiplication; use equal sharing and equal grouping to model division.	**Goal 7.** Use repeated addition, skip counting, arrays, area, and scaling to model multiplication and division.	**Goal 7.** Use repeated addition, arrays, area, and scaling to model multiplication and division; use ratios expressed as words, fractions, percents, and with colons; solve problems involving ratios of parts of a set to the whole set.	**Goal 6.** Use ratios and scaling to model size changes and to solve size-change problems; represent ratios as fractions, percents, and decimals, and using a colon; model and solve problems involving part-to-whole and part-to-part ratios; model rate and ratio number stories with proportions; use and explain cross multiplication and other strategies to solve proportions.

Everyday Mathematics

Content Strand: DATA AND CHANCE

Program Goal: Select and Create Appropriate Graphical Representations of Collected or Given Data

Content	Kindergarten	First Grade	Second Grade	Third Grade	Fourth Grade	Fifth Grade	Sixth Grade
Data collection and representation	**Goal 1.** Collect and organize data to create class-constructed tally charts, tables, and bar graphs.	**Goal 1.** Collect and organize data to create tally charts, tables, bar graphs, and line plots.	**Goal 1.** Collect and organize data or use given data to create tally charts, tables, graphs, and line plots.	**Goal 1.** Collect and organize data or use given data to create charts, tables, graphs, and line plots.	**Goal 1.** Collect and organize data or use given data to create charts, tables, graphs, and line plots.	**Goal 1.** Collect and organize data or use given data to create graphic displays with reasonable titles, labels, keys, and intervals.	**Goal 1.** Collect and organize data or use given data to create graphic displays with reasonable titles, labels, keys, and intervals.

Program Goal: Analyze and Interpret Data

Content	Kindergarten	First Grade	Second Grade	Third Grade	Fourth Grade	Fifth Grade	Sixth Grade
Data analysis	**Goal 2.** Use graphs to answer simple questions.	**Goal 2.** Use graphs to answer simple questions and draw conclusions; find the maximum and minimum of a data set.	**Goal 2.** Use graphs to ask and answer simple questions and draw conclusions; find the maximum, minimum, mode, and median of a data set.	**Goal 2.** Use graphs to ask and answer simple questions and draw conclusions; find the maximum, minimum, range, mode, and median of a data set.	**Goal 2.** Use the maximum, minimum, range, median, mode, and graphs to ask and answer questions, draw conclusions, and make predictions.	**Goal 2.** Use the maximum, minimum, range, median, mode, and mean and graphs to ask and answer questions, draw conclusions, and make predictions.	**Goal 2.** Use data landmarks, measures of spread, and graphs to ask and answer questions, draw conclusions, and make predictions; compare and contrast the median and mean of a data set.

Program Goal: Understand and Apply Basic Concepts of Probability

Content	Kindergarten	First Grade	Second Grade	Third Grade	Fourth Grade	Fifth Grade	Sixth Grade
Qualitative probability	**Goal 3.** Describe events using *certain, possible, impossible,* and other basic probability terms.	**Goal 3.** Describe events using *certain, likely, unlikely, impossible,* and other basic probability terms.	**Goal 3.** Describe events using *certain, likely, unlikely, impossible,* and other basic probability terms; explain the choice of language.	**Goal 3.** Describe events using *certain, very likely, likely, unlikely, very unlikely, impossible,* and other basic probability terms; explain the choice of language.	**Goal 3.** Describe events using *certain, very likely, likely, unlikely, very unlikely, impossible,* and other basic probability terms; use *more likely, equally likely, same chance, 50–50, less likely,* and other basic probability terms to compare events; explain the choice of language.	**Goal 3.** Describe events using *certain, very likely, likely, unlikely, very unlikely, impossible,* and other basic probability terms; use *more likely, equally likely, same chance, 50–50, less likely,* and other basic probability terms to compare events; explain the choice of language.	

Everyday Mathematics

Content Strand: DATA AND CHANCE *cont.*

Program Goal: Understand and Apply Basic Concepts of Probability *cont.*

Content	Kindergarten	First Grade	Second Grade	Third Grade	Fourth Grade	Fifth Grade	Sixth Grade
Quantitative probability				**Goal 4.** Predict the outcomes of simple experiments and test the predictions using manipulatives; express the probability of an event by using "___ out of ___" language.	**Goal 4.** Predict the outcomes of experiments and test the predictions using manipulatives; summarize the results and use them to predict future events; express the probability of an event as a fraction.	**Goal 4.** Predict the outcomes of experiments, test the predictions using manipulatives, and summarize the results; compare predictions based on theoretical probability with experimental results; use summaries and comparisons to predict future events; express the probability of an event as a fraction, decimal, or percent.	**Goal 3.** Use the Multiplication Counting Principle, tree diagrams, and other counting strategies to identify all possible outcomes for a situation; predict results of experiments, test the predictions using manipulatives, and summarize the findings; compare predictions based on theoretical probability with experimental results; calculate probabilities and express them as fractions, decimals, and percents; explain how sample size affects results; use the results to predict future events.

Everyday Mathematics

Content Strand: MEASUREMENT AND REFERENCE FRAMES

Program Goal: Understand the Systems and Processes of Measurement; Use Appropriate Techniques, Tools, Units, and Formulas in Making Measurements

Content	Kindergarten	First Grade	Second Grade	Third Grade	Fourth Grade	Fifth Grade	Sixth Grade
Length, weight, and angles	**Goal 1.** Use nonstandard tools and techniques to estimate and compare weight and length; identify standard measuring tools.	**Goal 1.** Use nonstandard tools and techniques to estimate and compare weight and length; measure length with standard measuring tools.	**Goal 1.** Estimate length with and without tools; measure length to the nearest inch and centimeter; use standard and nonstandard tools to measure and estimate weight.	**Goal 1.** Estimate length with and without tools; measure length to the nearest $\frac{1}{2}$ inch and $\frac{1}{2}$ centimeter; draw and describe angles as records of rotations.	**Goal 1.** Estimate length with and without tools; measure length to the nearest $\frac{1}{4}$ inch and $\frac{1}{2}$ centimeter; use tools to measure and draw angles; estimate the size of angles without tools.	**Goal 1.** Estimate length with and without tools; measure length with tools to the nearest $\frac{1}{8}$ inch and millimeter; estimate the measure of angles with and without tools; use tools to draw angles with given measures.	**Goal 1.** Estimate length with and without tools; measure length with tools to the nearest $\frac{1}{16}$ inch and millimeter; estimate the measure of angles with and without tools; use tools to draw angles with given measures.
Area, perimeter, volume, and capacity			**Goal 2.** Partition rectangles into unit squares and count unit squares to find areas.	**Goal 2.** Describe and use strategies to measure the perimeter of polygons; find the areas of rectangles.	**Goal 2.** Describe and use strategies to measure the perimeter and area of polygons, to estimate the area of irregular shapes, and to find the volume of rectangular prisms.	**Goal 2.** Describe and use strategies to find the perimeter of polygons and the area of circles; choose and use appropriate methods, including formulas, to find the areas of rectangles, parallelograms, and triangles, and the volume of a prism; define *pi* as the ratio of a circle's circumference to its diameter.	**Goal 2.** Choose and use appropriate formulas to calculate the circumference of circles and to solve area, perimeter, and volume problems.
Units and systems of measurement			**Goal 3.** Describe relationships between days in a week and hours in a day.	**Goal 3.** Describe relationships among inches, feet, and yards; describe relationships between minutes in an hour, hours in a day, days in a week.	**Goal 3.** Describe relationships among U.S. customary units of measure and among metric units of measure.	**Goal 3.** Describe relationships among U.S. customary units of measure and among metric units of measure.	

Everyday Mathematics

Content Strand: MEASUREMENT AND REFERENCE FRAMES *cont.*

Program Goal: Understand the Systems and Processes of Measurement; Use Appropriate Techniques, Tools, Units, and Formulas in Making Measurements *cont.*

Content	Kindergarten	First Grade	Second Grade	Third Grade	Fourth Grade	Fifth Grade	Sixth Grade
Money	**Goal 2.** Identify pennies, nickels, dimes, quarters, and dollar bills.	**Goal 2.** Know and compare the value of pennies, nickels, dimes, quarters, and dollar bills; make exchanges between coins.	**Goal 4.** Make exchanges between coins and bills.				

Program Goal: Use and Understand Reference Frames

Content	Kindergarten	First Grade	Second Grade	Third Grade	Fourth Grade	Fifth Grade	Sixth Grade
Temperature	**Goal 3.** Describe temperature using appropriate vocabulary, such as *hot, warm,* and *cold;* identify a thermometer as a tool for measuring temperature.	**Goal 3.** Identify a thermometer as a tool for measuring temperature; read temperatures on Fahrenheit and Celsius thermometers to the nearest 10°.	**Goal 5.** Read temperature on both the Fahrenheit and Celsius scales.				
Time	**Goal 4.** Describe and use measures of time periods relative to a day and week; identify tools that measure time.	**Goal 4.** Use a calendar to identify days, weeks, months, and dates; tell and show time to the nearest half and quarter hour on an analog clock.	**Goal 6.** Tell and show time to the nearest five minutes on an analog clock; tell and write time in digital notation.	**Goal 4.** Tell and show time to the nearest minute on an analog clock; tell and write time in digital notation.			
Coordinate systems					**Goal 4.** Use ordered pairs of numbers to name, locate, and plot points in the first quadrant of a coordinate grid.	**Goal 4.** Use ordered pairs of numbers to name, locate, and plot points in all four quadrants of a coordinate grid.	**Goal 3.** Use ordered pairs of numbers to name, locate, and plot points in all four quadrants of a coordinate grid.

Everyday Mathematics

Content Strand: GEOMETRY

Program Goal: Investigate Characteristics and Properties of Two- and Three-Dimensional Geometric Shapes

Content	Kindergarten	First Grade	Second Grade	Third Grade	Fourth Grade	Fifth Grade	Sixth Grade
Lines and angles			**Goal 1.** Draw line segments and identify parallel line segments.	**Goal 1.** Identify and draw points, intersecting and parallel line segments and lines, rays, and right angles.	**Goal 1.** Identify, draw, and describe points, intersecting and parallel line segments and lines, rays, and right, acute, and obtuse angles.	**Goal 1.** Identify, describe, compare, name, and draw right, acute, obtuse, straight, and reflex angles; determine angle measures in vertical and supplementary angles and by applying properties of sums of angle measures in triangles and quadrangles.	**Goal 1.** Identify, describe, classify, name, and draw angles; determine angle measures by applying properties of orientations of angles and of sums of angle measures in triangles and quadrangles.
Plane and solid figures	**Goal 1.** Identify and describe plane and solid figures including circles, squares, rectangles, triangles, spheres, and cubes.	**Goal 1.** Identify and describe plane and solid figures including circles, triangles, squares, rectangles, spheres, cylinders, rectangular prisms, pyramids, cones, and cubes.	**Goal 2.** Identify, describe, and model plane and solid figures including circles, triangles, squares, rectangles, hexagons, trapezoids, rhombuses, spheres, cylinders, rectangular prisms, pyramids, cones, and cubes.	**Goal 2.** Identify, describe, model, and compare plane and solid figures including circles, polygons, spheres, cylinders, rectangular prisms, pyramids, cones, and cubes using appropriate geometric terms including the terms *face, vertex, edge,* and *base.*	**Goal 2.** Describe, compare, and classify plane and solid figures, including polygons, circles, spheres, cylinders, rectangular prisms, cones, cubes, and pyramids, using appropriate geometric terms including *vertex, base, face, edge,* and *congruent.*	**Goal 2.** Describe, compare, and classify plane and solid figures using appropriate geometric terms; identify congruent figures and describe their properties.	**Goal 2.** Identify and describe similar and congruent figures and describe their properties; construct a figure that is congruent to another figure using a compass and straightedge.

Program Goal: Apply Transformations and Symmetry in Geometric Situations

Content	Kindergarten	First Grade	Second Grade	Third Grade	Fourth Grade	Fifth Grade	Sixth Grade
Transformations and symmetry	**Goal 2.** Identify shapes having line symmetry.	**Goal 2.** Identify shapes having line symmetry; complete line-symmetric shapes or designs.	**Goal 3.** Create and complete two-dimensional symmetric shapes or designs.	**Goal 3.** Create and complete two-dimensional symmetric shapes or designs; locate multiple lines of symmetry in a two-dimensional shape.	**Goal 3.** Identify, describe, and sketch examples of reflections; identify and describe examples of translations and rotations.	**Goal 3.** Identify, describe, and sketch examples of reflections, translations, and rotations.	**Goal 3.** Identify, describe, and sketch (including plotting on the coordinate plane) instances of reflections, translations, and rotations.

Everyday Mathematics

Content Strand: PATTERNS, FUNCTIONS, AND ALGEBRA

Program Goal: Understand Patterns and Functions

Content	Kindergarten	First Grade	Second Grade	Third Grade	Fourth Grade	Fifth Grade	Sixth Grade
Patterns and functions	**Goal 1.** Extend, describe, and create visual, rhythmic, and movement patterns; use rules, which will lead to functions, to sort, make patterns, and play "What's My Rule?" and other games.	**Goal 1.** Extend, describe, and create numeric, visual, and concrete patterns; solve problems involving function machines, "What's My Rule?" tables, and Frames-and-Arrows diagrams.	**Goal 1.** Extend, describe, and create numeric, visual, and concrete patterns; describe rules for patterns and use them to solve problems; use words and symbols to describe and write rules for functions involving addition and subtraction and use those rules to solve problems.	**Goal 1.** Extend, describe, and create numeric patterns; describe rules for patterns and use them to solve problems; use words and symbols to describe and write rules for functions involving addition, subtraction, and multiplication and use those rules to solve problems.	**Goal 1.** Extend, describe, and create numeric patterns; describe rules for patterns and use them to solve problems; use words and symbols to describe and write rules for functions that involve the four basic arithmetic operations and use those rules to solve problems.	**Goal 1.** Extend, describe, and create numeric patterns; describe rules for patterns and use them to solve problems; write rules for functions involving the four basic arithmetic operations; represent functions using words, symbols, tables, and graphs and use those representations to solve problems.	**Goal 1.** Extend, describe, and create numeric patterns; describe rules for patterns and use them to solve problems; represent patterns and rules using algebraic notation; represent functions using words, algebraic notation, tables, and graphs; translate from one representation to another and use representations to solve problems involving functions.

Program Goal: Use Algebraic Notation to Represent and Analyze Situations and Structures

Content	Kindergarten	First Grade	Second Grade	Third Grade	Fourth Grade	Fifth Grade	Sixth Grade
Algebraic notation and solving number sentences	**Goal 2.** Read and write expressions and number sentences using the symbols +, −, and =.	**Goal 2.** Read, write, and explain expressions and number sentences using the symbols +, −, and = and the symbols > and < with cues; solve equations involving addition and subtraction.	**Goal 2.** Read, write, and explain expressions and number sentences using the symbols +, −, =, >, and <; solve number sentences involving addition and subtraction; write expressions and number sentences to model number stories.	**Goal 2.** Read, write, and explain number sentences using the symbols +, −, ×, ÷, =, >, and <; solve number sentences; write expressions and number sentences to model number stories.	**Goal 2.** Use conventional notation to write expressions and number sentences using the four basic arithmetic operations; determine whether number sentences are true or false; solve open sentences and explain the solutions; write expressions and number sentences to model number stories.	**Goal 2.** Determine whether number sentences are true or false; solve open number sentences and explain the solutions; use a letter variable to write an open sentence to model a number story; use a pan-balance model to solve linear equations in one unknown.	**Goal 2.** Determine whether equalities and inequalities are true or false; solve open number sentences and explain the solutions; use a pan-balance model to solve linear equations in one or two unknowns; use trial-and-error and equivalent equations strategies to solve linear equations in one unknown.

Everyday Mathematics

Program Goal: Use Algebraic Notation to Represent and Analyze Situations and Structures *cont.*

Content	Kindergarten	First Grade	Second Grade	Third Grade	Fourth Grade	Fifth Grade	Sixth Grade
Order of operations				**Goal 3.** Recognize that numeric expressions can have different values depending on the order in which operations are carried out; understand that grouping symbols can be used to affect the order in which operations are carried out.	**Goal 3.** Evaluate numeric expressions containing grouping symbols; insert grouping symbols to make number sentences true.	**Goal 3.** Evaluate numeric expressions containing grouping symbols and nested grouping symbols; insert grouping symbols and nested grouping symbols to make number sentences true; describe and use the precedence of multiplication and division over addition and subtraction.	**Goal 3.** Describe and apply the conventional order of operations.
Properties of the arithmetic operations		**Goal 3.** Apply the Commutative and Associative Properties of Addition and the Additive Identity to basic addition fact problems.	**Goal 3.** Describe the Commutative and Associative Properties of Addition and the Additive Identity and apply them to mental arithmetic problems.	**Goal 4.** Describe and apply the Commutative and Associative Properties of Addition and Multiplication and the Multiplicative Identity; apply the Distributive Property of Multiplication over Addition.	**Goal 4.** Describe and apply the Distributive Property of Multiplication over Addition.	**Goal 4.** Describe and apply properties of arithmetic.	**Goal 4.** Describe and apply properties of arithmetic and multiplicative and additive inverses.

Assessment Overviews

This section summarizes the assessment opportunities in each unit. Ongoing assessments, such as the Informing Instruction and Recognizing Student Achievement notes, are listed by lesson. Portfolio opportunities, paired or linked Math Boxes, and Writing/Reasoning prompts are also highlighted. You will find information on periodic assessments as well. Modifications for each unit's Progress Check Written Assessment, tips for implementing Open Response tasks (including rubrics for each task), and sample student responses for each rubric level are provided.

Contents

Beginning-of-Year Assessment Goals

The Beginning-of-Year Assessment (pages 212A–C) can be used to gauge children's readiness for the content they will encounter early in third grade. This allows you to plan your instruction accordingly. The following table provides the goals for all the problems in the Beginning-of-Year Assessment.

Problem(s)	Grade-Level Goal
1, 2	**Operations and Computation 1:** Demonstrate automaticity with all addition and subtraction facts through 10 + 10; use basic facts to compute fact extensions such as 80 + 70.
3	**Operations and Computation 2:** Use manipulatives, mental arithmetic, paper-and-pencil algorithms and models, and calculators to solve problems involving the addition and subtraction of whole numbers and decimals in a money context; describe the strategies used and explain how they work.
4	**Measurement and Reference Frames 2:** Describe and use strategies to measure the perimeter of polygons; find the areas of rectangles.
5	**Measurement and Reference Frames 1:** Estimate length with and without tools; measure length to the nearest $\frac{1}{2}$ inch and $\frac{1}{2}$ centimeter; draw and describe angles as records of rotations.
6, 7	**Patterns, Functions, and Algebra 1:** Extend, describe, and create numeric patterns; describe rules for patterns and use them to solve problems; use words and symbols to describe and write rules for functions involving addition, subtraction, and multiplication and use those rules to solve problems.
8	**Operations and Computation 6:** Recognize and describe change, comparison, and parts-and-total situations; use repeated addition, arrays, and skip counting to model multiplication; use equal sharing and equal grouping to model division.

Assessment Overview

In this unit, children review content from previous grades including work with number sequences and patterns, calculators, and money. Use the information in this section to develop your assessment plan for Unit 1.

Ongoing Assessment

Opportunities for using and collecting ongoing assessment information are highlighted in Informing Instruction and Recognizing Student Achievement notes. Student products, along with observations and suggested writing prompts, provide a range of useful assessment information.

Informing Instruction

The Informing Instruction notes highlight children's thinking and point out common misconceptions. Informing Instruction in Unit 1: Lessons 1-2, 1-4, 1-8, 1-9, 1-10, and 1-11.

Recognizing Student Achievement

The Recognizing Student Achievement notes highlight specific tasks from which teachers can collect assessment data to monitor and document children's progress toward meeting Grade-Level Goals.

Lesson	Content Assessed	Where to Find It
1♦1	**Extend numerical patterns.** [Patterns, Functions, and Algebra Goal 1]	*TLG*, p. 20
1♦2	**Describe and extend numerical patterns.** [Patterns, Functions, and Algebra Goal 1]	*TLG*, p. 26
1♦3	**Write whole numbers.** [Number and Numeration Goal 1]	*TLG*, p. 29
1♦4	**Show and write the time in digital notation to the nearest minute.** [Measurement and Reference Frames Goal 4]	*TLG*, p. 34
1♦5	**Write whole numbers using standard base-10 notation.** [Number and Numeration Goal 1]	*TLG*, p. 40
1♦6	**Use numerical expressions to represent equivalent names for whole numbers.** [Number and Numeration Goal 4]	*TLG*, p. 44
1♦7	**Use basic terms of probability.** [Data and Chance Goal 3]	*TLG*, p. 49
1♦8	**Add and subtract multidigit numbers.** [Operations and Computation Goal 2]	*TLG*, p. 53
1♦9	**Solve addition and subtraction problems.** [Operations and Computation Goal 2]	*TLG*, p. 58
1♦10	**Compare values of coin and bill combinations.** [Number and Numeration Goal 6]	*TLG*, p. 64
1♦11	**Order whole numbers.** [Number and Numeration Goal 6]	*TLG*, p. 68
1♦12	**Solve problems involving number patterns.** [Patterns, Functions, and Algebra Goal 1]	*TLG*, p. 76
1♦13	**Solve basic subtraction facts.** [Operations and Computation Goal 1]	*TLG*, p. 82

Math Boxes

Math Boxes, one of several types of tasks highlighted in the Recognizing Student Achievement notes, have an additional useful feature. Math Boxes in most lessons are paired or linked with Math Boxes in one or two other lessons that have similar problems. Paired or linked Math Boxes in Unit 1: 1-5 and 1-7; 1-6 and 1-8; 1-9, 1-11, and 1-13; and 1-10 and 1-12.

Writing/Reasoning Prompts

In Unit 1, a variety of writing prompts encourage children to explain their strategies and thinking, to reflect on their learning, and to make connections to other mathematics or life experiences. Here are some of the Unit 1 suggestions:

Lesson	Writing/Reasoning Prompts	Where to Find It
1♦5	Explain the meaning of the equal sign (=) in the number sentence.	*TLG*, p. 40
1♦6	Explain your strategies for finding the missing numbers on the grid.	*TLG*, p. 45
1♦10	Explain how you found the median.	*TLG*, p. 65
1♦11	Explain how you figured out what the date will be in two weeks.	*TLG*, p. 71

Portfolio Opportunities

Portfolios are a versatile tool for assessment. They help children reflect on their mathematical growth and help teachers understand and document that growth. Each unit identifies several student products that can be selected and stored in a portfolio. Here are some of the Unit 1 suggestions:

Lesson	Portfolio Opportunities	Where to Find It
1♦4	Children make a clock booklet and record time to the nearest minute.	*TLG*, p. 36
1♦7	Children write about the language of chance.	*TLG*, p. 50
1♦11	Children explain how to find what the date will be in two weeks.	*TLG*, p. 71
1♦12	Children make and solve Frames-and-Arrows puzzles.	*TLG*, p. 77
1♦13	Children make a daily schedule of activities.	*TLG*, p. 83

Periodic Assessment

Every Progress Check lesson includes opportunities to observe children's progress and to collect student products in a variety of ways—Self Assessment, Oral and Slate Assessment, Written Assessment, and an Open Response task. For more details, see the first page of Progress Check 1, Lesson 1-14 on page 84, of the *Teacher's Lesson Guide*.

Progress Check Modifications

Written Assessments are one way children demonstrate what they know. The table below shows modifications for the Written Assessment in this unit. Use these to maximize opportunities for children to demonstrate what they know. Modifications can be given individually or written on the board for the class.

Problem(s)	Modifications for Written Assessment
1, 2, 3	For Problems 1–3, use tool-kit coins to model the problems.
7	For Problem 7, write one name using both addition and subtraction.
8	For Problem 8, use counters to model the problems.
9, 10	For Problems 9 and 10, use a number line or number grid to help you fill in the missing numbers.

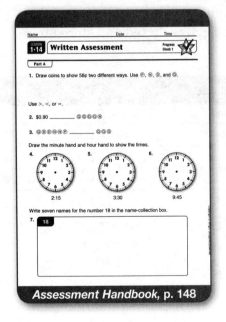

Assessment Handbook, p. 148

The Written Assessment for Unit 1 Progress Check is on pages 148–150.

Open Response, *Counting Coins*

Description

For this task, children make coin combinations for a given amount of money, using twice as many nickels as dimes.

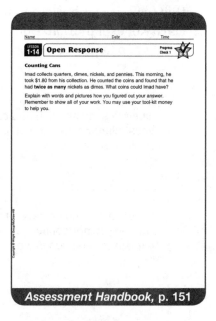

Focus

◆ **Use paper-and-pencil algorithms to solve problems involving the addition of decimals in a money context.**
[Operations and Computation Goal 2]

◆ **Use rules to solve problems.**
[Patterns, Functions, and Algebra Goal 1]

Implementation Tips

◆ Provide tool-kit coins.

◆ Discuss and use counters to model the meaning of *twice as many.*

Modifications for Meeting Diverse Needs

◆ Have children start out with a collection of twice as many nickels as dimes and build to a total of $1.80 using quarters and pennies.

◆ Have children solve the problem more than one way and write a description of how they found different ways to solve the problem.

Improving Open Response Skills

After children complete the task, have them share their solution strategies. Have children work in groups to write a description of one of the shared strategies. Have them display their descriptions. Children discuss, compare, and contrast the different strategies.

Note: The wording and formatting of the text on the student samples that follow may vary slightly from the actual task your children will complete. These minor discrepancies will not affect the implementation of the task.

Rubric

This rubric is designed to help you assess levels of mathematical performance on this task. It emphasizes mathematical understanding with only a mention of clarity of explanation. Consider the expectations of standardized tests in your area when applying a rubric. Modify this sample rubric as appropriate.

4	Makes a coin combination that totals $1.80, using twice as many nickels as dimes. Illustrates the solution and clearly explains a strategy for solving the problem. Uses vocabulary words such as *double, twice as many, added,* and *counted*. Might show multiple solutions.
3	Makes a coin combination that totals $1.80, using twice as many nickels as dimes with only minor counting or addition errors. Illustrates the solution and attempts to explain the solution in words, but the explanation might be incomplete.
2	Makes any coin combination that totals $1.80, or makes a coin combination that uses twice as many nickels as dimes, but does not total $1.80. Attempts to explain the solution, but the explanation might be incomplete or incorrect.
1	Attempts to solve the problem, but does not understand the concept of *twice as many* or how to make a coin combination that totals $1.80. Attempts to explain a solution, but there are errors in the strategy.
0	Does not attempt to understand or solve the problem.

Sample Student Responses

This Level 4 paper illustrates the following features: Only the specified coins are used in the coin combination. The value of the coin combination is $1.80. There are twice as many nickels as dimes (6 dimes and 12 nickels). The explanation describes starting out with twice as many nickels as dimes and then adding the balance that is needed in quarters and pennies. There is a second solution with 5 dimes and 10 nickels.

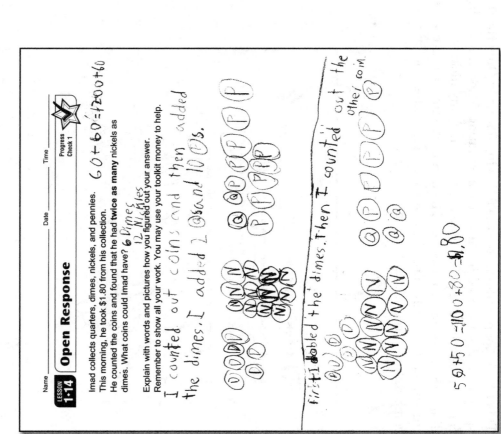

Name _____ Date _____ Time _____

LESSON 1·14 **Open Response**   Progress Check 1

Imad collects quarters, dimes, nickels, and pennies. This morning, he took $1.80 from his collection. He counted the coins and found that he had **twice as many** nickels as dimes. What coins could Imad have? 6 Dimes 12 Nickles

Explain with words and pictures how you figured out your answer. Remember to show all your work. You may use your toolkit money to help.

I counted out coins and then added the dimes. I added 2 Qs and 10 Ps.

$60 + 60' = 120 + 60$

first I dobled the dimes. Then I counted out the other coin.

$50 + 50 = 100 + 80 = 1.80

This Level 4 paper illustrates the following features: Only the specified coins are used in the coin combination. The value of the coin combination is $1.80. There are twice as many nickels as dimes (9 dimes and 18 nickels). The explanation describes beginning with dimes that totaled half of $1.80 and then adding double the number of nickels. The number sentence matches the illustration.

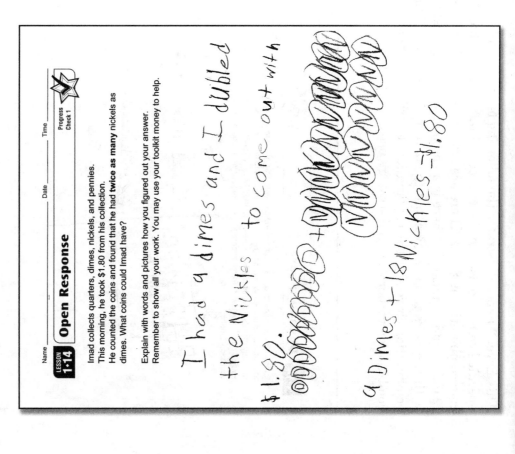

Name _____ Date _____ Time _____

LESSON 1·14 **Open Response**   Progress Check 1

Imad collects quarters, dimes, nickels, and pennies. This morning, he took $1.80 from his collection. He counted the coins and found that he had **twice as many** nickels as dimes. What coins could Imad have?

Explain with words and pictures how you figured out your answer. Remember to show all your work. You may use your toolkit money to help.

I had 9 dimes and I dubled the Niukles to come out with $1.80.

9 Dimes + 18Nickles = $1.80

This Level 3 paper illustrates the following features: Only the specified coins are used in the coin combination. The value of the coin combination is $1.80. There are twice as many nickels as dimes (8 dimes and 16 nickels). The number sentence represents the subtotal for each coin. The explanation describes the final combination rather than the strategy used.

This Level 3 paper illustrates the following features: Only the specified coins are used in the coin combination. The value of the coin combination is $1.80. There are twice as many nickels as dimes (9 dimes and 18 nickels). There is a small error in the illustration with one extra nickel drawn, but the description lists the final combination correctly. The explanation describes the final combination rather than the strategy used.

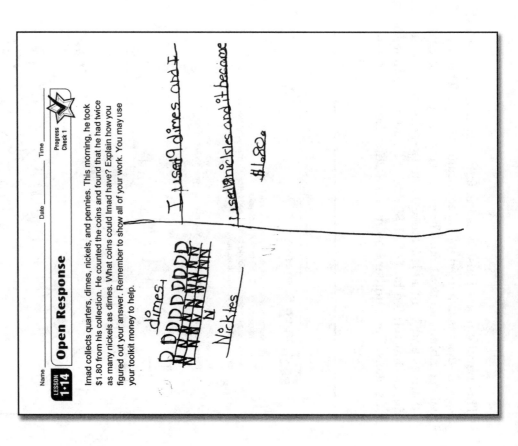

This Level 2 paper illustrates the following features: Only the specified coins are used in the coin combination. The value of the coin combination is $1.25. There are twice as many nickels as dimes (6 dimes and 12 nickels). The value calculated is incorrect. The explanation describes the final combination rather than the strategy used.

LESSON 1·14 **Open Response**

Progress Check 1

Imad collects quarters, dimes, nickels, and pennies. This morning, he took $1.80 from his collection. He counted the coins and found that he had twice as many nickels as dimes. What coins could Imad have? Explain how you figured out your answer. Remember to show all of your work. You may use your toolkit money to help.

Ⓓ Ⓝ
Ⓓ Ⓝ
Ⓓ Ⓝ
Ⓓ Ⓝ
Ⓓ Ⓝ
Ⓓ Ⓝ
= $1.25

I yousd 6 dimes and I
yousd 12 Nickels and
to adds op to $1.25

This Level 1 paper illustrates the following features: Only the specified coins are used in the coin combination. The value of the coin combination is $2.05. There is no apparent relationship between the numbers of dimes and nickels. There is no explanation.

LESSON 1·14 **Open Response**

Progress Check 1

Imad collects quarters, dimes, nickels, and pennies. This morning, he took $1.80 from his collection. He counted the coins and found that he had **twice as many** nickels as dimes. What coins could Imad have?

Explain with words and pictures how you figured out your answer. Remember to show all your work. You may use your toolkit money to help.

I Used
10 Dimes

2 Qurters

3 Nickles

8 Nickeles

Unit 2

Assessment Overview

In this unit, children work on developing their fact power with basic and extended facts and on developing paper-and-pencil algorithms for solving addition and subtraction problems. Use the information in this section to develop your assessment plan for Unit 2.

Ongoing Assessment

Opportunities for using and collecting ongoing assessment information are highlighted in Informing Instruction and Recognizing Student Achievement notes. Student products, along with observations and suggested writing prompts, provide a range of useful assessment information.

Informing Instruction

The Informing Instruction notes highlight children's thinking and point out common misconceptions. Informing Instruction in Unit 2: Lessons 2-1, 2-3, 2-4, 2-5, and 2-8.

Recognizing Student Achievement

The Recognizing Student Achievement notes highlight specific tasks from which teachers can collect assessment data to monitor and document children's progress toward meeting Grade-Level Goals.

Lesson	Content Assessed	Where to Find It
2•1	**Write whole numbers.** [Number and Numeration Goal 1]	*TLG*, p. 104
2•2	**Solve basic facts and write fact families.** [Operations and Computation Goal 1]	*TLG*, p. 107
2•3	**Solve "What's My Rule?" tables.** [Patterns, Functions, and Algebra Goal 1]	*TLG*, p. 115
2•4	**Write number models.** [Patterns, Functions, and Algebra Goal 2]	*TLG*, p. 121
2•5	**Determine the value of digits in a given number.** [Number and Numeration Goal 1]	*TLG*, p. 127
2•6	**Write number stories.** [Operations and Computation Goal 6]	*TLG*, p. 132
2•7	**Solve multidigit addition problems.** [Operations and Computation Goal 2]	*TLG*, p. 138
2•8	**Understand multidigit subtraction problems.** [Operations and Computation Goal 2]	*TLG*, p. 144
2•9	**Write equivalent names for numbers.** [Number and Numeration Goal 4]	*TLG*, p. 150

Math Boxes

Math Boxes, one of several types of tasks highlighted in the Recognizing Student Achievement notes, have an additional useful feature. Math Boxes in most lessons are paired or linked with Math Boxes in one or two other lessons that have similar problems. Paired or linked Math Boxes in Unit 2: 2-1 and 2-3; 2-2 and 2-4; 2-5, 2-7, and 2-9; and 2-6 and 2-8.

Writing/Reasoning Prompts

In Unit 2, a variety of writing prompts encourage children to explain their strategies and thinking, to reflect on their learning, and to make connections to other mathematics or life experiences. Here are some of the Unit 2 suggestions:

Lesson	Writing/Reasoning Prompts	Where to Find It
2◆3	Explain your strategy for finding change.	*TLG*, p. 115
2◆4	Explain how you found the numbers for the first two and the last two frames.	*TLG*, p. 121
2◆7	Explain how you found the length of the fence.	*TLG*, p. 139
2◆8	Explain how you figured out what the time would be in 30 minutes.	*TLG*, p. 145

Portfolio Opportunities

Portfolios are a versatile tool for assessment. They help children reflect on their mathematical growth and help teachers understand and document that growth. Each unit identifies several student products that can be selected and stored in a portfolio. Here are some of the Unit 2 suggestions:

Lesson	Portfolio Opportunities	Where to Find It
2◆4	Children write rules and complete "What's My Rule?" tables.	*TLG*, p. 121
2◆6	Children solve comparison number stories. Children write comparison statements about data.	*TLG*, p. 134
2◆7	Children write and solve addition number stories involving distance.	*TLG*, p. 140
2◆9	Children solve addition and subtraction problems.	*TLG*, p. 151

Periodic Assessment

Every Progress Check lesson includes opportunities to observe children's progress and to collect student products in a variety of ways—Self Assessment, Oral and Slate Assessment, Written Assessment, and an Open Response task. For more details, see the first page of Progress Check 2, Lesson 2-10, page 152, of the *Teacher's Lesson Guide*.

Progress Check Modifications

Written Assessments are one way children demonstrate what they know. The table below shows modifications for the Written Assessment in this unit. Use these to maximize opportunities for children to demonstrate what they know. Modifications can be given individually or written on the board for the class.

Problem(s)	Modifications for Written Assessment
1, 2, 13, 14	For Problems 1, 2, 13, and 14, use base-10 blocks to model the problems.
5	For Problem 5, use all five number cards to make 9.
6, 7	For Problems 6 and 7, use a number grid to help you solve the problems.
10	For Problem 10, make a place-value chart and write each digit in its correct place value.

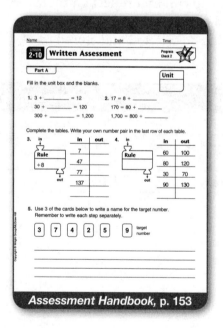

Assessment Handbook, p. 153

The Written Assessment for Unit 2 Progress Check is on pages 153–155.

Open Response, *A Birthday Dinner*

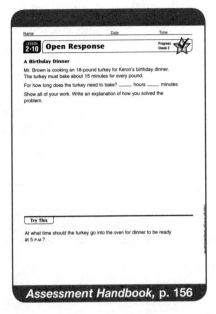

Assessment Handbook, p. 156

Description

For this task, children use addition and subtraction to solve an elapsed time problem.

Focus

◆ **Use paper-and-pencil algorithms to solve problems involving the addition and subtraction of whole numbers.**
[Operations and Computation Goal 2]

◆ **Tell and show time on an analog clock.**
[Measurement and Reference Frames Goal 4]

Implementation Tips

◆ Provide tool-kit clocks.

◆ Review quarter-hours and make a visual representation of $\frac{1}{4}$ hour.

Modifications for Meeting Diverse Needs

◆ Have children model the problem by moving the hands on the tool-kit clock and tallying each hour as they go.

◆ Have children record advice they would give to others who are solving time problems like this one. For example, "You have to remember that an hour has 60 minutes. It is easier if you use a clock and count around the clock face. If you remember that there are 4 quarter-hours in one hour, you can count by 4s."

Improving Open Response Skills

Before children begin the task, read it together. Give children a minute or two to think about how they will solve the problem. Have them share ideas in their small groups on how they plan to organize their work.

Note: The wording and formatting of the text on the student samples that follow may vary slightly from the actual task your children will complete. These minor discrepancies will not affect the implementation of the task.

Rubric

This rubric is designed to help you assess levels of mathematical performance on this task. It emphasizes mathematical understanding with only a mention of clarity of explanation. Consider the expectations of standardized tests in your area when applying a rubric. Modify this sample rubric as appropriate.

4	Calculates the baking time in hours and minutes. Converts total minutes to hours and minutes. Determines what time the turkey should go in the oven. Clearly explains the strategy used for calculating the baking time.
3	Calculates the baking time in minutes and converts them to hours and minutes. Determines what time the turkey should go in the oven, but there might be small errors. Attempts to explain the strategy used, but the explanation might be incomplete.
2	Provides some evidence of understanding how to solve the problem, but there might be errors. Attempts to convert total minutes to hours and minutes to find the baking time, but there might be errors. Might determine what time the turkey should go in the oven, but it might be incorrect.
1	Shows little evidence of using a strategy that makes sense in the context of the problem. Makes errors in calculations, conversions, or in the explanation.
0	Does not attempt to solve the problem.

Sample Student Responses

This Level 4 paper illustrates the following features: The correct baking time in minutes is calculated and then converted to hours and minutes by forming and counting groups of 4 pounds (15 minutes per pound, 1 hour per group). There is an organized chart that clearly labels each group as 1 hour. The starting time is calculated. The explanation is correct and complete.

This Level 4 paper illustrates the following features: The correct baking time in minutes is calculated and then converted to hours and minutes by repeatedly subtracting groups of 60 minutes (1 hour) from the total minutes. The work is clearly labeled and explained. The starting time is calculated.

Name _____ Date _____ Time _____

LESSON 2·10 Open Response

Progress Check 2

Mr. Brown is cooking an 18-pound turkey for Keron's birthday dinner. The turkey must bake about 15 minutes for every pound.

For how long does the turkey need to bake? __4__ hours __30__ minutes

Show all your work. Write an explanation of how you solved the problem.

① hours
1 pound = 15
2 pound = 30
3 pound = 45
4 pound = 60

② hours
5 pound = 15
6 pound = 30
7 pound = 45
8 pound = 60

③ hours
9 pound = 15
10 pound = 30
11 pound = 45
12 pound = 60

④ hours
13 pound = 15
14 pound = 30
15 pound = 45
16 pound = 60

⑤ minutes
17 pound = 15
18 pound = 30

First, I draw 4 pounds is
1 hours another I put 4
pounds is 2 hours I draw
4 pounds is 3 hours and
If I draw 4 more pounds
is 4 hours and that
4 hours is 16 time
and to be 18 time
is 30 minutes more
and now I now that
answer the answer is
4 hours and 30
minutes.

Try This!
At what time should the turkey go into the oven for dinner to be ready at 5 p.m.?

At 12:30 beouse if you put the turkey
at 12:30 you Add 4 hours and it gave
me 4:30 so I Add up 30 m. more
and it gave me 5:00

Use with Lesson 2-10

Name _____ Date _____ Time _____

LESSON 2·10 Open Response

Progress Check 2

Mr. Brown is cooking an 18-pound turkey for Keron's birthday dinner. The turkey must bake about 15 minutes for every pound.

For how long does the turkey need to bake? __4__ hours __30__ minutes

Show all your work. Write an explanation of how you solved the problem.

First I added 15+15+15+15+15+15 = 270 1 hour
and more 15's so it + 60 2 hour
was 270 min so I subtracted 210 2 hour
Second I subtracted 270-60   + 150 3 hours
and it gave me 210-60   + 90   3 hours
it gave me 150-60 it was -60 4 hours
90-60 = 40-60=30 over   30
I added with the four.1ours 1:00 + 30
Third I got my answer.   4:30
finally I got my answer
and solved the problem.

$$15, 15, 15, 15, 15, 15, 15, 15, 15, 15, 15, 15, 15, 15, 15, 15, 15, 15$$
270

Try This!
At what time should the turkey go into the oven for dinner to be ready at 5 p.m.?

At the 12:30 becous 4 hours & 30 min +12:30 = 5:00pm

Use with Lesson 2-10

This Level 2 paper illustrates the following features: The correct baking time is calculated in minutes by adding 18 sets of 15. Groups of 60 minutes are subtracted from the total, but then instead of counting the number of hours and adding the last 30 minutes, 30 was taken to be the final answer in hours and minutes.

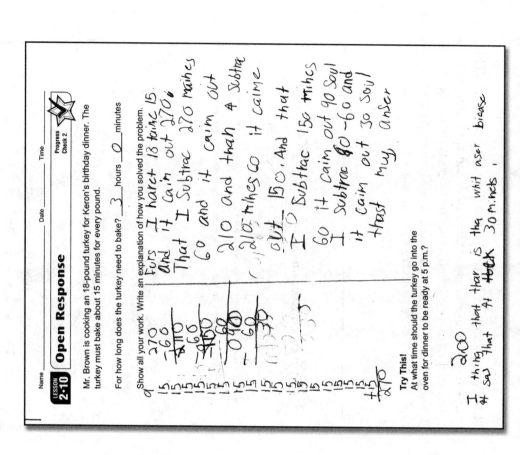

This Level 3 paper illustrates the following features: The correct baking time is calculated by making repeated additions of 15 minutes and then recorded in hours and minutes. No conversion is necessary. The explanation is confusing and incomplete. The extra hour is not carried in calculating the starting time.

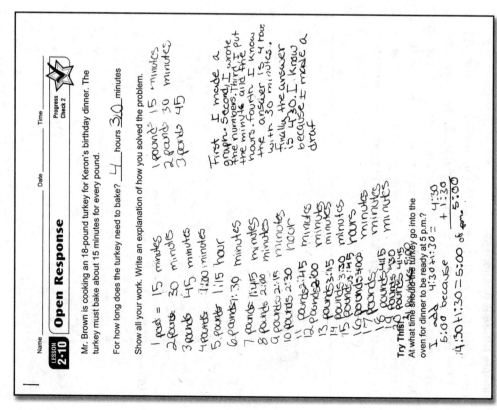

This Level 2 paper illustrates the following features: The product of 18 × 15 is found by adding 18 fifteen times. The baking time in minutes is correct but the conversion to hours and minutes is incorrect. The explanation and work shown provide no evidence for how the hours and minutes are calculated.

This Level 1 paper illustrates the following features: The correct baking time appears to be calculated by multiplying, but the work shown and the explanation do not support the answer.

Level 2 paper

Name _____ Date _____ Time _____

LESSON 2·10 **Open Response**

Progress Check 2

Mr. Brown is cooking an 18-pound turkey for Keron's birthday dinner. The turkey must bake about 15 minutes for every pound.

For how long does the turkey need to bake? __7__ hours __30__ minutes

Show all your work. Write an explanation of how you solved the problem.

18
×15
270

18+18+18+18+18+18+18+18+18+18+18+18+18+18+18 =
270

Fast I tot of maltiplicqtion and I maltipicaty
18 × 15 bot I Cqutade 18 tams 15 so it ge de
he 270 so tqt is How I sold my prodlem.

Try This!
At what time should the turkey go into the oven for dinner to be ready at 5 p.m.?

3:00 Plose the 30 mints - 2:30
so The Torkel Cah Finis qt 3:00 so
the Tarke can de geeled cockt

Level 1 paper

Name _____ Date _____ Time _____

LESSON 2·10 **Open Response**

Progress Check 2

Mr. Brown is cooking an 18-pound turkey for Keron's birthday dinner. The turkey must bake about 15 minutes for every pound.

For how long does the turkey need to bake? __4__ hours __30__ minutes

Show all your work. Write an explanation of how you solved the problem.

I solved This problem
I count The numbers and
I Put the number in the
PePer and I draw a pictu

15
×18
270
16

250
18
4:30

Try This!
At what time should the turkey go into the oven for dinner to be ready at 5 p.m.?

I do I cout the number
in the line 500×200=700

Assessment Overview 67

Assessment Overview

In this unit, children measure lengths of objects and explore perimeter and area. Use the information in this section to develop your assessment plan for Unit 3.

Ongoing Assessment

Opportunities for using and collecting ongoing assessment information are highlighted in Informing Instruction and Recognizing Student Achievement notes. Student products, along with observations and suggested writing prompts, provide a range of useful assessment information.

Informing Instruction

The Informing Instruction notes highlight children's thinking and point out common misconceptions. Informing Instruction in Unit 3: Lessons 3-2, 3-4, and 3-9.

Recognizing Student Achievement

The Recognizing Student Achievement notes highlight specific tasks from which teachers can collect assessment data to monitor and document children's progress toward meeting Grade-Level Goals.

Lesson	Content Assessed	Where to Find It
3•1	Explain the need for standard units of measure. [Measurement and Reference Frames Goal 1]	*TLG*, p. 173
3•2	Measure line segments to the nearest $\frac{1}{2}$ inch. [Measurement and Reference Frames Goal 1]	*TLG*, p. 179
3•3	Make ballpark estimates and record number models. [Operations and Computation Goal 5]	*TLG*, p. 183
3•4	Measure to the nearest centimeter. [Measurement and Reference Frames Goal 1]	*TLG*, p. 192
3•5	Use the Commutative and Associative Properties of Addition for 3- and 4-addend problems. [Patterns, Functions, and Algebra Goal 4]	*TLG*, p. 197
3•6	Tell time to the nearest five minutes. [Measurement and Reference Frames Goal 4]	*TLG*, p. 202
3•7	Demonstrate knowledge of basic subtraction facts. [Operations and Computation Goal 1]	*TLG*, p. 209
3•8	Calculate the area of rectangles. [Measurement and Reference Frames Goal 2]	*TLG*, p. 215
3•9	Find the area of rectangular shapes. [Measurement and Reference Frames Goal 2]	*TLG*, p. 222

Math Boxes

Math Boxes, one of several types of tasks highlighted in the Recognizing Student Achievement notes, have an additional useful feature. Math Boxes in most lessons are paired or linked with Math Boxes in one or two other lessons that have similar problems. Paired or linked Math Boxes in Unit 3: 3-1 and 3-3; 3-2 and 3-4; 3-5, 3-7, and 3-9; and 3-6 and 3-8.

Writing/Reasoning Prompts

In Unit 3, a variety of writing prompts encourage children to explain their strategies and thinking, reflect on their learning, and make connections to other mathematics or life experiences. Here are some of the Unit 3 suggestions:

Lesson	Writing/Reasoning Prompts	Where to Find It
3•1	Explain how you solved the addition problem.	*TLG*, p. 174
3•4	Explain how you know which numbers are greater.	*TLG*, p. 192
3•6	Explain whether you would use a ruler or a yardstick to measure the height of the classroom door.	*TLG*, p. 204
3•7	Explain what the term *area* means.	*TLG*, p. 210

Portfolio Opportunities

Portfolios are a versatile tool for assessment. They help children reflect on their mathematical growth and help teachers understand and document that growth. Each unit identifies several student products that can be selected and stored in a portfolio. Here are some of the Unit 3 suggestions:

Lesson	Portfolio Opportunities	Where to Find It
3•1	Children explain how they solved an addition problem.	*TLG*, p. 174
3•4	Children explain how to find the greater number.	*TLG*, p. 192
3•6	Children explain which measuring tool to use to measure the height of the classroom door.	*TLG*, p. 204
3•7	Children explain what the term *area* means.	*TLG*, p. 210
3•8	Children simulate buying items on a shopping trip, and record what they pay and how much change they receive.	*TLG*, p. 215

Periodic Assessment

Every Progress Check lesson includes opportunities to observe children's progress and to collect student products in a variety of ways—Self Assessment, Oral and Slate Assessment, Written Assessment, and an Open Response task. For more details, see the first page of Progress Check 3, Lesson 3-10, page 224, of the *Teacher's Lesson Guide*.

Progress Check Modifications

Written Assessments are one way children demonstrate what they know. The table below shows modifications for the Written Assessment in this unit. Use these to maximize opportunities for children to demonstrate what they know. Modifications can be given individually or written on the board for the class.

Problem(s)	Modifications for Written Assessment
3, 4, 14	For Problems 3, 4, and 14, use Ruler A to measure each line segment.
5, 6, 11, 15	For Problems 5, 6, 11, and 15, use Ruler D to measure each line segment.
7	For Problem 7, explain how you found the perimeter of the rectangle.
13	For Problem 13, use page 246 in your *Student Reference Book* to find the equivalent measures.

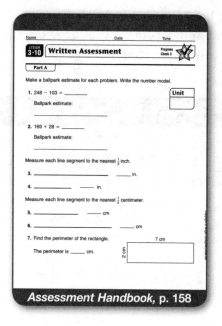

The Written Assessment for Unit 3 Progress Check is on pages 158–160.

Open Response, *Building a Fence*

Description

For this task, children find the maximum area of a rectangle with a given perimeter.

Focus

◆ **Compare and order whole numbers.**
[Number and Numeration Goal 6]

◆ **Count unit squares to find the perimeters and areas of rectangles.**
[Measurement and Reference Frames Goal 2]

Implementation Tips

◆ Provide centimeter-grid paper.

◆ Review the meaning of *perimeter* and *area*. Illustrate this vocabulary on the board.

Modifications for Meeting Diverse Needs

Assessment Handbook, p. 161

◆ Provide children with centimeter-grid paper and chenille sticks or pipe cleaners about 24 centimeters in length. Twist the ends of the pipe cleaners together and shape into a rectangle. Have children place their models on the grid paper to help find and draw rectangles with a perimeter of 24.

◆ Have children find all possible rectangles that have a perimeter of 24 and explain how they know they have found all possible rectangles. Have them describe any patterns they see.

Improving Open Response Skills

Before children begin the task, have them look over the problem and generate a list of vocabulary words that they might use in the explanation— for example, *rectangle, square, measuring, adding, subtracting, counting, perimeter, area.*

Note: The wording and formatting of the text on the student samples that follow may vary slightly from the actual task your children will complete. These minor discrepancies will not affect the implementation of the task.

Rubric

This rubric is designed to help you assess levels of mathematical performance on this task. It emphasizes mathematical understanding with only a mention of clarity of explanation. Consider the expectations of standardized tests in your area when applying a rubric. Modify this sample rubric as appropriate.

4   Finds the dimensions of the rectangle with the largest area and a perimeter of 24 units. Draws or describes only rectangles with perimeters of 24 units. Identifies the largest possible area of 36 square units. Demonstrates an understanding of perimeter and area. Labels all work clearly. Completely describes the steps that are followed and explains a strategy for finding the largest area.

3   Finds the dimensions of the rectangle with the largest area and a perimeter of 24 units. Draws or describes only rectangles with perimeters of 24 units. Identifies the largest possible area of 36 square units. Demonstrates an understanding of both perimeter and area. Labels work. Describes some of the steps that are followed and explains a strategy for finding the largest area.

2   Draws or describes some rectangles with perimeters of 24 units. Might identify the largest possible area of 36 square units. Demonstrates some understanding of perimeter and area, but might have minor misconceptions. Might label work. Attempts to describe some of the steps that were followed.

1   Demonstrates little evidence of understanding perimeter and area. Might label work. Might attempt to describe some of the steps that were followed, but the description might make no sense in the context of the problem.

0   Does not attempt to solve the problem.

Sample Student Responses

This Level 4 paper illustrates the following features: All possible rectangles with a perimeter of 24 units are drawn and labeled. The rectangle with the maximum area (36 square units) is chosen. The explanation describes the steps for finding the largest area and describes counting the squares to find the area.

This Level 4 paper illustrates the following features: All possible rectangles with a perimeter of 24 units are drawn and labeled. The rectangle with the largest area (36 square units) is chosen. The explanation describes manipulating the dimensions to maintain the same perimeter and counting squares to find the area.

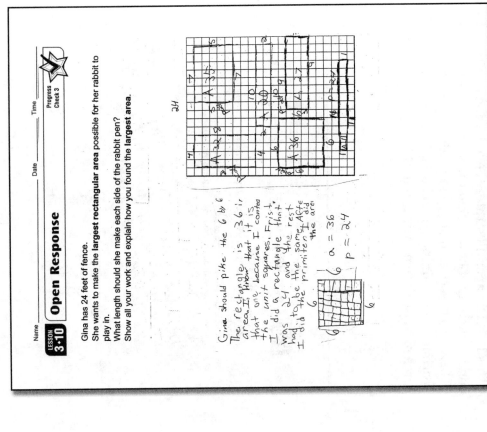

Name _____ Date _____ Time _____

LESSON 3·10 | **Open Response** | Progress Check 3

Gina has 24 feet of fence.
She wants to make the **largest rectangular area** possible for her rabbit to play in.
What length should she make each side of the rabbit pen?
Show all your work and explain how you found the **largest area.**

Gina should pick the rectangle that has the area of 36. First I drawed all the possibilitys of shapes that the perimeter is 24. Then I counted all the square inside each rectangule. I put the number of squares in the middle of the rectangle so I wont forget. Then I answered the qudian.

Name _____ Date _____ Time _____

LESSON 3·10 | **Open Response** | Progress Check 3

Gina has 24 feet of fence.
She wants to make the **largest rectangular area** possible for her rabbit to play in.
What length should she make each side of the rabbit pen?
Show all your work and explain how you found the **largest area.**

Gina should pike the 6 by 6
The rectangle is 36 is
area I know that it is
that one because I counted
the unit squares. First
I did a rectangle that
was 24 and the rest
had to be the same Acte
I did the primiter I did
the area

$a = 36$
$p = 24$

This Level 3 paper illustrates the following features: All possible rectangles with a perimeter of 24 units are drawn and labeled. The rectangle with the largest area (36 square units) is chosen. The explanation describes some steps of the solution strategy, but does not describe how to calculate area.

This Level 2 paper illustrates the following features: There is some understanding of how to find the areas and perimeters of rectangles. There is a description of adjusting the size of the rectangle to get a perimeter of 24 units. The solution is the rectangle with the largest area of those drawn rather than the largest possible area.

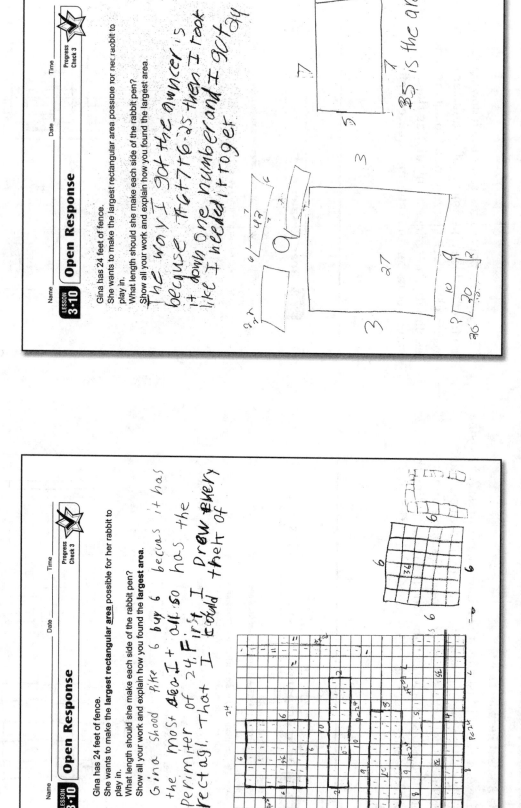

This Level 1 paper illustrates the following features: The correct answer is indicated, but there is no justification for this choice in the explanation. The illustration of the answer is incorrect for the dimensions given and the label is confusing. Some of the rectangles drawn do not have a perimeter of 24 units.

This Level 2 paper illustrates the following features: There is some understanding of how to find the areas and perimeters of rectangles. The rectangle drawn has a perimeter of 24 units, but the area is 32 square units. There is no evidence of a strategy for finding the rectangle with the largest area.

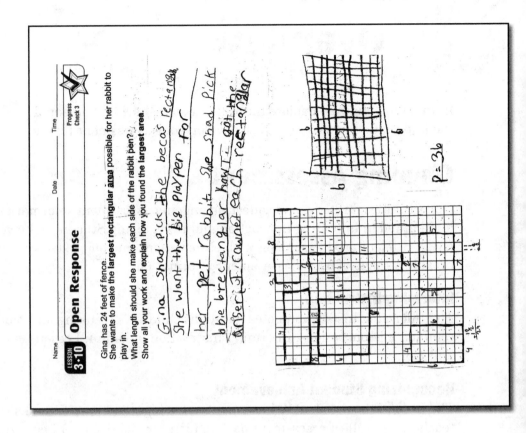

Name _____ Date _____ Time _____

LESSON
3·10   **Open Response**   Progress
                                                            Check 3

Gina has 24 feet of fence.
She wants to make the **largest rectangular area** possible for her rabbit to play in.
What length should she make each side of the rabbit pen?
Show all your work and explain how you found the **largest area.**

Gina shad pick the becas rectangoar
She want the big Playpen for
her pet rabbit She shad Pick
b ble brecangiar howI got the
anser I counet each restangiar

P = 36

Name _____ Date _____ Time _____

LESSON
3·10   **Open Response**   Progress
                                                            Check 3

Gina has 24 feet of fence.
She wants to make the largest rectangular area possible for her rabbit to play in.
What length should she make each side of the rabbit pen?
Show all your work and explain how you found the largest area.

Hight = 4
Leadth = 8
Perimiter = 24

Area = 32

I picked it because the cat could not only run
in a straight line it could run everywhere

In this unit, children explore multiples, equal sharing, and equal grouping. Use the information in this section to develop your assessment plan for Unit 4.

Ongoing Assessment

Opportunities for using and collecting ongoing assessment information are highlighted in Informing Instruction and Recognizing Student Achievement notes. Student products, along with observations and suggested writing prompts, provide a range of useful assessment information.

Informing Instruction

The Informing Instruction notes highlight children's thinking and point out common misconceptions. Informing Instruction in Unit 4: Lessons 4-1, 4-4, and 4-8.

Recognizing Student Achievement

The Recognizing Student Achievement notes highlight specific tasks from which teachers can collect assessment data to monitor and document children's progress toward meeting Grade-Level Goals.

Lesson	Content Assessed	Where to Find It
4•1	**Solve multiplication facts.** [Operations and Computation Goal 3]	*TLG,* p. 243
4•2	**Use arrays and multiples of equal groups to demonstrate the meaning of multiplication.** [Operations and Computation Goal 6]	*TLG,* p. 251
4•3	**Tell time to nearest minute and write time in digital notation.** [Measurement and Reference Frames Goal 4]	*TLG,* p. 257
4•4	**Use equal sharing to demonstrate the meaning of division.** [Operations and Computation Goal 6]	*TLG,* p. 261
4•5	**Find the area of rectangular shapes.** [Measurement and Reference Frames Goal 2]	*TLG,* p. 270
4•6	**Use the +, −, and = symbols.** [Patterns, Functions, and Algebra Goal 2]	*TLG,* p. 273
4•7	**Use equal sharing and equal grouping to demonstrate the meaning of division.** [Operations and Computation Goal 6]	*TLG,* p. 279
4•8	**Solve multiplication facts.** [Operations and Computation Goal 3]	*TLG,* p. 286
4•9	**Use number lines to order whole numbers and fractions.** [Number and Numeration Goal 6]	*TLG,* p. 289
4•10	**Collect and organize data.** [Data and Chance Goal 1]	*TLG,* p. 296

Math Boxes

Math Boxes, one of several types of tasks highlighted in the Recognizing Student Achievement notes, have an additional useful feature. Math Boxes in most lessons are paired or linked with Math Boxes in one or two other lessons that have similar problems. Paired or linked Math Boxes in Unit 4: 4-1 and 4-3; 4-2 and 4-4; 4-5 and 4-7; 4-6 and 4-9; and 4-8 and 4-10.

Writing/Reasoning Prompts

In Unit 4, a variety of writing prompts encourage children to explain their strategies and thinking, to reflect on their learning, and to make connections to other mathematics or life experiences. Here are some of the Unit 4 suggestions:

Lesson	Writing/Reasoning Prompts	Where to Find It
4◆1	Draw a different polygon with the same perimeter as in Problem 4. Explain how you know that the two polygons have equal perimeters.	*TLG*, p. 246
4◆2	Explain why estimates are helpful.	*TLG*, p. 252
4◆6	Describe what happens when a number is divided by 1.	*TLG*, p. 276
4◆7	Explain how you found the range.	*TLG*, p. 281
4◆8	Explain how you found one of your answers.	*TLG*, p. 286
4◆9	Explain how you figured out the number you wrote in the first empty frame.	*TLG*, p. 293

Portfolio Opportunities

Portfolios are a versatile tool for assessment. They help children reflect on their mathematical growth and help teachers understand and document that growth. Each unit identifies several student products that can be selected and stored in a portfolio. Here are some of the Unit 4 suggestions:

Lesson	Portfolio Opportunities	Where to Find It
4◆1	Children write multistep multiplication number stories.	*TLG*, p. 247
4◆4	Children find mystery numbers and identify patterns.	*TLG*, p. 265
4◆5	Children write and explain their own fact shortcuts for multiplication facts.	*TLG*, p. 271
4◆6	Children record patterns they find on a Multiplication/Division Facts Table.	*TLG*, p. 277
4◆9	Children make scale drawings of classroom objects.	*TLG*, p. 293

Periodic Assessment

Every Progress Check lesson includes opportunities to observe children's progress and to collect student products in a variety of ways—Self Assessment, Oral and Slate Assessment, Written Assessment, and an Open Response task. For more details, see the first page of Progress Check 4, Lesson 4-11, page 300, of the *Teacher's Lesson Guide*.

Progress Check Modifications

Written Assessments are one way children demonstrate what they know. The table below shows modifications for the Written Assessment in this unit. Use these to maximize opportunities for children to demonstrate what they know. Modifications can be given individually or written on the board for the class.

Problem(s)	Modifications for Written Assessment
3	For Problem 3, use base-10 blocks to model the problem.
4	For Problem 4, record the product above each multiplication fact before inserting the relation symbol.
7	For Problem 7, describe how the class 100-grid pattern is the same and how it is different from the pattern in this section of the number grid.
8, 9	For Problems 8 and 9, draw pictures to help you solve the problem.

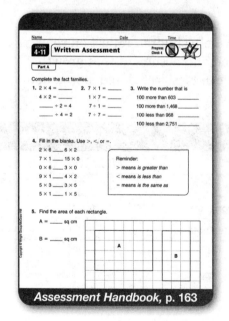

Assessment Handbook, p. 163

The Written Assessment for Unit 4 Progress Check is on pages 163–165.

Open Response, *A Multiplication Problem*

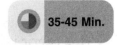

35-45 Min.

Description

For this task, children find a pattern that can be used to solve multiplication problems.

Focus

◆ **Use arrays, mental arithmetic, and paper-and-pencil algorithms to solve problems involving the multiplication of whole numbers.** [Operations and Computation Goal 4]

◆ **Describe numeric patterns and use them to solve problems.**
[Patterns, Functions, and Algebra Goal 1]

Implementation Tips

◆ Emphasize the phrase "without doing multiplication."

◆ Encourage children to check if their answers are reasonable.

Assessment Handbook, p. 166

Modifications for Meeting Diverse Needs

◆ Provide quarter-inch grid paper so children can draw arrays. Provide tool-kit quarters to represent the 25s.

◆ Have children write a rule for finding the difference between any two multiplication problems when one of the factors is the same.

Improving Open Response Skills

Before children begin the task, read the problem together. Give children a few minutes to look at it. Display Level 4 of the rubric on the board or overhead and review it with children. Have them translate Level 4 of the rubric into their own words. Record the children's language on chart paper and display this during the task. Have children check their work with the posted Level 4 description before turning in their papers.

Note: The wording and formatting of the text on the student samples that follow may vary slightly from the actual task your children will complete. These minor discrepancies will not affect the implementation of the task.

Rubric

This rubric is designed to help you assess levels of mathematical performance on this task. It emphasizes mathematical understanding with only a mention of clarity of explanation. Consider the expectations of standardized tests in your area when applying a rubric. Modify this sample rubric as appropriate.

4 Finds the difference without using multiplication. Clearly and completely describes the solution strategy with words, numbers, or pictures. Uses notation and symbols correctly, and all computation is correct.

3 Finds the difference without using multiplication. Describes the solution strategy with words, numbers, or pictures. Might make some errors in the use of notation and symbols. All computation is correct.

2 Might use multiplication in finding a difference. There is some understanding of the problem, but there might be errors in computation. Describes the solution strategy, but the description might be incomplete or incorrect.

1 Might attempt to find a difference with or without using multiplication, but the solution or the explanation makes no sense in the context of the problem.

0 Does not attempt to solve the problem.

Sample Student Responses

This Level 4 paper illustrates the following features: Shows repeated addition of 25 for eight 25s and for nine 25s. Shows and explains finding the difference between the two sums to find the answer.

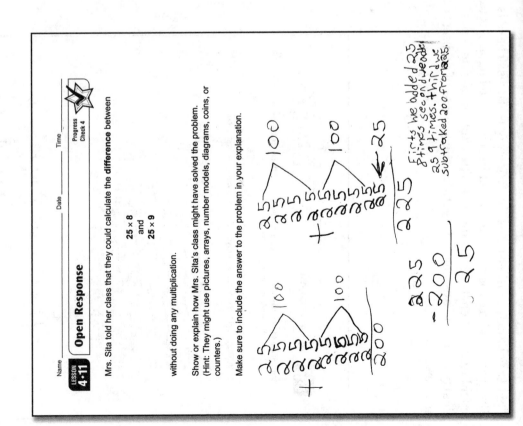

This Level 4 paper illustrates the following features: There is a clear illustration beginning with an 8 × 25 array. Then, as the explanation and illustration indicate, a ninth row of 25 is added, clearly showing that the difference between the two products is 25.

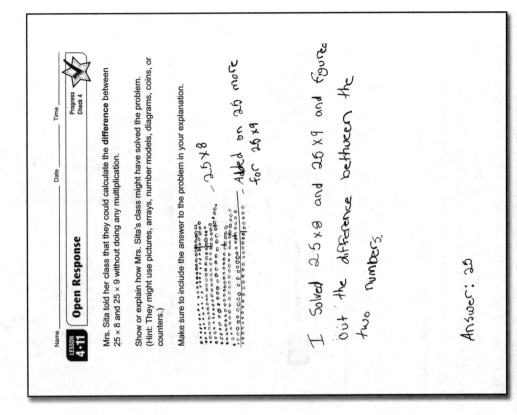

This Level 3 paper illustrates the following features: There is an illustration of groups of 25 arranged in rows. The ongoing total is calculated and each row is labeled. The explanation does not clearly state the answer, but restates the process of adding the last row.

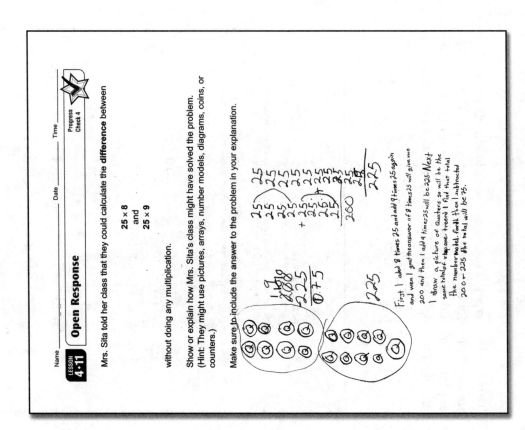

This Level 2 paper illustrates the following features: Shows collections of quarters to represent 25s. One group has 8 quarters and the other has 9 quarters. Both are labeled with a total. There is a computation error in the subtraction problem, and the final answer makes no sense.

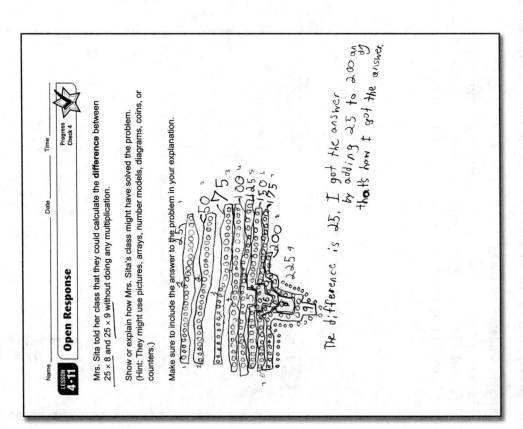

This Level 1 paper illustrates the following features: The numbers and arrays recorded on the page make no sense in the context of the problem.

This Level 2 paper illustrates the following features: The strategy described involves multiplication and subtraction. The instructions indicate that multiplication should not be used.

Name _____ Date _____ Time _____

LESSON 4·11   **Open Response**   Progress Check 4

Mrs. Sita told her class that they could calculate the **difference** between 25 × 8 and 25 × 9 without doing any multiplication.

Show or explain how Mrs. Sita's class might have solved the problem. (Hint: They might use pictures, arrays, number models, diagrams, coins, or counters.)

Make sure to include the answer to the problem in your explanation.

50
+17
67

−25
+25
5 0

8
+9
17

I added everything together.

Name _____ Date _____ Time _____

LESSON 4·11   **Open Response**   Progress Check 4

Mrs. Sita told her class that they could calculate the **difference** between 25 × 8 and 25 × 9 without doing any multiplication.

Show or explain how Mrs. Sita's class might have solved the problem. (Hint: They might use pictures, arrays, number models, diagrams, coins, or counters.)

Make sure to include the answer to the problem in your explanation.

25 × 8 = 200 < 25
25 × 9 = 225

You can answer the problem by answering the two problems and then see the difference in the answers that you got on 25×8a 25×9 and 25×8=200 and 25×9=225an the difference is 25.

Assessment Overview

In this unit, children explore place value and compare and order whole numbers through millions and decimals through thousandths. Use the information in this section to develop your assessment plan for Unit 5.

Ongoing Assessment

Opportunities for using and collecting ongoing assessment information are highlighted in Informing Instruction and Recognizing Student Achievement notes. Student products, along with observations and suggested writing prompts, provide a range of useful assessment information.

Informing Instruction

The Informing Instruction notes highlight children's thinking and point out common misconceptions. Informing Instruction in Unit 5: Lessons 5-1, 5-3, 5-4, 5-6, and 5-7.

Recognizing Student Achievement

The Recognizing Student Achievement notes highlight specific tasks from which teachers can collect assessment data to monitor and document children's progress toward meeting Grade-Level Goals.

Lesson	Content Assessed	Where to Find It
5◆1	Write whole numbers up to five digits. [Number and Numeration Goal 1]	*TLG*, p. 319
5◆2	Find the maximum, minimum, and range of a data set. [Data and Chance Goal 2]	*TLG*, p. 327
5◆3	Compare numbers. [Number and Numeration Goal 6]	*TLG*, p. 331
5◆4	Compare numbers. [Number and Numeration Goal 6]	*TLG*, p. 339
5◆5	Use basic facts to compute extended facts. [Operations and Computation Goal 1]	*TLG*, p. 345
5◆6	Use multiples of 10 to count base-10 blocks. [Number and Numeration Goal 3]	*TLG*, p. 349
5◆7	Read and write money totals in decimal notation. [Number and Numeration Goal 1]	*TLG*, p. 353
5◆8	Describe relationships between units of time. [Measurement and Reference Frames Goal 3]	*TLG*, p. 361
5◆9	Compare decimals. [Number and Numeration Goal 6]	*TLG*, p. 366
5◆10	Compare decimals. [Number and Numeration Goal 6]	*TLG*, p. 372
5◆11	Determine the values of digits in decimal numbers. [Number and Numeration Goal 1]	*TLG*, p. 377
5◆12	Solve multiplication facts up to 10 × 10. [Operations and Computation Goal 3]	*TLG*, p. 382

Math Boxes

Math Boxes, one of several types of tasks highlighted in the Recognizing Student Achievement notes, have an additional useful feature. Math Boxes in most lessons are paired or linked with Math Boxes in one or two other lessons that have similar problems. Paired or linked Math Boxes in Unit 5: 5-1 and 5-3; 5-2 and 5-4; 5-5 and 5-7; 5-6 and 5-8; 5-9 and 5-11; and 5-10 and 5-12.

Writing/Reasoning Prompts

In Unit 5, a variety of writing prompts encourage children to explain their strategies and thinking, to reflect on their learning, and to make connections to other mathematics or life experiences. Here are some of the Unit 5 suggestions:

Lesson	Writing/Reasoning Prompts	Where to Find It
5•3	Show how you used the data set to find the maximum, minimum, and range.	*TLG*, p. 334
5•4	Explain how you know which operation to use.	*TLG*, p. 340
5•5	Explain how you solved the problem using another method.	*TLG*, p. 345
5•6	Explain whether the money amounts can be written without the zeros.	*TLG*, p. 350
5•9	Explain why the area is measured in square units.	*TLG*, p. 366

Portfolio Opportunities

Portfolios are a versatile tool for assessment. They help children reflect on their mathematical growth and help teachers understand and document that growth. Each unit identifies several student products that can be selected and stored in a portfolio. Here are some of the Unit 5 suggestions:

Lesson	Portfolio Opportunities	Where to Find It
5•9	Children estimate and measure the lengths of objects in the room.	*TLG*, p. 367
5•9	Children explain how they use tenths and hundredths in metric measurements.	*TLG*, p. 367
5•11	Children record decimals greater than 0 and less than 1 and place them on a number line.	*TLG*, p. 378
5•12	Children determine the maximum, minimum, range, mode, and median for a data set.	*TLG*, p. 383
5•12	Children find data landmarks for heights of 8-year-old children.	*TLG*, p. 383

Periodic Assessment

Every Progress Check lesson includes opportunities to observe children's progress and to collect student products in a variety of ways—Self Assessment, Oral and Slate Assessment, Written Assessment, and an Open Response task. For more details, see the first page of Progress Check 5, Lesson 5-13, page 384, of the *Teacher's Lesson Guide*.

Progress Check Modifications

Written Assessments are one way children demonstrate what they know. The table below shows modifications for the Written Assessment in this unit. Use these to maximize opportunities for children to demonstrate what they know. Modifications can be given individually or written on the board for the class.

Problem(s)	Modifications for Written Assessment
1, 2, 19, 20	For Problems 1, 2, 19, and 20, make a place-value mat and record each number in its correct place value.
7, 8	For Problems 7 and 8, use counters to help you solve the problems.
9, 10	For Problems 9 and 10, use a number grid to help you solve the problems.
17	For Problem 17, explain how you know whether 0.19 or 0.65 is worth more.

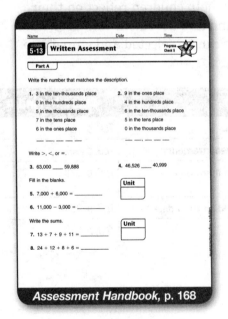

Assessment Handbook, p. 168

The Written Assessment for Unit 5 Progress Check is on pages 168–170.

Open Response, *Playing with Place Value*

25-35 Min.

Description

For this task, children place digit cards in the *Number Top-It* game to make the largest number.

Focus

◆ **Read and write whole numbers up to 1,000,000, and identify the values of the digits in those places.**
[Number and Numeration Goal 1]

◆ **Compare and order whole numbers up to 1,000,000.** [Number and Numeration Goal 6]

Implementation Tips

◆ Review the rules for *Number Top-It*. Emphasize that the largest number wins the round. Remind children that they may draw any of the digits 0 to 9 on their next turns.

◆ Remind children that Problem 1 is the middle of a game.

Assessment Handbook, p. 171

Modifications for Meeting Diverse Needs

◆ Provide a *Number Top-It* gameboard and number cards for children to model the game.

◆ Ask children if they like the teacher's added rule in Problem 2. Have them explain their answers. *(Sample answer: It is a good rule because then you don't know who wins the game until the end. It is a good rule because you can always make your number larger.)*

Improving Open Response Skills

After children complete the task, have them use a separate sheet of paper to organize their answers into two columns. Have them label the top of the first column *What Janine should do*. Have them label the top of the second column *Why Janine should do it*. Explain that entries in the first column are the advice they gave to Janine, while entries in the second column are the reasons for the advice. Have them attach this paper to their original task. Remind children that whenever they are asked to "explain their answers," the explanation should include both what they did and why they did it.

Note: The wording and formatting of the text on the student samples that follow may vary slightly from the actual task your children will complete. These minor discrepancies will not affect the implementation of the task.

Rubric

This rubric is designed to help you assess levels of mathematical performance on this task. It emphasizes mathematical understanding with only a mention of clarity of explanation. Consider the expectations of standardized tests in your area when applying a rubric. Modify this sample rubric as appropriate.

4   For Problem 1, places the 7 in the thousands or ten-thousands place and includes a valid and clearly-explained justification for the placement. For Problem 2, switches the 7 from the tens place with the 4 in the ten-thousands place and clearly explains that this is the largest number with one switch.

3   For Problem 1, places the 7 in the thousands or ten-thousands place and indicates that this is the largest number. For Problem 2, switches the 7 from the tens place with the 4 in the ten-thousands place, but might make other switches as well. Explains the steps but might not explain the reasoning.

2   For Problem 1, places the 7 to make the largest number, but might not describe a 5-digit number. For Problem 2, makes a larger number, but might switch digits to make the largest number. Explains the steps in both problems but might not explain any reasoning.

1   Might show some understanding of place value, but gives answers and explanations that might not make sense in the context of the problem.

0   Does not attempt to solve the problem.

Sample Student Responses

This Level 4 paper illustrates the following features: In Problem 1, the 7 is put in the thousands place. The choice is justified by explaining there are higher cards. In Problem 2, only one switch is made—between the 4 and the 7 in the tens place. The explanation describes that this makes the largest number.

This Level 4 paper illustrates the following features: In Problem 1, the 7 is put in the ten-thousands place. The choice is justified by explaining that getting higher cards is unlikely. In Problem 2, only one switch is made—between the 4 and the 7 in the tens place. The explanation describes that this makes the largest number.

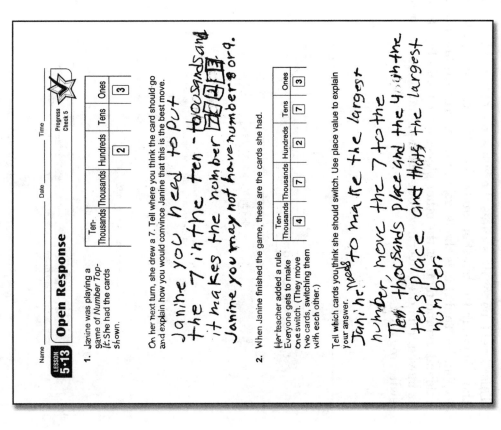

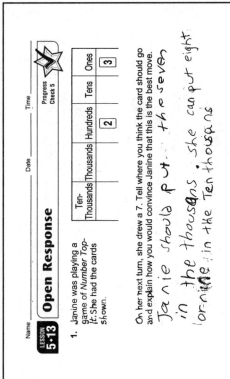

This Level 3 paper illustrates the following features: In Problem 1, the 7 is put in the ten-thousands place. The choice is justified by explaining that this is the largest number. The explanation shows a misunderstanding that the other places have 0s. In Problem 2, the 7 is moved from the tens place, but the explanation does not refer to switching digits.

LESSON 5·13 **Open Response** Progress Check 5

1. Janine was playing a game of *Number Top-It.* She had the cards shown.

Ten-Thousands	Thousands	Hundreds	Tens	Ones
7	0	2	0	3

On her next turn, she drew a 7. Tell where you think the card should go and explain how you would convince Janine that this is the best move.

I want to do the largest number. She must move it he seven from the tens to the ten thousands. She would have 70,203.

2. When Janine finished the game, these are the cards she had.

Her teacher added a rule. Everyone gets to make one switch. (They move two cards, switching them with each other.)

Ten-Thousands	Thousands	Hundreds	Tens	Ones
4	7	2	7	3

Tell which cards you think she should switch. Use place value to explain your answer.

I think she should move the seven to the ten thousands and the other seven to the thousands. That's how she could have the biggest number.

This Level 3 paper illustrates the following features: In Problem 1, the 7 is put in the thousands place. The choice is justified by explaining that the number is smaller if 7 is in the tens place. In Problem 2, only one switch is made—between the 4 and the 7 in the tens place. The explanation does not justify the answer.

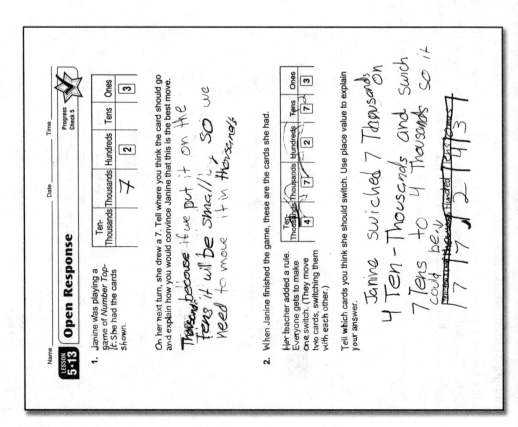

LESSON 5·13 **Open Response** Progress Check 5

1. Janine was playing a game of *Number Top-It.* She had the cards shown.

Ten-Thousands	Thousands	Hundreds	Tens	Ones
	7	2		3

On her next turn, she drew a 7. Tell where you think the card should go and explain how you would convince Janine that this is the best move.

The tens because if we put it on the tens it will be smaller, so we need to move it in thousands.

2. When Janine finished the game, these are the cards she had.

Her teacher added a rule. Everyone gets to make one switch. (They move two cards, switching them with each other.)

Ten-Thousands	Thousands	Hundreds	Tens	Ones
4	7	2	7	3

Tell which cards you think she should switch. Use place value to explain your answer.

Janine switched 7 Thousands on 4 Ten-Thousands and swich 7 Tens to 4 Thousands so it could be v

7 7 7 2 7 4 3

This Level 1 paper illustrates the following features: The illustration in Problem 1 does not match the explanation of the steps. The explanations for both problems describe a strategy for making the smallest number instead of the largest one.

This Level 2 paper illustrates the following features: In Problem 1, the 7 is moved into the hundreds place. The choice is justified by explaining that 7 is the largest number, but the rules of the game are not taken into account. For Problem 2, the digits are all rearranged into the largest number, which does not follow the instructions.

Level 1 paper (right):

Name _____ Date _____ Time _____

LESSON 5·13 | **Open Response**

Progress Check 5

1. Janine was playing a game of *Number Top-It*. She had the cards shown.

Ten-Thousands	Thousands	Hundreds	Tens	Ones
7	0	2	0	3

On her next turn, she drew a 7. Tell where you think the card should go and explain how you would convince Janine that this is the best move.

I think jushe will make the seven in the ones so she could make a smallest number

2. When Janine finished the game, these are the cards she had.

Her teacher added a rule. Everyone gets to make one switch. (They move two cards, switching them with each other.)

Ten-Thousands	Thousands	Hundreds	Tens	Ones
4	7	2	7	3

Tell which cards you think she should switch. Use place value to explain your answer.

I think se should move th eseven to the ones sign and the other seven to the tens so she wold have the smallest number.

Use w _esson 5-13

3U05L13M05

Level 2 paper (left):

Name _____ Date _____ Time _____

LESSON 5·13 | **Open Response**

Progress Check 5

1. Janine was playing a game of *Number Top-It*. She had the cards shown.

Ten-Thousands	Thousands	Hundreds	Tens	Ones
		2		3

On her next turn, she drew a 7. Tell where you think the card should go and explain how you would convince Janine that this is the best move.

I want Janine do the largest number that move the seven to the hounine and the 3 to the tens and the 2 to the ones thos the way she can to the largest number and she will get 732.

2. When Janine finished the game, these are the cards she had.

Her teacher added a rule. Everyone gets to make one switch. (They move two cards, switching them with each other.)

Ten-Thousands	Thousands	Hundreds	Tens	Ones
4	7	2	7	3

Tell which cards you think she should switch. Use place value to explain your answer.

I think the Janine has to moove the 7 to the ten thousands and the other seven to the thousands and the four to hundreds and the 2 to the tens and the 2 to the 3 ones

Use w _esson 5-13

3U05L13M05

Assessment Overview 91

Unit 6

Assessment Overview

In this unit, children explore, describe, compare, and contrast the attributes of polygons and polyhedrons. Use the information in this section to develop your assessment plan for Unit 6.

Ongoing Assessment

Opportunities for using and collecting ongoing assessment information are highlighted in Informing Instruction and Recognizing Student Achievement notes. Student products, along with observations and suggested writing prompts, provide a range of useful assessment information.

Informing Instruction

The Informing Instruction notes highlight children's thinking and point out common misconceptions. Informing Instruction in Unit 6: Lessons 6-3, 6-5, and 6-8.

Recognizing Student Achievement

The Recognizing Student Achievement notes highlight specific tasks from which teachers can collect assessment data to monitor and document children's progress toward meeting Grade-Level Goals.

Lesson	Content Assessed	Where to Find It
6◆1	Draw line segments. [Geometry Goal 1]	*TLG*, p. 405
6◆2	Identify parallel and intersecting lines and segments. [Geometry Goal 1]	*TLG*, p. 411
6◆3	Read decimal numbers. [Number and Numeration Goal 1]	*TLG*, p. 417
6◆4	Draw line segments, rays, and lines. [Geometry Goal 1]	*TLG*, p. 424
6◆5	Identify points and draw line segments to form a quadrangle. [Geometry Goal 1]	*TLG*, p. 427
6◆6	Measure line segments to the nearest $\frac{1}{2}$ centimeter. [Measurement and Reference Frames Goal 1]	*TLG*, p. 435
6◆7	Demonstrate automaticity with multiplication facts. [Operations and Computation Goal 3]	*TLG*, p. 442
6◆8	Recognize a right angle. [Geometry Goal 1]	*TLG*, p. 448
6◆9	Complete symmetric shapes. [Geometry Goal 3]	*TLG*, p. 452
6◆10	Model decimals with base-10 blocks and shaded grids, and write the decimal represented by the base-10 blocks. [Number and Numeration Goal 1]	*TLG*, p. 459
6◆11	Identify properties of solid figures—pyramids and prisms. [Geometry Goal 2]	*TLG*, p. 465
6◆12	Demonstrate automaticity with multiplication facts. [Operations and Computation Goal 3]	*TLG*, p. 471

Math Boxes

Math Boxes, one of several types of tasks highlighted in the Recognizing Student Achievement notes, have an additional useful feature. Math Boxes in most lessons are paired or linked with Math Boxes in one or two other lessons that have similar problems. Paired or linked Math Boxes in Unit 6: 6-1 and 6-3; 6-2 and 6-4; 6-5 and 6-7; 6-6 and 6-8; 6-9 and 6-11; and 6-10 and 6-12.

Writing/Reasoning Prompts

In Unit 6, a variety of writing prompts encourage children to explain their strategies and understandings, to reflect on their learning, and to make connections to other mathematics or life experiences. Here are some of the Unit 6 suggestions:

Lesson	Writing/Reasoning Prompts	Where to Find It
6◆1	Explain how much of the grid needs to be shaded to fill in the whole grid.	TLG, p. 406
6◆2	Explain how using money might help someone understand which decimal is larger.	TLG, p. 412
6◆8	Explain how shaded grids help you figure out which decimal is smaller.	TLG, p. 448
6◆10	Explain the difference between 0.40 and 0.4.	TLG, p. 460
6◆11	Explain how you figured out the solution and then draw a picture of what you did.	TLG, p. 466

Portfolio Opportunities

Portfolios are a versatile tool for assessment. They help children reflect on their mathematical growth and help teachers understand and document that growth. Each unit identifies several student products that can be selected and stored in a portfolio. Here are some of the Unit 6 suggestions:

Lesson	Portfolio Opportunities	Where to Find It
6◆7	Children draw a regular polygon and then explain why it is regular.	TLG, p. 442
6◆9	Children solve pattern-block puzzles involving shapes with symmetry and then describe the blocks they used to solve each riddle.	TLG, p. 455
6◆10	Children create an 8-point design.	TLG, p. 458
6◆13	Children write directions for drawing a 2-dimensional figure.	TLG, p. 477

Periodic Assessment

Every Progress Check lesson includes opportunities to observe children's progress and to collect student products in a variety of ways—Self Assessment, Oral and Slate Assessment, Written Assessment, and an Open Response task. For more details, see the first page of Progress Check 6, Lesson 6-13, page 474, of the *Teacher's Lesson Guide*.

Progress Check Modifications

Written Assessments are one way children demonstrate what they know. The table below shows modifications for the Written Assessment in this unit. Use these to maximize opportunities for children to demonstrate what they know. Modifications can be given individually or written on the board for the class.

Problem(s)	Modifications for Written Assessment
4	For Problem 4, explain how you know if a pair of lines is parallel.
11–14	For Problems 11–13, build each number with base-10 blocks. Use these to help you solve Problem 14.
21	For Problem 21, use page 109 in the *Student Reference Book* to find other names for the shape.

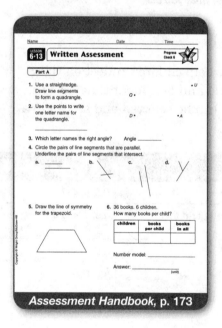

Assessment Handbook, p. 173

The Written Assessment for Unit 6 Progress Check is on pages 173–175.

Open Response, *Writing Directions*

30-40 Min.

Description

For this task, children apply their knowledge of polygons in writing directions for drawing a 2-dimensional figure.

Focus

◆ **Identify intersecting and parallel line segments.** [Geometry Goal 1]

◆ **Identify and describe plane figures using appropriate geometric terms.** [Geometry Goal 2]

Implementation Tips

◆ Have children start by trying to draw the figure themselves.

◆ Have children check their work by trying to draw the figure based on the directions they wrote.

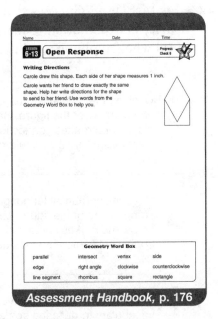

Assessment Handbook, p. 176

Modifications for Meeting Diverse Needs

◆ Make a Geometry Word Box on the board and have volunteers illustrate the vocabulary words. Before starting the task, have children review the vocabulary in the Word Box. As children review each word, have them trace parts of the original figure with their fingers. Leave the words and illustrations on display for children to refer to when they complete the task.

◆ Have children write the directions without using the words *square* or *rhombus.*

Improving Open Response Skills

After children complete the task, have them translate Level 4 of the rubric into their own words. Post Level 4 of the rubric in children's language on chart paper. Have children discuss in their groups what the statements in the rubric mean. After the discussion, have children take their own papers and try to improve or enhance their instructions according to the rubric.

Note: The wording and formatting of the text on the student samples that follow may vary slightly from the actual task your children will complete. These minor discrepancies will not affect the implementation of the task.

Rubric

This rubric is designed to help you assess levels of mathematical performance on this task. It emphasizes mathematical understanding with only a mention of clarity of explanation. Consider the expectations of standardized tests in your area when applying a rubric. Modify this sample rubric as appropriate.

4	Uses mathematical language, including Word Box vocabulary, to describe the main components of the figure. Refers to all sides being one inch. Explains the steps clearly and makes connections between the steps. The instructions might need some clarification, but they could result in drawing the figure.
3	Uses mathematical language, including Word Box vocabulary, to describe some main components of the figure. Might refer to all sides being one inch. Explains some steps and makes some connections between the steps. The instructions might need some clarification or steps added, but they make sense in the context of the problem.
2	There is evidence of some understanding of the task. Attempts to use Word Box vocabulary to describe some components of the figure, but there might be no connections between the components. The instructions make some sense in the context of the problem, but there might be errors.
1	Shows little evidence of understanding the task. Might attempt to use Word Box vocabulary to describe some components of the figure, but the instructions might demonstrate conceptual errors.
0	Does not attempt to solve the problem.

This Level 4 paper illustrates the following features: The instructions include several vocabulary words from the Word Box. The main components of a square and a rhombus are described as having all one inch long sides. The instructions suggest how to put the rhombus in the open square explaining how they touch. The steps are correct, but some clarification is required.

This Level 4 paper illustrates the following features: The instructions include several vocabulary words from the Word Box. The main components are described in terms of parallel and intersecting line segments—all of which are one inch in length. The instructions suggest how the final figure resembles "a rhombus going into a square." The steps are correct, but some clarification is required.

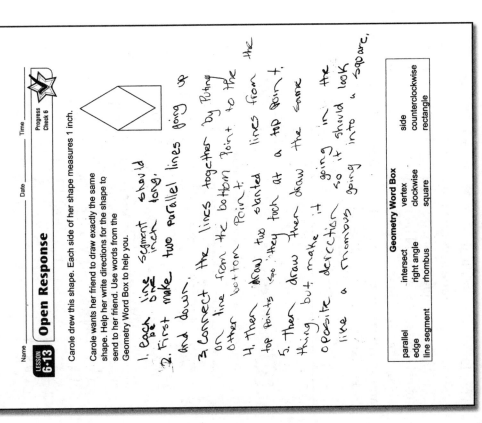

First student response (left):

LESSON 6·13 — Open Response — Progress Check 6

Carole drew this shape. Each side of her shape measures 1 inch.

Carole wants her friend to draw exactly the same shape. Help her write directions for the shape to send to her friend. Use words from the Geometry Word Box to help you.

Draw a rhombus with each side one in. long. Then draw a squar with one open side deferly under the rhombus. Make shure that the top to linse are tuching the the corners on the side of the rhombus.

Geometry Word Box		
parallel	intersect	vertex	side
edge	right angle	clockwise	counterclockwise
line segment	rhombus	square	rectangle

Second student response (right):

LESSON 6·13 — Open Response — Progress Check 6

Carole drew this shape. Each side of her shape measures 1 inch.

Carole wants her friend to draw exactly the same shape. Help her write directions for the shape to send to her friend. Use words from the Geometry Word Box to help you.

1. Each line segment should be one inch long.

2. First make two parallel lines going up and down.

3. Connect the lines together by puting on line from the bottom point to the other bottom point.

4. Then draw two slanted lines from the top points so they touch at a top point.

5. Then draw then draw the same thing but make it going in the oposite dereccton so it should look like a rhombus going into a square.

Geometry Word Box		
parallel	intersect	vertex	side
edge	right angle	clockwise	counterclockwise
line segment	rhombus	square	rectangle

This Level 3 paper illustrates the following features: The instructions include several vocabulary words from the Word Box. The main components are described as being a 1-inch square and two triangles. The instructions provide basic information about the relationship between these shapes, but more information and clarification are required to understand what the final figure looks like.

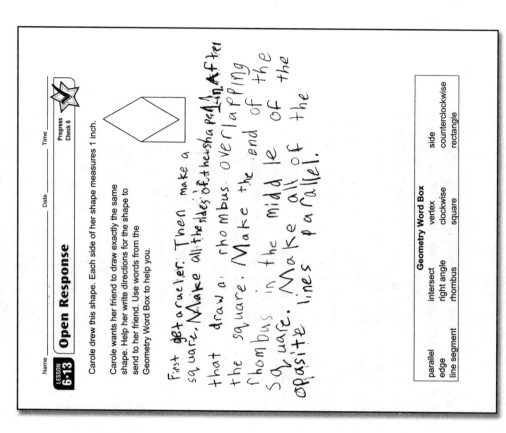

LESSON 6·13 **Open Response** Progress Check 6

Carole drew this shape. Each side of her shape measures 1 inch.

Carole wants her friend to draw exactly the same shape. Help her write directions for the shape to send to her friend. Use words from the Geometry Word Box to help you.

draw a square
that has one inch on
each side. Then erase
the top line. Then draw a
triangle that has no bottum
upsidedown in the squre. Then draw a
another triangle that has no bo turn
right side up but make sure it has
all eacwell side that they are an inch.

Geometry Word Box		
parallel	intersect	vertex	side
edge	right angle	clockwise	counterclockwise
line segment	rhombus	square	rectangle

This Level 3 paper illustrates the following features: The instructions include several vocabulary words from the Word Box. The main components are described as being a 1-inch square and an "overlapping" rhombus. The instructions provide basic information about the relationship between these shapes, but more information and clarification are required to understand what the final figure looks like.

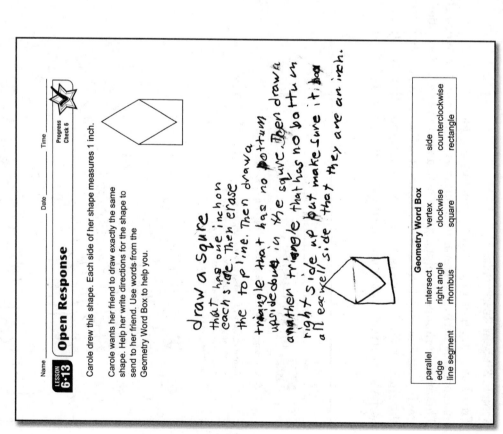

LESSON 6·13 **Open Response** Progress Check 6

Carole drew this shape. Each side of her shape measures 1 inch.

Carole wants her friend to draw exactly the same shape. Help her write directions for the shape to send to her friend. Use words from the Geometry Word Box to help you.

First get a rectaler. Then make a
square. Make all the sides of the isha pell in After
that draw a rhombus overlapping
the square. Make the end of the
rhombus in the middle of the
square. Make all of the
opasite lines parallel.

Geometry Word Box		
parallel	intersect	vertex	side
edge	right angle	clockwise	counterclockwise
line segment	rhombus	square	rectangle

This Level 2 paper illustrates the following features: The instructions include several vocabulary words from the Word Box. One main component of the figure is described in detail—the rhombus. The instructions describe drawing the rhombus, but no mention is made of the other components of the figure.

This Level 1 paper illustrates the following features: The instructions include several vocabulary words from the Word Box. Some of the features of the figure are described. Although the instructions highlight some of the features, no connections are made between the features that would lead to drawing the figure.

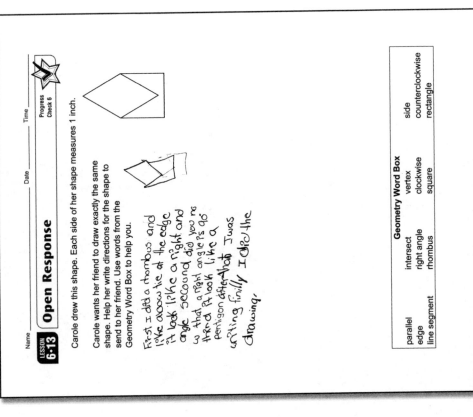

Level 2 paper:

Name _____ Date _____ Time _____

LESSON 6·13 **Open Response**

Progress Check 6

Carole drew this shape. Each side of her shape measures 1 inch.

Carole wants her friend to draw exactly the same shape. Help her write directions for the shape to send to her friend. Use words from the Geometry Word Box to help you.

Directions: ① draw a rhombus.
② make sure the rhombus has parallel lines. ③ make sure the rhombus has 3 edges
④ then draw it.

Geometry Word Box

parallel	intersect	vertex	side
edge	right angle	clockwise	counterclockwise
line segment	rhombus	square	rectangle

Level 1 paper:

Name _____ Date _____ Time _____

LESSON 6·13 **Open Response**

Progress Check 6

Carole drew this shape. Each side of her shape measures 1 inch.

Carole wants her friend to draw exactly the same shape. Help her write directions for the shape to send to her friend. Use words from the Geometry Word Box to help you.

First I did a rhombus and I like draw the at the edge it look like a right and angle Second did you no whata right angle's go the d it look like a pentagon after that I was writing finily I did the drawing.

Geometry Word Box

parallel	intersect	vertex	side
edge	right angle	clockwise	counterclockwise
line segment	rhombus	square	rectangle

Mid-Year Assessment Goals

The Mid-Year Assessment (pages 213–216) provides an additional opportunity that you may use as part of your balanced assessment plan. It covers some of the important concepts and skills presented in *Third Grade Everyday Mathematics*. It should be used to complement the ongoing and periodic assessments that appear within lessons and at the end of units. The following table provides the goals for all the problems in the Mid-Year Assessment.

Problem(s)	Grade-Level Goal
1	**Operations and Computation 1:** Demonstrate automaticity with all addition and subtraction facts through 10 + 10; use basic facts to compute fact extensions such as 80 + 70.
2	**Operations and Computation 6:** Recognize and describe change, comparison, and parts-and-total situations; use repeated addition, arrays, and skip counting to model multiplication; use equal sharing and equal grouping to model division.
3	**Measurement and Reference Frames 4:** Tell and show time to the nearest minute on an analog clock; tell and write time in digital notation.
4	**Operations and Computation 2:** Use manipulatives, mental arithmetic, paper-and-pencil algorithms and models, and calculators to solve problems involving the addition and subtraction of whole numbers and decimals in a money context; describe the strategies used and explain how they work.
5	**Operations and Computation 6:** Recognize and describe change, comparison, and parts-and-total situations; use repeated addition, arrays, and skip counting to model multiplication; use equal sharing and equal grouping to model division.
6	**Measurement and Reference Frames 1:** Estimate length with and without tools; measure length to the nearest $\frac{1}{2}$ inch and $\frac{1}{2}$ centimeter; draw and describe angles as records of rotations.
7	**Data and Chance 1:** Collect and organize data or use given data to create charts, tables, graphs, and line plots.
8	**Operations and Computation 6:** Recognize and describe change, comparison, and parts-and-total situations; use repeated addition, arrays, and skip counting to model multiplication; use equal sharing and equal grouping to model division.
9	**Operations and Computation 1:** Demonstrate automaticity with all addition and subtraction facts through 10 + 10; use basic facts to compute fact extensions such as 80 + 70.
10	**Measurement and Reference Frames 1:** Estimate length with and without tools; measure length to the nearest $\frac{1}{2}$ inch and $\frac{1}{2}$ centimeter; draw and describe angles as records of rotations.
11	**Operations and Computation 6:** Recognize and describe change, comparison, and parts-and-total situations; use repeated addition, arrays, and skip counting to model multiplication; use equal sharing and equal grouping to model division.
12	**Measurement and Reference Frames 1:** Estimate length with and without tools; measure length to the nearest $\frac{1}{2}$ inch and $\frac{1}{2}$ centimeter; draw and describe angles as records of rotations.

Assessment Overview

In this unit, children extend their work with multiplication to products with factors of multiples of 10, 100, and 1,000. Use the information in this section to develop your assessment plan for Unit 7.

Ongoing Assessment

Opportunities for using and collecting ongoing assessment information are highlighted in Informing Instruction and Recognizing Student Achievement notes. Student products, along with observations and suggested writing prompts, provide a range of useful assessment information.

Informing Instruction

The Informing Instruction notes highlight children's thinking and point out common misconceptions. Informing Instruction in Unit 7: Lessons 7-4, 7-5, 7-6, and 7-7.

Recognizing Student Achievement

The Recognizing Student Achievement notes highlight specific tasks from which teachers can collect assessment data to monitor and document children's progress toward meeting Grade-Level Goals.

Lesson	Content Assessed	Where to Find It
7◆1	Compute multiplication facts. [Operation and Computation Goal 3]	*TLG*, p. 577
7◆2	Use arrays to model multiplication. [Operations and Computation Goal 6]	*TLG*, p. 583
7◆3	Find and use rules to solve multiplication and division problems. [Patterns, Functions, and Algebra Goal 1]	*TLG*, p. 589
7◆4	Show that parentheses affect the order of operations. [Patterns, Functions, and Algebra Goal 3]	*TLG*, p. 597
7◆5	Show that the operation inside the parentheses is carried out first. [Patterns, Functions, and Algebra Goal 3]	*TLG*, p. 602
7◆6	Use relationships between units of time to solve number stories. [Measurement and Reference Frames Goal 3]	*TLG*, p. 610
7◆7	Explain how an estimate is obtained. [Operations and Computation Goal 5]	*TLG*, p. 616
7◆8	Multiply 2-digit numbers by a 1-digit number. [Operations and Computation Goal 4]	*TLG*, p. 620
7◆9	Identify and describe solid figures. [Geometry Goal 2]	*TLG*, p. 625

Math Boxes

Math Boxes, one of several types of tasks highlighted in the Recognizing Student Achievement notes, have an additional useful feature. Math Boxes in most lessons are paired or linked with Math Boxes in one or two other lessons that have similar problems. Paired or linked Math Boxes in Unit 7: 7-1 and 7-3; 7-2 and 7-4; 7-5, 7-7, and 7-9; and 7-6 and 7-8.

Writing/Reasoning Prompts

In Unit 7, a variety of writing prompts encourage children to explain their strategies and thinking, to reflect on their learning, and to make connections to other mathematics or life experiences. Here are some of the Unit 7 suggestions:

Lesson	Writing/Reasoning Prompts	Where to Find It
7•3	Explain how rays and lines are alike and how they are different.	*TLG*, p. 591
7•4	Write your own polygon riddle.	*TLG*, p. 598
7•6	Describe a pattern you see and write three more facts that follow the same pattern.	*TLG*, p. 611
7•7	Write each number sentence and find a different answer by moving the parentheses.	*TLG*, p. 616

Portfolio Opportunities

Portfolios are a versatile tool for assessment. They help children reflect on their mathematical growth and help teachers understand and document that growth. Each unit identifies several student products that can be selected and stored in a portfolio. Here are some of the Unit 7 suggestions:

Lesson	Portfolio Opportunities	Where to Find It
7•2	Children identify and describe patterns that they see in 9s facts.	*TLG*, p. 587
7•4	Children write their own polygon riddle.	*TLG*, p. 598
7•6	Children describe a pattern they see, and write three more facts that follow the same pattern.	*TLG*, p. 611
7•7	Children explain why and how they would make estimates when they shop.	*TLG*, p. 616
7•9	Children answer questions related to a ratio problem.	*TLG*, p. 627

Periodic Assessment

Every Progress Check lesson includes opportunities to observe children's progress and to collect student products in a variety of ways—Self Assessment, Oral and Slate Assessment, Written Assessment, and an Open Response task. For more details, see the first page of Progress Check 7, Lesson 7-10 on page 630, of the *Teacher's Lesson Guide*.

Progress Check Modifications

Written Assessments are one way children demonstrate what they know. The table below shows modifications for the Written Assessment in this unit. Use these to maximize opportunities for children to demonstrate what they know. Modifications can be given individually or written on the board for the class.

Problem(s)	Modifications for Written Assessment
1–10	For Problems 1–10, use counters and build arrays to find the products.
16–17	For Problems 16–17, use base-10 blocks to model the numbers and solve the problems.
17a	For Problem 17a, Rita wrote $500 - 200 = 300$ for her ballpark estimate. Dani wrote $460 - 150 = 310$. Explain which ballpark estimate you think is correct and why.
18–21	For Problems 18–21, write the value of the expression in parentheses, and rewrite the problem using the value you recorded in place of the expression in parentheses.

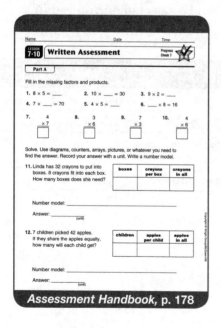

Assessment Handbook, p. 178

The Written Assessment for the Unit 7 Progress Check is on pages 178–180.

Open Response, *Button Dolls*

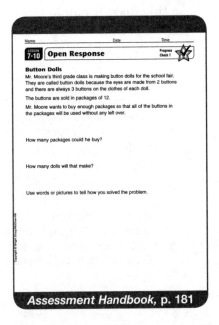

Assessment Handbook, p. 181

40-50 Min.

Description

For this task, children solve a multistep problem involving equal groups.

Focus

◆ **Find multiples of 2, 5, and 10.**
[Number and Numeration Goal 3]

◆ **Use repeated addition, arrays, and skip counting to model multiplication; use equal sharing and equal grouping to model division.** [Operations and Computation Goal 6]

◆ **Use numeric patterns to solve problems.**
[Patterns, Functions, and Algebra Goal 1]

Implementation Tips

◆ Have children draw pictures or use tallies to help them solve the problem.

◆ Provide counters for children who want to model the problem.

Modifications for Meeting Diverse Needs

◆ Create pictures for children to manipulate. On a sheet of paper, draw 4 simple dolls that clearly show the 5 buttons. Copy and cut apart these dolls for children to use. Also, provide pictures of button packages (3 × 4 arrays). Children can match the number of dolls (2) that can be made from each package and use counters to indicate the remaining buttons (2). When they have enough remaining buttons (counters) to form a new doll, they should trade them in for another doll. Repeat the process until there are no leftover buttons (counters).

◆ Have children find a second solution to the problem and describe a rule they can use to find many solutions.

Improving Open Response Skills

After children complete the task, discuss and list the most important components of a successful open response paper. For example, there should be evidence of using multiples for both 12 and 5; the description should explain how the number of dolls and packages are derived. After the discussion, give children a few minutes to improve their papers.

Note: The wording and formatting of the text on the student samples that follow may vary slightly from the actual task your children will complete. These minor discrepancies will not affect the implementation of the task.

Rubric

This rubric is designed to help you assess levels of mathematical performance on this task. It emphasizes mathematical understanding with only a mention of clarity of explanation. Consider the expectations of standardized tests in your area when applying a rubric. Modify this sample rubric as appropriate.

4 Determines a number of packages such that the total number of buttons can be equally distributed among the dolls. Tells how many dolls can be made from the buttons. Clearly explains and illustrates a strategy that includes multiples or equal groups of both 5 and 12.

3 Determines the total number of packages such that the total number of buttons can be equally distributed among the dolls. Tells how many dolls can be made from the buttons. Explains or illustrates some steps of a strategy that includes multiples or equal groups of both 5 and 12. There might be small errors in recording the answers.

2 Determines a number of packages and of dolls. There might be errors, but there is evidence of some understanding of the problem and of the need for groups of 5 or 12. Attempts to explain or illustrate some steps of a strategy.

1 Attempts to determine a number of packages and of dolls. There might be errors. There is little evidence of understanding the problem or the need for groups of 5 or 12.

0 Does not attempt to solve the problem.

Sample Student Responses

This Level 4 paper illustrates the following features: The explanation clearly describes a search for a multiple of both 12 and 5. The "picture" is a series of number sentences that justify the solution of 5 packages and 12 dolls, showing that 60 is the first multiple of 12 that does not have a remainder when divided by 5.

This Level 4 paper illustrates the following features: The illustration clearly shows packages containing 12 buttons each. The buttons in the packages are grouped by 5s and recorded as dolls. The explanation describes adding packages and grouping buttons until there are no remaining buttons.

Mr. Moore's third grade class is making button dolls for the school fair. They are called button dolls because the eyes are made from 2 buttons and there are always 3 buttons on the clothes of each doll.

The buttons are sold in packages of 12.

Mr. Moore wants to buy enough packages so that all of the buttons in the packages will be used without any left over.

How many packages could he buy? 5

How many dolls will that make? 12

Use words or pictures to tell how you solved the problem.

$12 \div 5 = X$
$24 \div 5 = X$
$36 \div 5 = X$
$48 \div 5 = X$
$60 \div 5 = 12$

I first start with 12. Then I do ÷ by 5 because 2+3=5 for how many buttons for each doll. I keep adding 12 till I have an answer that has 0 or 5 in the ones place.

Mr. Moore's third grade class is making button dolls for the school fair. They are called button dolls because the eyes are made from 2 buttons and there are always 3 buttons on the clothes of each doll.

The buttons are sold in packages of 12.

Mr. Moore wants to buy enough packages so that all of the buttons in the packages will be used without any left over.

How many packages could he buy? 5 packages

How many dolls will that make? 12 dolls

Use words or pictures to tell how you solved the problem.

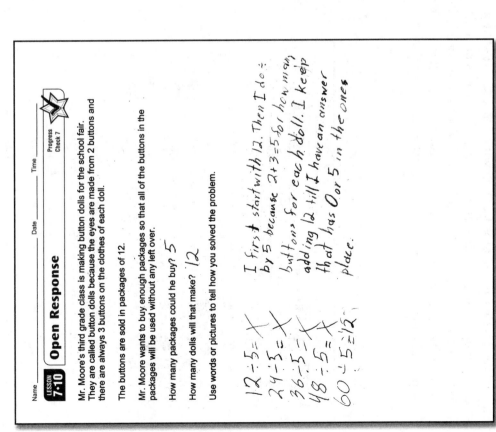

My answer is 5 packages and 12 dolls. I solved it by drawing dolls and making "move" packages till there is no left over buttons.

This Level 3 paper illustrates the following features: It illustrates buttons in rows of 6 so that these can be shown in packages of 12. The buttons are then grouped by 5s. A record of how to group extra buttons is added. The explanation describes some steps of solving the problem, but it is confusing and some steps are missing.

This Level 3 paper illustrates the following features: It shows a strategy of drawing packages and crossing off buttons as dolls are drawn in the illustration. The explanation does not describe the illustrated strategy but does provide a description of how to find multiple solutions to the problem using the patterns.

This Level 1 paper illustrates the following features: It shows 12 buttons in each package and 5 buttons on each doll in the illustration. There is no evidence of understanding the problem beyond the setup. The answer given is incorrect.

This Level 2 paper illustrates the following features: It shows buttons for 12 dolls grouped by 5s in the illustration. There is some evidence of an understanding of the problem but without an explanation to clarify work.

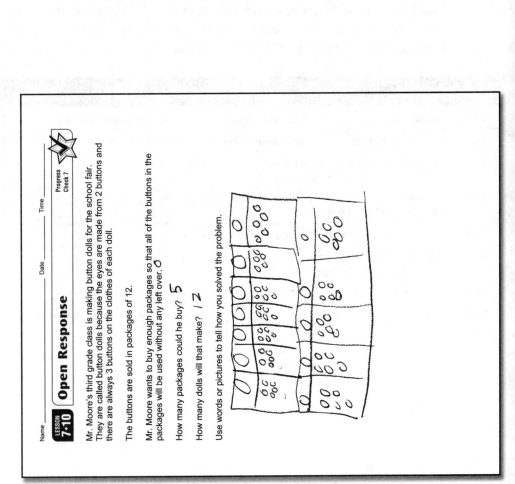

Name _____ Date _____ Time _____

LESSON 7·10 Open Response Progress Check 7

Mr. Moore's third grade class is making button dolls for the school fair. They are called button dolls because the eyes are made from 2 buttons and there are always 3 buttons on the clothes of each doll.

The buttons are sold in packages of 12.

Mr. Moore wants to buy enough packages so that all of the buttons in the packages will be used without any left over.

How many packages could he buy?

How many dolls will that make?

Use words or pictures to tell how you solved the problem.

box   dolls

her are 7 Pack gis,3
and 96 Button Dolls.

Name _____ Date _____ Time _____

LESSON 7·10 Open Response Progress Check 7

Mr. Moore's third grade class is making button dolls for the school fair. They are called button dolls because the eyes are made from 2 buttons and there are always 3 buttons on the clothes of each doll.

The buttons are sold in packages of 12.

Mr. Moore wants to buy enough packages so that all of the buttons in the packages will be used without any left over. 0

How many packages could he buy? 5

How many dolls will that make? 12

Use words or pictures to tell how you solved the problem.

Assessment Overview

In this unit, children review the uses of fractions and fraction notation, and work toward a solid understanding of equivalent fractions. Use the information in this section to develop your assessment plan for Unit 8.

Ongoing Assessment

Opportunities for using and collecting ongoing assessment information are highlighted in Informing Instruction and Recognizing Student Achievement notes. Student products, along with observations and suggested writing prompts, provide a range of useful assessment information.

Informing Instruction

The Informing Instruction notes highlight children's thinking and point out common misconceptions. Informing Instruction in Unit 8: Lessons 8-1, 8-4, 8-7, and 8-8.

Recognizing Student Achievement

The Recognizing Student Achievement notes highlight specific tasks from which teachers can collect assessment data to monitor and document children's progress toward meeting Grade-Level Goals.

Lesson	Content Assessed	Where to Find It
8◆1	**Identify and write fractions that name regions.** [Number and Numeration Goal 2]	*TLG*, p. 652
8◆2	**Describe events using basic probability terms.** [Data and Chance Goal 3]	*TLG*, p. 657
8◆3	**Demonstrate how parentheses affect the order of operations.** [Patterns, Functions, and Algebra Goal 3]	*TLG*, p. 663
8◆4	**Identify the value of digits in numbers though hundred-thousands.** [Number and Numeration Goal 1]	*TLG*, p. 666
8◆5	**Make and test predictions for simple experiments.** [Data and Chance Goal 4]	*TLG*, p. 674
8◆6	**Describe relationships between equivalent units of time.** [Measurement and Reference Frames Goal 3]	*TLG*, p. 680
8◆7	**Use Fraction Cards to find equivalent fractions.** [Number and Numeration Goal 5]	*TLG*, p. 685
8◆8	**Solve problems involving fractional parts of a collection.** [Number and Numeration Goal 2]	*TLG*, p. 691

Math Boxes

Math Boxes, one of several types of tasks highlighted in the Recognizing Student Achievement notes, have an additional useful feature. Math Boxes in most lessons are paired or linked with Math Boxes in one or two other lessons that have similar problems. Paired or linked Math Boxes in Unit 8: 8-1 and 8-3; 8-2 and 8-4; 8-5 and 8-7; and 8-6 and 8-8.

Writing/Reasoning Prompts

In Unit 8, a variety of writing prompts encourage children to explain their strategies and thinking, to reflect on their learning, and to make connections to other mathematics or life experiences. Here are some of the Unit 8 suggestions:

Lesson	Writing/Reasoning Prompts	Where to Find It
8•3	Explain how knowing that $5 \times 9 = 45$ helps you know that $5 \times 900 = 4,500$.	*TLG*, p. 663
8•4	Explain how to find the probability of drawing a red or blue block.	*TLG*, p. 669
8•7	Explain the meaning of *share equally*.	*TLG*, p. 686
8•8	Explain whether $\frac{1}{5}$ is more or less than $\frac{1}{2}$.	*TLG*, p. 693

Portfolio Opportunities

Portfolios are a versatile tool for assessment. They help children reflect on their mathematical growth and help teachers understand and document that growth. Each unit identifies several student products that can be selected and stored in a portfolio. Here are some of the Unit 8 suggestions:

Lesson	Portfolio Opportunities	Where to Find It
8•3	Children explain how knowing that $5 \times 9 = 45$ helps you know that $5 \times 900 = 4,500$.	*TLG*, p. 663
8•5	Children look for a rule about how fractions equivalent to $\frac{1}{2}$ are related to one another.	*TLG*, p. 676
8•5	Children make poster-size name-collection boxes for familiar fractions.	*TLG*, p. 676
8•7	Children explain the meaning of *share equally*.	*TLG*, p. 686
8•8	Children explain whether $\frac{1}{5}$ is more or less than $\frac{1}{2}$.	*TLG*, p. 693

Periodic Assessment

Every Progress Check lesson includes opportunities to observe children's progress and to collect student products in a variety of ways—Self Assessment, Oral and Slate Assessment, Written Assessment, and an Open Response task. For more details, see the first page of Progress Check 8, Lesson 8-9 on page 694, of the *Teacher's Lesson Guide*.

Progress Check Modifications

Written Assessments are one way children demonstrate what they know. The table below shows modifications for the Written Assessment in this unit. Use these to maximize opportunities for children to demonstrate what they know. Modifications can be given individually or written on the board for the class.

Problem(s)	Modifications for Written Assessment
6	For Problem 6, make a place-value chart, and write each digit in its correct place.
8	For Problem 8, use counters to model the problem.
13	For Problem 13, explain how you know which fraction names are equivalent to $\frac{3}{4}$. Draw a picture that supports your explanation.
15	For Problem 15, use quarters and dimes to model the problem.

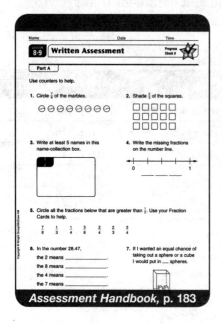

Assessment Handbook, p. 183

The Written Assessment for the Unit 8 Progress Check is on pages 183–185.

Open Response, *Solving a Coin Problem*

25-35 Min.

Description

For this task, children find the number and value of coins in a collection based on what fraction each type of coin represents in the collection.

Focus

◆ **Read, write, and model fractions; solve problems involving fractional parts of a collection; describe strategies used.**
[Number and Numeration Goal 2]

◆ **Use manipulatives, mental arithmetic, and paper-and-pencil algorithms to solve problems involving the addition of decimals in a money context.**
[Operations and Computation Goal 2]

Implementation Tips

◆ Provide tool-kit coins for children to model the problem.

Modifications for Meeting Diverse Needs

◆ Provide 24 counters. For each fraction, have children model 24 divided into the required number of parts. For example, for "$\frac{1}{3}$ *were pennies,*" have children divide 24 into thirds and then find $\frac{1}{3}$. When they have figured out the number of coins needed for each type of coin, have them use tool-kit coins to find the total value.

◆ Have children record number sentences they can use to solve Problems 1 and 3. Have them describe the relationship between division and finding the fraction of a collection.

Improving Open Response Skills

After children complete the task, ask children to share their ideas in small groups. Have them reflect on and record what was difficult and what was easy about the task and describe how they think they can improve their work.

Note: The wording and formatting of the text on the student samples that follow may vary slightly from the actual task your children will complete. These minor discrepancies will not affect the implementation of the task.

Assessment Handbook, p. 186

Rubric

This rubric is designed to help you assess levels of mathematical performance on this task. It emphasizes mathematical understanding with only a mention of clarity of explanation. Consider the expectations of standardized tests in your area when applying a rubric. Modify this sample rubric as appropriate.

4 Identifies the correct number of coins for each type. Shows how to find each fraction of 24. Clearly and completely explains how to find the number of dimes. Calculates the value of the coin combination and shows all work using correct notation.

3 Identifies the correct number of coins for each type. Shows some work illustrating how to find each fraction of 24. Explains some steps for how to find the number of dimes. Calculates the value of the coin combination and shows work, but there might be minor notation errors.

2 Attempts to find the number of coins for each type. Shows some work related to finding a fraction of 24. The explanation for finding the number of dimes makes some sense, but it might have errors. Attempts to calculate the value of the coins.

1 Attempts to find a number of coins for each type and a total value for the coins, but there might be errors. There is little evidence of understanding how to find the fraction of a collection.

0 Does not attempt to solve the problem.

Sample Student Responses

This Level 4 paper illustrates the following features: It shows the correct numbers of coins. The number sentences record using division to find the fraction of the collection. The explanation for finding the number of dimes describes how to divide the total into a number of groups according to the denominator of the fraction. The correct total for the coin combination is given.

This Level 4 paper illustrates the following features: It shows the correct numbers of coins. The illustration shows dividing 24 into groups as designated by the denominator. The explanation of how to find the number of dimes reflects the same process in words. The correct total for the coin combination is given.

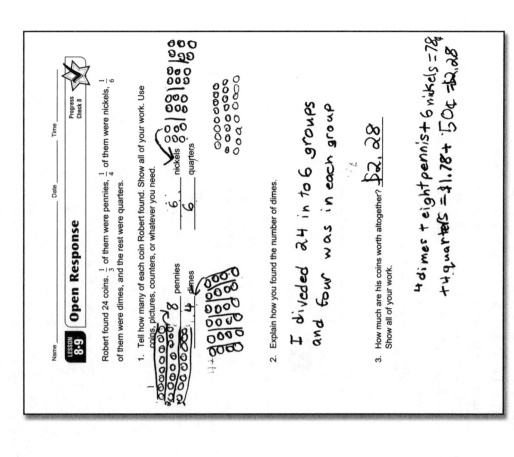

This Level 3 paper illustrates the following features: It shows the correct numbers of coins. The number sentences record using multiplication to find the fraction of the collection. The explanation for finding the number of dimes using multiplication makes sense but is incomplete. The correct total for the coin combination is given, but the decimal point and dollar sign are missing.

This Level 3 paper illustrates the following features: It shows the correct numbers of coins. The number sentences record using multiplication to find the fraction of the collection. The explanation for finding the number of dimes using multiplication makes sense but is incomplete. The correct total for the coin combination is given, but the dollar sign is missing.

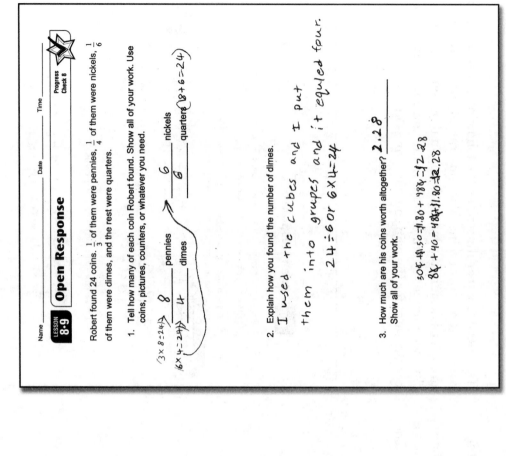

Name _____ Date _____ Time _____

LESSON 8·9 **Open Response**

Progress Check 8

Robert found 24 coins. $\frac{1}{3}$ of them were pennies, $\frac{1}{4}$ of them were nickels, $\frac{1}{6}$ of them were dimes, and the rest were quarters.

1. Tell how many of each coin Robert found. Show all of your work. Use coins, pictures, counters, or whatever you need.

(3 × 8=24→) 8 pennies
(6×4=24→) 4 dimes
6 nickels
6 quarters (8 + 6 =24)

2. Explain how you found the number of dimes.
I used the cubes and I put them into grupes and it equled four. 24÷6 or 6×4=24

3. How much are his coins worth altogether? **2.28**
Show all of your work.

50¢ 4¢1.50=1.80 + 98¢ =2.28
8¢ + 40=48¢+1.80=2.28

Name _____ Date _____ Time _____

LESSON 8·9 **Open Response**

Progress Check 8

21 17 11

Robert found 24 coins. $\frac{1}{3}$ of them were pennies, $\frac{1}{4}$ of them were nickels, $\frac{1}{6}$ of them were dimes, and the rest were quarters.

1. Tell how many of each coin Robert found. Show all of your work. Use coins, pictures, counters, or whatever you need.

8 pennies
4 dimes
6 nickels
6 quarters

8×3=24
4×6=24
6×4=24

8+30+40+150= 228

2. Explain how you found the number of dimes.
I did 4×6 and I knew it was 24 and that is how I got the answer.

3. How much are his coins worth altogether? 228
Show all of your work.

8+30+40 +150 = 2.28

This Level 1 paper illustrates the following features: It shows the correct numbers of coins, but there is no indication of the strategy used to calculate the fraction of the collection. The explanation for finding the number of dimes might refer to a valid strategy, but there is not enough information. Problem 3 is misinterpreted.

This Level 2 paper illustrates the following features: It shows number sentences that record attempts to use multiplication and division to find the fraction of the collection. The explanation for finding the number of dimes might make sense in the context of the problem, but combined with the other work shown, it is confusing. The total for the coin combination is incorrect.

Name _____ Date _____ Time _____

LESSON 8-9 Open Response Progress Check 8

Robert found 24 coins. $\frac{1}{3}$ of them were pennies, $\frac{1}{4}$ of them were nickels, $\frac{1}{6}$ of them were dimes, and the rest were quarters.

1. Tell how many of each coin Robert found. Show all of your work. Use coins, pictures, counters, or whatever you need.

8 pennies   6 nickels
4 dimes   6 quarters

2. Explain how you found the number of dimes. I stuck all of the counters and I got 4 dimes

3. How much are his coins worth altogether? $ 4+6+6=24 Show all of your work.

Name _____ Date _____ Time _____

LESSON 8-9 Open Response Progress Check 8

Robert found 24 coins. $\frac{1}{3}$ of them were pennies, $\frac{1}{4}$ of them were nickels, $\frac{1}{6}$ of them were dimes, and the rest were quarters.

1. Tell how many of each coin Robert found. Show all of your work. Use coins, pictures, counters, or whatever you need.

$8 \times 3 = 24$ 8 pennies
$6 \div 3 = 6$
$24 \div 2 = 6$ dimes
     nickels
     quarters
$18 + 6 = 24$

2. Explain how you found the number of dimes. Because 6 is 1 of 12 and 12 is 2 of 24 6 would be the answer.

3. How much are his coins worth altogether? $12.48 Show all of your work.

$2 + 3 + 2 + 8 = $12.48

Assessment Overview   117

Unit 9 Assessment Overview

In this unit, children further explore multiplication including the introduction of both partial-products and lattice algorithms for multiplication. Use the information in this section to develop your assessment plan for Unit 9.

Ongoing Assessment

Opportunities for using and collecting ongoing assessment information are highlighted in Informing Instruction and Recognizing Student Achievement notes. Student products, along with observations and suggested writing prompts, provide a range of useful assessment information.

Informing Instruction

The Informing Instruction notes highlight children's thinking and point out common misconceptions. Informing Instruction in Unit 9: Lessons 9-1, 9-2, 9-3, 9-6, 9-7, 9-8, 9-9, 9-11, and 9-12.

Recognizing Student Achievement

The Recognizing Student Achievement notes highlight specific tasks from which teachers can collect assessment data to monitor and document children's progress toward meeting Grade-Level Goals.

Lesson	Content Assessed	Where to Find It
9•1	**Solve problems involving multiples of 10, 100, and 1,000.** [Number and Numeration Goal 3]	*TLG*, p. 716
9•2	**Use strategies to solve 1-digit by 2-digit multiplication problems.** [Operations and Computation Goal 4]	*TLG*, p. 721
9•3	**Predict the outcome of an experiment.** [Data and Chance Goal 4]	*TLG*, p. 728
9•4	**Solve multiplication problems.** [Operations and Computation Goal 4]	*TLG*, p. 733
9•5	**Compare fractions.** [Number and Numeration Goal 6]	*TLG*, p. 739
9•6	**Use concrete materials to model common fractions.** [Number and Numeration Goal 2]	*TLG*, p. 743
9•7	**Solve problems involving fractional parts of a region.** [Number and Numeration Goal 2]	*TLG*, p. 752
9•8	**Demonstrate that parentheses affect the order of operations.** [Patterns, Functions, and Algebra Goal 3]	*TLG*, p. 758
9•9	**Identify and describe polygons.** [Geometry Goal 2]	*TLG*, p. 764
9•10	**Describe angle rotations.** [Measurement and Reference Frames Goal 1]	*TLG*, p. 770
9•11	**Describe angle rotations.** [Measurement and Reference Frames Goal 1]	*TLG*, p. 776
9•12	**Demonstrate automaticity with multiplication facts.** [Operations and Computation Goal 3]	*TLG*, p. 782
9•13	**Find the areas of rectangular shapes.** [Measurement and Reference Frames Goal 2]	*TLG*, p. 788

Math Boxes

Math Boxes, one of several types of tasks highlighted in the Recognizing Student Achievement notes, have an additional useful feature. Math Boxes in most lessons are paired or linked with Math Boxes in one or two other lessons that have similar problems. Paired or linked Math Boxes in Unit 9: 9-1 and 9-3; 9-2 and 9-4; 9-5 and 9-7; 9-6 and 9-8; 9-9, 9-11, and 9-13; and 9-10 and 9-12.

Writing/Reasoning Prompts

In Unit 9, a variety of writing prompts encourage children to explain their strategies and thinking, to reflect on their learning, and to make connections to other mathematics or life experiences. Here are some of the Unit 9 suggestions:

Lesson	Writing/Reasoning Prompts	Where to Find It
9◆2	Explain how you figured out which numbers to write on the number line.	*TLG*, p. 722
9◆6	Explain how you decided if the game was fair.	*TLG*, p. 746
9◆7	Explain how you can equally share the leftover pizza among 4 people.	*TLG*, p. 752
9◆9	Explain how you found all the factors for 24.	*TLG*, p. 764

Portfolio Opportunities

Portfolios are a versatile tool for assessment. They help children reflect on their mathematical growth and help teachers understand and document that growth. Each unit identifies several student products that can be selected and stored in a portfolio. Here are some of the Unit 9 suggestions:

Lesson	Portfolio Opportunities	Where to Find It
9◆1	Children write multiplication and division number stories.	*TLG*, p. 717
9◆2	Children calculate weekly allowances according to three different plans.	*TLG*, p. 723
9◆4	Children find sums of whole numbers by multiplying a partial sum a certain number of times.	*TLG*, p. 735
9◆9	Children solve problems related to the musical composition *Vexations*.	*TLG*, p. 765
9◆10	Children find number patterns by building equilateral triangles.	*TLG*, p. 769

Periodic Assessment

Every Progress Check lesson includes opportunities to observe children's progress and to collect student products in a variety of ways—Self Assessment, Oral and Slate Assessment, Written Assessment, and an Open Response task. For more details, see the first page of Progress Check 9, Lesson 9-14 on page 790, of the *Teacher's Lesson Guide*.

Progress Check Modifications

Written Assessments are one way children demonstrate what they know. The table below shows modifications for the Written Assessment in this unit. Use these to maximize opportunities for children to demonstrate what they know. Modifications can be given individually or written on the board for the class.

Problem(s)	Modifications for Written Assessment
1	For Problem 1, use base-10 blocks to model four 40s and solve the problem.
4	For Problem 4, explain how you figured out which fraction is the largest. Draw pictures to support your explanation.
5–8	For Problems 5–8, write the value of the expression in parentheses, and rewrite the problem using the value you recorded in place of the expression in parentheses.
16	For Problem 16, do the partial products for this problem to find Lora's mistake.

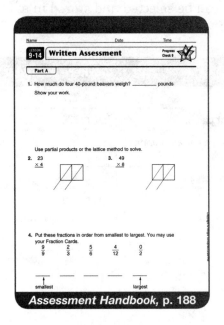

Assessment Handbook, p. 188

The Written Assessment for the Unit 9 Progress Check is on pages 188–190.

Open Response, *Factor Patterns*

Description

For this task, children identify patterns in the relationships between factors and products and use the patterns to solve a problem.

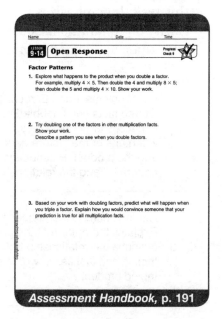

Assessment Handbook, p. 191

Focus

◆ **Use mental arithmetic and paper-and-pencil algorithms to solve problems involving the multiplication of 2-digit whole numbers by 1-digit whole numbers; describe the strategies used.**
[Operations and Computation Goal 4]

◆ **Describe numeric patterns; describe rules for patterns and use them to solve problems.**
[Patterns, Functions, and Algebra Goal 1]

Implementation Tips

◆ Review the meaning of *factor* and *product*.

Modifications for Meeting Diverse Needs

◆ Provide children with a chart to help them organize their work for Problems 1 and 2. For example:

	Factors	Problem	Product
Original Problem	4, 5	4 × 5 =	
Doubling One Factor (4)	**8**, 5	**8** × 5 =	
Doubling the Other Factor (5)	4, **10**	4 × **10** =	

◆ Have children predict what will happen to the product if both factors are doubled. Have them check their predictions.

Improving Open Response Skills

After children complete the task, have them analyze several explanations for Problem 3 (without the number sentences). Consider using some of the explanations included in the Sample Student Responses beginning on page 123 of this book. Record each explanation on a piece of chart paper and give one to a group. Have children determine and record what information is missing from each explanation. Have them work together to write a clearer and more complete explanation.

Note: The wording and formatting of the text on the student samples that follow may vary slightly from the actual task your children will complete. These minor discrepancies will not affect the implementaton of the task.

Rubric

This rubric is designed to help you assess levels of mathematical performance on this task. It emphasizes mathematical understanding with only a mention of clarity of explanation. Consider the expectations of standardized tests in your area when applying a rubric. Modify this sample rubric as appropriate.

4 For Problems 1 and 2, records number sentences that show the original fact and the altered facts (with doubled factors). For Problem 1, writes number sentences for both variations of doubled factors. Clearly explains the pattern of the product doubling when one of the factors doubles, and describes the relationship between the factor and the product. Extends the doubling pattern to tripling, and clearly explains the pattern for and the relationship between factor and product.

3 Records number sentences that show the original altered facts (with doubled factors). Explains the pattern of the product doubling when one of the factors doubles. Might describe the relationship between factor and product. Extends the doubling pattern to tripling and justifies in words or with an example how a tripled factor results in a tripled product.

2 Records number sentences that show the original and altered facts (with doubled factors). Attempts to describe a pattern that results from doubling a factor. Recognizes that the doubling pattern can be extended to tripling and attempts to describe in words or with an example how a tripled factor results in a tripled product. The explanation might require clarification, or it might be incomplete.

1 Records number sentences, but they might not reflect doubling factors, or there might be errors. Attempts to describe some pattern, but there might be little evidence of understanding the problem.

0 Does not attempt to solve the problem.

This Level 4 paper illustrates the following features: It shows number sentences that clearly illustrate doubling or tripling a factor recorded for all three problems. The explanation clearly states the relationship between the doubled factor and product. The pattern of tripled products and factors is identified, applied, and clearly described in Problem 3.

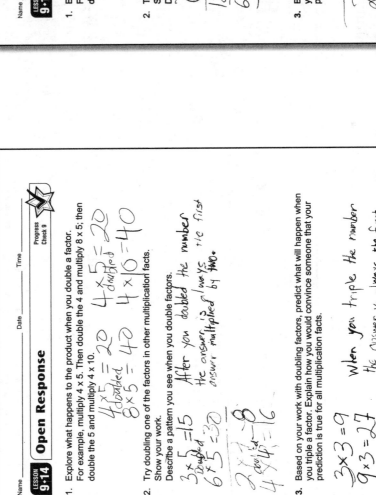

This Level 4 paper illustrates the following features: It shows number sentences that clearly illustrate doubling each factor recorded for the first two problems. The explanation clearly states the relationship between the doubled factor and product. The pattern of tripled products and factors is identified, applied, and clearly described in Problem 3, and the intermediate step of doubling is shown.

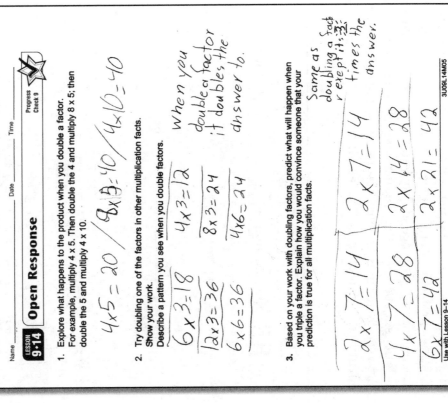

This Level 3 paper illustrates the following features: It shows number sentences that illustrate doubling or tripling a factor recorded for all three problems. The explanation describes modifying both the factor and the product, but it does not clearly make the connection between the factor and the product. The pattern of tripled products and factors is identified, applied, and described in Problem 3.

This Level 3 paper illustrates the following features: It shows number sentences that illustrate doubling a factor recorded for the first two problems. For Problem 3, the number sentence is connected to one number sentence in Problem 2. The explanation describes the relationship between the factor and the products, but does not make the connection between the factor and product. The pattern of tripling the product is identified and applied in Problem 3.

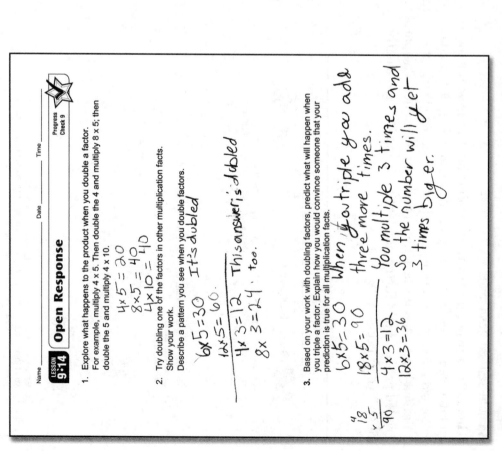

Left paper:

Name _____ Date _____ Time _____

LESSON 9·14 **Open Response** Progress Check 9

1. Explore what happens to the product when you double a factor. For example, multiply 4 x 5. Then double the 4 and multiply 8 x 5; then double the 5 and multiply 4 x 10.

   4x5 = 20
   8x5 = 40
   4x10 = 40

2. Try doubling one of the factors in other multiplication facts. Show your work. Describe a pattern you see when you double factors.

   6x5=30   It's dubled
   18x5= 60.
   4x3=12   Thisanswer's dubled
   8x 3=24, too.

3. Based on your work with doubling factors, predict what will happen when you triple a factor. Explain how you would convince someone that your prediction is true for all multiplication facts.

   6x5=30   When you triple you add
   18x5= 90   three more times.
   4x3=12   You multiple 3 times and
   12x3=36   So the number will get
   3 times bigger.

   18
   x5
   ——
   90

Right paper:

Name _____ Date _____ Time _____

LESSON 9·14 **Open Response** Progress Check 9

1. Explore what happens to the product when you double a factor. For example, multiply 4 x 5. Then double the 4 and multiply 8 x 5; then double the 5 and multiply 4 x 10.

   4x5=20   4x10=40
   8x5=40

2. Try doubling one of the factors in other multiplication facts. Show your work. Describe a pattern you see when you double factors.

   3X6=18   when you double
   6x6=36   the first product
   12x3=36   then you get
   the second
   and 3rd answer.
   2x4=0
   4x4=16   8x2=16

3. Based on your work with doubling factors, predict what will happen when you triple a factor. Explain how you would convince someone that your prediction is true for all multiplication facts.

   4x12=48
   you add the product (16) 3 times
   and get the answer (48).

This Level 1 paper illustrates the following features: It shows number sentences that illustrate doubling a factor recorded for Problem 2. For Problem 3, the number sentences illustrate tripling a factor. The pattern described in Problem 2 applies to the situation, but it cannot be generalized. The explanation for Problem 3 makes no sense and provides no evidence of understanding the problem.

Name _____ Date _____ Time _____

Open Response

Progress
Check 9

1. Explore what happens to the product when you double a factor.
   For example, multiply 4 × 5. Then double the 4 and multiply 8 × 5; then double the 5 and multiply 4 × 10.

   10 11 0

2. Try doubling one of the factors in other multiplication facts.
   Show your work.
   Describe a pattern you see when you double factors.

   $6 \times 2 = 12$ the first product is the next one factor.
   $12 \times 2 = 24$
   $24 \times 2 = 48$

3. Based on your work with doubling factors, predict what will happen when you triple a factor. Explain how you would convince someone that your prediction is true for all multiplication facts.

   $2 \times 6 = 12$ they add number
   $6 \times 6 = 36$ to the factor and
   $18 \times 6 = 108$ they get the answer.

This Level 2 paper illustrates the following features: It shows number sentences that illustrate doubling a factor recorded for the first two problems. For Problem 3, the number sentence illustrates doubling and tripling a factor. The explanation in Problem 2 describes the relationship between doubling factors and doubling products. The explanation in Problem 3 appears to be incorrect, but the work shows some evidence of understanding the problem.

Name _____ Date _____ Time _____

Open Response

Progress
Check 9

1. Explore what happens to the product when you double a factor.
   For example, multiply 4 × 5. Then double the 4 and multiply 8 × 5; then double the 5 and multiply 4 × 10.

   $5 \times 5 = 25$
   $10 \times 5 = 50$

2. Try doubling one of the factors in other multiplication facts.
   Show your work.
   Describe a pattern you see when you double factors.

   $2 \times 24 = 48$
   $4 \times 24 = 96$

   Not onley does part of the problem duble ther ancer does

3. Based on your work with doubling factors, predict what will happen when you triple a factor. Explain how you would convince someone that your prediction is true for all multiplication facts.

   $5 \times 6 = 30$
   $10 \times 6 = 60$
   $15 \times 6 = 90$

   in the ancer it a does pluse by 30. $30 + 30 = 60$ $60 + 30 = 90$

Unit 10

Assessment Overview

In this unit, children build on previous work with measurement and extend their work with data landmarks including mean, median, and mode. Use the information in this section to develop your assessment plan for Unit 10.

Ongoing Assessment

Opportunities for using and collecting ongoing assessment information are highlighted in Informing Instruction and Recognizing Student Achievement notes. Student products, along with observations and suggested writing prompts, provide a range of useful assessment information.

Informing Instruction

The Informing Instruction notes highlight children's thinking and point out common misconceptions. Informing Instruction in Unit 10: Lessons 10-2, 10-3, 10-6, and 10-9.

Recognizing Student Achievement

The Recognizing Student Achievement notes highlight specific tasks from which teachers can collect assessment data to monitor and document children's progress toward meeting Grade-Level Goals.

Lesson	Content Assessed	Where to Find It
10◆1	Measure to the nearest $\frac{1}{2}$ inch and $\frac{1}{2}$ cm. [Measurement and Reference Frames Goal 1]	*TLG*, p. 811
10◆2	Write decimal numbers and identify the value of the digits. [Number and Numeration Goal 1]	*TLG*, p. 815
10◆3	Demonstrate automaticity with multiplication facts through 10 × 10. [Operations and Computation Goal 3]	*TLG*, p. 822
10◆4	Demonstrate automaticity with multiplication facts through 10 × 10. [Operations and Computation Goal 3]	*TLG*, p. 828
10◆5	Draw conclusions about data representations. [Data and Chance Goal 2]	*TLG*, p. 833
10◆6	Complete a bar graph. [Data and Chance Goal 1]	*TLG*, p. 837
10◆7	Explain what *median* means. [Data and Chance Goal 2]	*TLG*, p. 841
10◆8	Predict the outcome of an experiment. [Data and Chance Goal 4]	*TLG*, p. 850
10◆9	Solve problems involving fractional parts of sets. [Number and Numeration Goal 2]	*TLG*, p. 856
10◆10	Find the median of a data set. [Data and Chance Goal 2]	*TLG*, p. 861

Math Boxes

Math Boxes, one of several types of tasks highlighted in the Recognizing Student Achievement notes, have an additional useful feature. Math Boxes in most lessons are paired or linked with Math Boxes in one or two other lessons that have similar problems. Paired or linked Math Boxes in Unit 10: 10-1 and 10-3; 10-2 and 10-4; 10-5 and 10-7; 10-6 and 10-8; and 10-9 and 10-10.

Writing/Reasoning Prompts

In Unit 10, a variety of writing prompts encourage children to explain their strategies and thinking, to reflect on their learning, and to make connections to other mathematics or life experiences. Here are some of the Unit 10 suggestions:

Lesson	Writing/Reasoning Prompts	Where to Find It
10◆3	Write 3 questions about a shape.	TLG, p. 823
10◆4	Draw a picture of the pizza and label the amount of pizza that each child ate. Show the amount left over. How much of the pizza did each child eat altogether?	TLG, p. 828
10◆5	Explain how you figured out which fractions were less than $\frac{2}{3}$.	TLG, p. 833
10◆8	Find the perimeter of a shape.	TLG, p. 850
10◆9	Explain how you found the mean weight of the newborn babies.	TLG, p. 856

Portfolio Opportunities

Portfolios are a versatile tool for assessment. They help children reflect on their mathematical growth and help teachers understand and document that growth. Each unit identifies several student products that can be selected and stored in a portfolio. Here are some of the Unit 10 suggestions:

Lesson	Portfolio Opportunities	Where to Find It
10◆2	Children find the volumes of progressively larger cubes.	TLG, p. 818
10◆3	Children write 3 questions about a shape.	TLG, p. 823
10◆4	Children apply fractions to solve the problem of a shared pizza.	TLG, p. 828
10◆5	Children explain how they figured out which fractions were less than $\frac{2}{3}$.	TLG, p. 833
10◆9	Children explain how they found the mean weight of newborn babies.	TLG, p. 856

Periodic Assessment

Every Progress Check lesson includes opportunities to observe children's progress and to collect student products in a variety of ways—Self Assessment, Oral and Slate Assessment, Written Assessment, and an Open Response task. For more details, see the first page of Progress Check 10, Lesson 10-11 on page 862, of the *Teacher's Lesson Guide*.

Progress Check Modifications

Written Assessments are one way children demonstrate what they know. The table below shows modifications for the Written Assessment in this unit. Use these to maximize opportunities for children to demonstrate what they know. Modifications can be given individually or written on the board for the class.

Problem(s)	Modifications for Written Assessment
3–5	For Problems 3–5, use a crayon or colored pencil to trace all of the $\frac{1}{2}$-inch marks before placing your dots on the ruler.
9, 10	For Problems 9 and 10, write each test score on a stick-on note and organize the stick-on notes to help you construct the data representations and find the data landmarks.
11	For Problem 11, list at least two reasons why you might want to find the median test score for the Spelling Test data.
15	For Problem 15, use an inch-grid paper and counters to model the number of puppies in each dog's litter. Move the counters to help you find the mean.

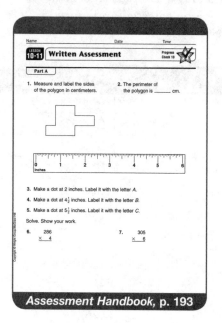

Assessment Handbook, p. 193

The Written Assessment for the Unit 10 Progress Check is on pages 193–195.

Open Response, *Writing About a Top Dog*

Description

For this task, children apply an estimation strategy using the mean to estimate the total number of words in an article.

Focus

◆ **Use mental arithmetic or paper-and-pencil algorithms to solve problems involving the multiplication of 2- and 3-digit whole numbers by 1-digit whole numbers; describe the strategies used.**
[Operations and Computation Goal 4]

◆ **Answer simple questions and draw conclusions based on data landmarks.**
[Data and Chance Goal 2]

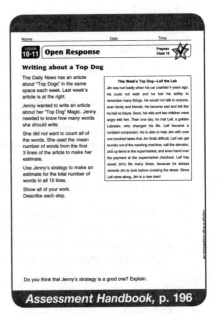

Assessment Handbook, p. 196

Implementation Tips

◆ Review the definition of *mean* and how to calculate the mean for a set of numbers.

Modifications for Meeting Diverse Needs

◆ Provide counters and grid paper. Have children use counters to build a bar graph for the first three numbers and even out the columns to find the mean. Emphasize that each column represents a line of the article. Have children discuss this estimation strategy, and have them plan together how they will solve the problem.

◆ Have children describe advantages and disadvantages of using Jenny's estimation strategy. (*Sample answer: Advantage: You don't have to try and count all the words; Disadvantage: You might use larger or smaller words and so the average number of words on a line for your article might be different.*)

Improving Open Response Skills

After children complete the task, have them reorganize their answers into two columns on a separate sheet of paper—*What* each step is and *Why* each step is required. For example, *What* could be "Got 30 and divided by 3"; *Why* could be "because there are three lines and I am finding the average per line." Have them attach this reorganization to their original task. Remind children that when they explain their answers, the explanation should include both of these parts.

Note: The wording and formatting of the text on the student samples that follow may vary slightly from the actual task your children will complete. These minor discrepancies will not affect the implementation of the task.

Rubric

This rubric is designed to help you assess levels of mathematical performance on this task. It emphasizes mathematical understanding with only a mention of clarity of explanation. Consider the expectations of standardized tests in your area when applying a rubric. Modify this sample rubric as appropriate.

4 Applies and clearly describes Jenny's strategy. Describes in numbers and words how to find the mean and an estimated total word count. Explains in the second part that estimating is faster than counting all of the words in the article, or justifies using the mean by comparing the results to the actual count.

3 Applies Jenny's strategy. Describes in numbers and words how to find the mean, and uses it to find an estimated total word count. Explains in the second part that estimating is faster than counting all of the words in the article, or justifies using the mean by comparing the results to the actual count.

2 Attempts to use Jenny's strategy. Demonstrates some understanding of the problem, but the description might be incomplete or unclear. The explanation in the second part makes some sense in the context of the problem, but it might not explain that estimating is faster than counting.

1 Attempts to make an estimate in for the first part. Might provide some information related to the problem, but shows little evidence of understanding. Explanation in the second part might be incomplete or incorrect.

0 Does not attempt to solve the problem.

Sample Student Responses

This Level 4 paper illustrates the following features: The steps for using Jenny's strategy to solve the problem are clearly described. The first two steps provide information about the numbers being used. The third step does not explain why 10 is multiplied by 15. The explanation for the second part refers to using the mean so that Jenny does not have to count all of the words.

This Level 4 paper illustrates the following features: The steps for using Jenny's strategy to solve the problem are clearly described in paragraph form. Every number is explained in the description. A partial-products algorithm is used. The explanation for the second part refers to using the mean so that Jenny does not have to count all of the words.

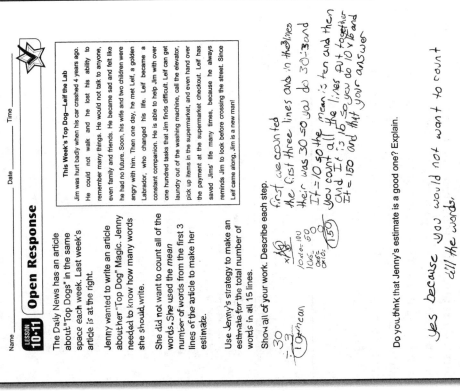

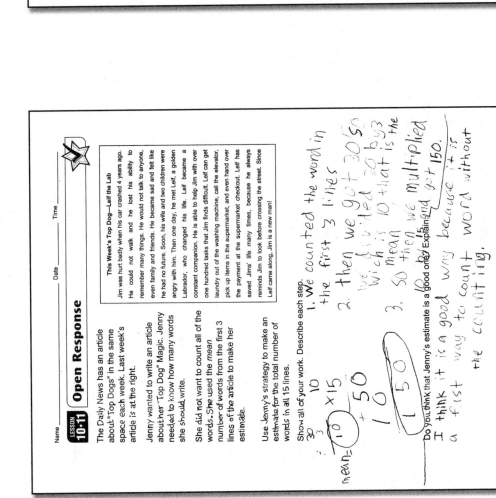

This Level 3 paper illustrates the following features: The steps for using Jenny's strategy to solve the problem are described in paragraph form. The numbers used in the strategy are not explained in the description. The multiplication algorithm used is not explained clearly in words. The explanation for the second part refers to using the mean so that Jenny does not have to count all of the words.

This Level 2 paper illustrates the following features: The arithmetic correctly represents steps from the problem, but there is no labeling and no explanation of what is going on in the steps. There is one number sentence that does not make sense ($10 \times 15 = 0$), but the correct computation is illustrated. The explanation for the second part refers to using the mean so that Jenny does not have to count all of the words.

LESSON 10·11 **Open Response**

The Daily News has an article about "Top Dogs" in the same space each week. Last week's article is at the right.

Jenny wanted to write an article about her "Top Dog" Magic. Jenny needed to know how many words she should write.

She did not want to count all of the words. She used the *mean* number of words from the first 3 lines of the article to make her estimate.

Use Jenny's strategy to make an estimate for the total number of words in all 15 lines.

Show all of your work. Describe each step.

This Week's Top Dog—Leif the Lab

Jim was hurt badly when his car crashed 4 years ago. He could not walk and he lost his ability to remember many things. He would not talk to anyone, even family and friends. He became sad and felt like he had no future. Soon, his wife and two children were angry with him. Then one day, he met Leif, a golden Labrador, who changed his life. Leif became a constant companion. He is able to help Jim with over one hundred tasks that Jim finds difficult. Leif can get laundry out of the washing machine, call the elevator, pick up items in the supermarket, and even hand over the payment at the supermarket checkout. Leif has saved Jims' life many times, because he always reminds Jim to look before crossing the street. Since Leif came along, Jim is a new man!

30
÷ 3
‾‾‾‾‾
mean 10

1. I counted the words in the first three lines
2. I got 30 and I ÷ it by three and got 10.
3. I counted all the lines and got 15.
4. I did 10 × 15 and got 150.

10
× 15
‾‾‾‾
5 0
10
‾‾‾‾
1 5 0

Do you think that Jenny's estimate is a good one? Explain.
Yes. Because it is to long to count and it is good to find the mean.

LESSON 10·11 **Open Response**

The Daily News has an article about "Top Dogs" in the same space each week. Last week's article is at the right.

Jenny wanted to write an article about her "Top Dog" Magic. Jenny needed to know how many words she should write.

She did not want to count all of the words. She used the *mean* number of words from the first 3 lines of the article to make her estimate.

Use Jenny's strategy to make an estimate for the total number of words in all 15 lines.

Show all of your work. Describe each step.

This Week's Top Dog—Leif the Lab

Jim was hurt badly when his car crashed 4 years ago. He could not walk and he lost his ability to remember many things. He would not talk to anyone, even family and friends. He became sad and felt like he had no future. Soon, his wife and two children were angry with him. Then one day, he met Leif, a golden Labrador, who changed his life. Leif became a constant companion. He is able to help Jim with over one hundred tasks that Jim finds difficult. Leif can get laundry out of the washing machine, call the elevator, pick up items in the supermarket, and even hand over the payment at the supermarket checkout. Leif has saved Jims' life many times, because he always reminds Jim to look before crossing the street. Since Leif came along, Jim is a new man!

30
‾‾‾
10
 9
‾‾
 30   3)30
       10

$10 \times 15 = 0$

10
× 15
‾‾‾‾
 50
150
‾‾‾‾
150

Do you think that Jenny's strategy is a good one? Explain.
I think that is a good strategy. because so that way she wont have to count all of the words.

This Level 2 paper illustrates the following features: The first two steps for finding the mean number of words in a line are correctly described. The steps describe breaking the article up into 3-line sections and multiplying the total number of sections by the 10-word average, which is not correct. The explanation for the second part refers to using the mean so that Jenny does not have to count all of the words.

This Level 1 paper illustrates the following features: The explanation begins by describing a total number of words for 3 sentences instead of the first 3 lines. The remaining description, "multiply by the number that you would use to get 15 then add a 0," makes no sense in the context of the problem. Although the correct answer is recorded, there is no evidence of understanding the problem. The explanation in the second part states that this is "easy compared to counting all the words."

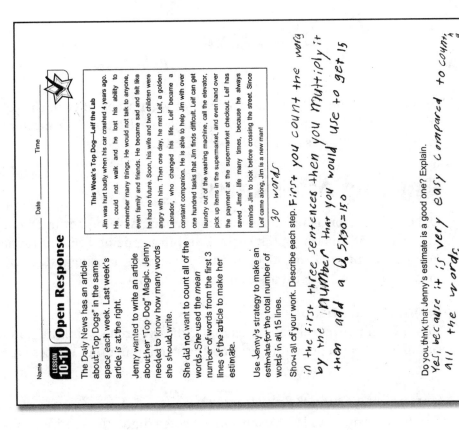

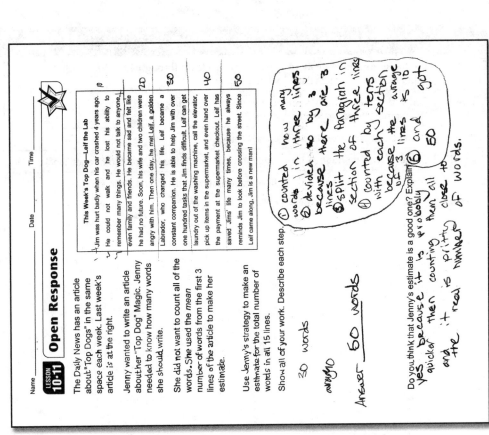

Assessment Overview

In this unit, children continue their work with probability in the context of spinners and wrap up their yearlong projects. Use the information in this section to develop your assessment plan for Unit 11.

Ongoing Assessment

Opportunities for using and collecting ongoing assessment information are highlighted in Informing Instruction and Recognizing Student Achievement notes. Student products, along with observations and suggested writing prompts, provide a range of useful assessment information.

Informing Instruction

The Informing Instruction notes highlight children's thinking and point out common misconceptions. Informing Instruction in Unit 11: Lessons 11-4 and 11-5.

Recognizing Student Achievement

The Recognizing Student Achievement notes highlight specific tasks from which teachers can collect assessment data to monitor and document children's progress toward meeting Grade-Level Goals.

Lesson	Content Assessed	Where to Find It
11♦1	Demonstrate automaticity with multiplication facts through 10 × 10. [Operations and Computation Goal 3]	*TLG*, p. 881
11♦2	Tell and write time to the nearest minute on an analog clock. [Measurement and Reference Frames Goal 4]	*TLG*, p. 886
11♦3	Collect and organize data. [Data and Chance Goal 1]	*TLG*, p. 891
11♦4	Interpret the language of probability to make a spinner. [Data and Chance Goal 3]	*TLG*, p. 896
11♦5	Draw conclusions based on data representations. [Data and Chance Goal 2]	*TLG*, p. 901

Math Boxes

Math Boxes, one of several types of tasks highlighted in the Recognizing Student Achievement notes, have an additional useful feature. Math Boxes in most lessons are paired or linked with Math Boxes in one or two other lessons that have similar problems. Paired or linked Math Boxes in Unit 11: 11-1 and 11-3; 11-2 and 11-4; and 11-5 and 11-6.

Writing/Reasoning Prompts

In Unit 11, a variety of writing prompts encourage children to explain their strategies and thinking, to reflect on their learning, and to make connections to other mathematics or life experiences. Here are some of the Unit 11 suggestions:

Lesson	Writing/Reasoning Prompts	Where to Find It
11♦1	Explain the estimation strategy you used. Find the exact answer to the problem.	*TLG*, p. 882
11♦4	Describe the steps you followed to find the median.	*TLG*, p. 897
11♦5	Explain how you figured out how much time Danielle spends skating in a week.	*TLG*, p. 903

Portfolio Opportunities

Portfolios are a versatile tool for assessment. They help children reflect on their mathematical growth and help teachers understand and document that growth. Each unit identifies several student products that can be selected and stored in a portfolio. Here are some of the Unit 11 suggestions:

Lesson	Portfolio Opportunities	Where to Find It
11♦1	Children explain an estimation strategy and then find the exact answer.	*TLG*, p. 882
11♦4	Children describe the steps they followed to find the median.	*TLG*, p. 897
11♦5	Children explain how they figured out how much time Danielle spends skating in a week.	*TLG*, p. 903

Periodic Assessment

Every Progress Check lesson includes opportunities to observe children's progress and to collect student products in a variety of ways—Self Assessment, Oral and Slate Assessment, Written Assessment, and an Open Response task. For more details, see the first page of Progress Check 11, Lesson 11-6 on page 905, of the *Teacher's Lesson Guide*.

Progress Check Modifications

Written Assessments are one way children demonstrate what they know. The table below shows modifications for the Written Assessment in this unit. Use these to maximize opportunities for children to demonstrate what they know. Modifications can be given individually or written on the board for the class.

Problem(s)	Modifications for Written Assessment
1–3	For Problems 1–3, make a place-value chart and record digits in the chart.
5	For Problem 5, write two more true statements for the spinner.
9	For Problem 9, collect the data from 3 other children before answering the question.
10, 11	For Problems 10 and 11, record a fraction next to each jar, and record the results of the drawings as fractions before solving the problem.

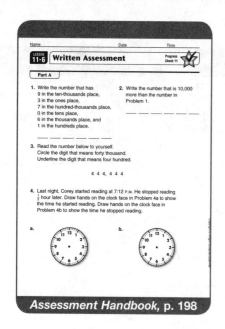

Assessment Handbook, p. 198

The Written Assessment for the Unit 11 Progress Check is on pages 198–200.

Open Response, *The Sandwich Spinner*

Description

For this task, children divide a spinner according to specified attributes and choose a representation of the likely results of spinning the spinner.

Focus

◆ **Model fractions; solve problems involving fractional parts of a region; describe strategies used.**
[Number and Numeration Goal 2]

◆ **Predict the outcomes of simple experiments.**
[Data and Chance Goal 4]

Implementation Tips

◆ Review the meaning of the phrases *half the time* and *twice as often as*.

Modifications for Meeting Diverse Needs

◆ Provide a spinner that is labeled with degrees and divided into six sections.
◆ Have children explain why Andy's and Jose's are not the most likely charts.

Improving Open Response Skills

Before children begin the task, have them read through it together and make a list of the necessary components for the task. Post this list while children are doing the task. For example, the spinner has to be divided and labeled; the correct tally chart has to be chosen; the explanation should include justification for why one tally chart works and the others do not work.

Note: The wording and formatting of the text on the student samples that follow may vary slightly from the actual task your children will complete. These minor discrepancies will not affect the implementation of the task.

Assessment Handbook, p. 201

Rubric

This rubric is designed to help you assess levels of mathematical performance on this task. It emphasizes mathematical understanding with only a mention of clarity of explanation. Consider the expectations of standardized tests in your area when applying a rubric. Modify this sample rubric as appropriate.

4 Divides the spinner correctly into $\frac{1}{2}$ for turkey, $\frac{1}{3}$ for peanut butter, and $\frac{1}{6}$ for cheese. Selects and clearly explains why Barb's tally chart is the most likely to be correct. The explanation refers to the fact that about $\frac{1}{2}$ of the people won turkey, and that there are almost twice as many peanut butter winners as cheese winners.

3 Divides the spinner correctly into $\frac{1}{2}$ for turkey, $\frac{1}{3}$ for peanut butter, and $\frac{1}{6}$ for cheese. Selects and explains why Barb's tally chart is most likely to be correct. The explanation refers to the fact that about $\frac{1}{2}$ of the people won turkey, or that there are almost twice as many peanut butter winners as cheese winners.

2 Divides the spinner with only minor errors into $\frac{1}{2}$ for turkey, $\frac{1}{3}$ for peanut butter, and $\frac{1}{6}$ for cheese. Selects and explains why Barb's tally chart is the most likely to be correct. The explanation refers to some relationship in the spinner, but might not mention specific proportional relationships between the three kinds of sandwiches.

1 Attempts to divide the spinner into sections for turkey, peanut butter, and cheese. Selects a tally chart, but the explanation provides little evidence of understanding the problem.

0 Does not attempt to solve the problem.

Sample Student Responses

This Level 4 paper illustrates the following features: The spinner is divided correctly based on first dividing it into 6 sections. The tallies are counted and the totals are recorded. The explanation describes that in Barb's chart, the tally for peanut butter (11) is about double the tally for cheese (5). The final check is that turkey has 17 tallies, which is about $\frac{1}{2}$ of the total of 33 tallies.

This Level 4 paper illustrates the following features: The spinner is divided correctly. The tallies are counted, and the totals are described in the explanation. The explanation refers to the turkey's tally of 17 as being about $\frac{1}{2}$ of the total. Since the tally for cheese is 5, and 5 + 5 is 10, the cheese and peanut butter ratio works in Barb's chart.

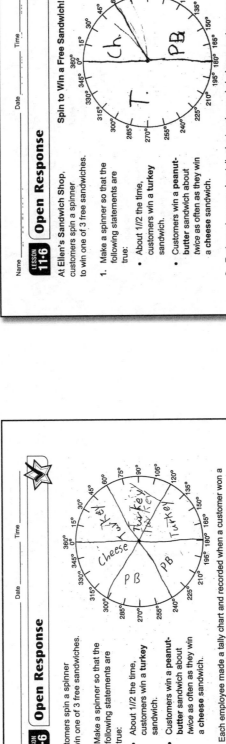

Left worksheet

Name _____ Date _____ Time _____

LESSON 11·6 Open Response

customers spin a spinner
to win one of 3 free sandwiches.

1. Make a spinner so that the
   following statements are
   true:
   - About 1/2 the time,
     customers win a **turkey**
     sandwich.
   - Customers win a **peanut-butter** sandwich about
     twice as often as they win
     a **cheese** sandwich.

2. Each employee made a tally chart and recorded when a customer won a
   sandwich. At the end of the day, their tally charts did not match.

Andy's	
Turkey	ℋℋ ℋℋ ℋℋ 15
Peanut Butter	ℋℋ ℋℋ ℐℐℐℐ 14
Cheese	ℐℐℐℐ 4

Barb's	
Turkey	ℋℋ ℋℋ ℋℋ ℐℐ 17
Peanut Butter	ℋℋ ℋℋ ℐ 11
Cheese	ℋℋ 5

Jose's	
Turkey	ℋℋ ℋℋ 10
Peanut Butter	ℋℋ ℋℋ ℐℐℐℐ 14
Cheese	ℋℋ ℐℐℐℐ 9

Which employee's tally chart is most likely to be correct?
Explain how you found your answer.

Barb's tally chart is most likely
to be correct. First I added the cheese
tally marks and the peanut butter
tally marks. Then I saw witch tallys
double closes to and it was 5 and 11!
Then I add up the turkey tally marks and I
got 17. I added up 5 and 11 and I got 16.
16 was closer to 17 and that ment that Barbs
talley chart was correct and thats how I solved it

Right worksheet

Name _____ Date _____ Time _____

LESSON 11·6 Open Response

At Ellen's Sandwich Shop,
customers spin a spinner
to win one of 3 free sandwiches.

Spin to Win a Free Sandwich!

1. Make a spinner so that the
   following statements are
   true:
   - About 1/2 the time,
     customers win a **turkey**
     sandwich.
   - Customers win a **peanut-butter** sandwich about
     twice as often as they win
     a **cheese** sandwich.

2. Each employee made a tally chart and recorded when a customer won a
   sandwich. At the end of the day, their tally charts did not match.

Andy's	
Turkey	ℋℋ ℋℋ ℋℋ
Peanut Butter	ℋℋ ℋℋ ℐℐℐℐ
Cheese	ℐℐℐℐ

Barb's	
Turkey	ℋℋ ℋℋ ℋℋ ℐℐ
Peanut Butter	ℋℋ ℋℋ ℐ
Cheese	ℋℋ

Jose's	
Turkey	ℋℋ ℋℋ
Peanut Butter	ℋℋ ℋℋ ℐℐℐℐ
Cheese	ℋℋ ℐℐℐℐ

Which employee's tally chart is most likely to be correct?
Explain how you found your answer.

I think Barbs because her Toatle
was 33 and her Turkey was 17
her P.B. was 11 and The Turkey
was half her cheese was 5.
5+5=10 so her P.B was 11.

This Level 3 paper illustrates the following features: The spinner is divided correctly. The explanation discusses why Andy's and Jose's charts are incorrect before explaining that Barb's has more turkey. The explanation refers to Barb's peanut butter tally being only one more than doubling the count for cheese.

This Level 3 paper illustrates the following features: The spinner is divided correctly. The explanation discusses why Andy's and Jose's charts are incorrect before explaining that Barb's has about $\frac{1}{2}$ turkey and that the total for cheese and peanut butter combined is about the same as the turkey.

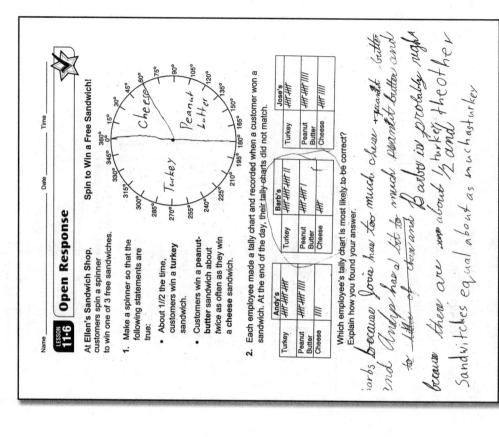

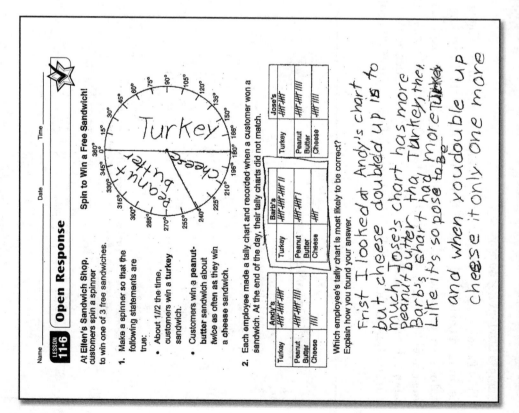

This Level 2 paper illustrates the following features: The spinner is divided correctly. The explanation suggests that Barb's is correct because people like turkey more than cheese. Since all three charts have more turkey than cheese, this is not a sufficient explanation.

This Level 1 paper illustrates the following features: The spinner is incorrectly divided into $\frac{1}{2}$ turkey and $\frac{1}{4}$ each for cheese and peanut butter. The explanation describes peanut butter and cheese being about the same, which matches the illustration but is incorrect for the problem.

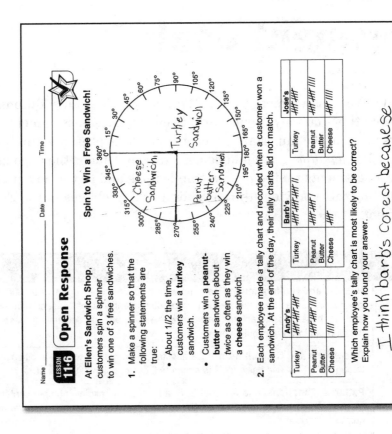

Name _____ Date _____ Time _____

LESSON 11·6   Open Response

Spin to Win a Free Sandwich!

At **Ellen's Sandwich Shop,** customers spin a spinner to win one of 3 free sandwiches.

1. Make a spinner so that the following statements are true:

   • About 1/2 the time, customers win a **turkey** sandwich.

   • Customers win a **peanut-butter** sandwich about *twice* as often as they win a **cheese** sandwich.

2. Each employee made a tally chart and recorded when a customer won a sandwich. At the end of the day, their tally charts did not match.

Which employee's tally chart is most likely to be correct? Explain how you found your answer.

I think barb's corect becaues the number of the penutbutter and the cheese is almost the same that's why I picked barb.

First, I look at the chart then I read the story then I wirth the anwers the I circle Barb's because people like Turkey More then cheese.

Assessment Overview   **141**

End-of-Year Assessment Goals

The End-of-Year Assessment (pages 217–225) provides an additional opportunity that you may use as part of your balanced assessment plan. It covers many of the important concepts and skills presented in *Third Grade Everyday Mathematics*. It should be used to complement the ongoing and periodic assessments that appear within lessons and at the end of units. The following table provides the goals for all the problems in the End-of-Year Assessment.

Problem(s)	Grade-Level Goal
1, 2, 34	**Number and Numeration 1:** Read and write whole numbers up to 1,000,000; read, write, and model with manipulatives decimals through hundredths; identify places in such numbers and the values of the digits in those places; translate between whole numbers and decimals represented in words, in base-10 notation, and with manipulatives.
3	**Operations and Computation 1:** Demonstrate automaticity with all addition and subtraction facts through 10 + 10; use basic facts to compute fact extensions such as 80 + 70.
4a, 23a, 28a, 29	**Patterns, Functions, and Algebra 2:** Read, write, and explain number sentences using the symbols +, −, ×, ÷, =, >, and <; solve number sentences; write expressions and number sentences to model number stories.
4b, 23b, 28b	**Operations and Computation 6:** Recognize and describe change, comparison, and parts-and-total situations; use repeated addition, arrays, and skip counting to model multiplication; use equal sharing and equal grouping to model division.
5	**Patterns, Functions, and Algebra 4:** Describe and apply the Commutative and Associative Properties of Addition and Multiplication and the Multiplicative Identity; apply the Distributive Property of Multiplication over Addition.
6	**Number and Numeration 3:** Find multiples of 2, 5, and 10.
7	**Geometry 3:** Create and complete two-dimensional symmetric shapes or designs; locate multiple lines of symmetry in a two-dimensional shape.
8, 33, 35	**Number and Numeration 6:** Compare and order whole numbers up to 1,000,000; use manipulatives to order decimals through hundredths; use area models and benchmark fractions to compare and order fractions.
9	**Data and Chance 3:** Describe events using *certain, very likely, likely, unlikely, very unlikely, impossible,* and other basic probability terms; explain the choice of language.
10	**Measurement and Reference Frames 2:** Describe and use strategies to measure the perimeter of polygons; find the areas of rectangles.
11	**Operations and Computation 5:** Make reasonable estimates for whole number addition, subtraction, multiplication, and division problems; explain how the estimates were obtained.
12	**Measurement and Reference Frames 4:** Tell and show time to the nearest minute on an analog clock; tell and write time in digital notation.
13	**Operations and Computation 3:** Demonstrate automaticity with multiplication facts through 10 × 10.
14	**Number and Numeration 5:** Use manipulatives and drawings to find and represent equivalent names for fractions; use manipulatives to generate equivalent fractions.

Problem(s)	Grade-Level Goal
15, 16	**Number and Numeration 2:** Read, write, and model fractions; solve problems involving fractional parts of a region or a collection; describe strategies used.
17	**Measurement and Reference Frames 1:** Estimate length with and without tools; measure length to the nearest $\frac{1}{2}$ inch and $\frac{1}{2}$ centimeter; draw and describe angles as records of rotations.
18	**Data and Chance 4:** Predict the outcomes of simple experiments and test the predictions using manipulatives; express the probability of an event by using "_____ out of _____" language.
19, 31	**Geometry 2:** Identify, describe, model, and compare plane and solid figures including circles, polygons, spheres, cylinders, rectangular prisms, pyramids, cones, and cubes using appropriate geometric terms including the terms *face, edge, vertex,* and *base.*
20, 27	**Operations and Computation 2:** Use manipulatives, mental arithmetic, paper-and-pencil algorithms and models, and calculators to solve problems involving the addition and subtraction of whole numbers and decimals in a money context; describe the strategies used and explain how they work.
21	**Patterns, Functions, and Algebra 1:** Extend, describe, and create numeric patterns; describe rules for patterns and use them to solve problems; use words and symbols to describe and write rules for functions involving addition, subtraction, and multiplication and use those rules to solve problems.
22	**Operations and Computation 4:** Use arrays, mental arithmetic, paper-and-pencil algorithms and models, and calculators to solve problems involving the multiplication of 2- and 3-digit whole numbers by 1-digit whole numbers; describe the strategies used.
24–26	**Measurement and Reference Frames 3:** Describe relationships among inches, feet, and yards; describe relationships between minutes in an hour, hours in a day, days in a week.
30	**Patterns, Functions, and Algebra 3:** Recognize that numeric expressions can have different values depending on the order in which operations are carried out; understand that grouping symbols can be used to affect the order in which operations are carried out.
32	**Geometry 1:** Identify and draw points, intersecting and parallel line segments and lines, rays, and right angles.
36	**Number and Numeration 4:** Use numerical expressions involving one or more of the basic four arithmetic operations to give equivalent names for whole numbers.
37	**Data and Chance 1:** Collect and organize data or use given data to create charts, tables, graphs, and line plots.
38	**Data and Chance 2:** Use graphs to ask and answer simple questions and draw conclusions; find the maximum, minimum, range, mode, and median of a data set.

Assessment Masters

Contents

LESSON 1·14 | **Self Assessment**

Check one box for each skill.

Skills	I can do this on my own and can explain how to do it.	I can do this on my own.	I can do this if I get help or look at an example.
1. Count money.			
2. Count by 2s and 10s.			
3. Complete Frames-and-Arrows puzzles.			
4. Write names in name-collection boxes.			
5. Tell time.			
6. Make tally charts and bar graphs.			

LESSON 1·14

Written Assessment

Part A

1. Draw coins to show 58¢ two different ways. Use Ⓟ, Ⓝ, Ⓓ, and Ⓠ.

Use >, <, or =.

2. $0.90 _____ ⓆⓆⓆⓆⓃ

3. ⓆⒹⒹⓃⓃⓅ _____ ⓆⓆⓆ

Draw the minute hand and hour hand to show the times.

4.

2:15

5.

3:30

6.

9:45

Write seven names for the number 18 in the name-collection box.

7.

18

LESSON 1·14 | **Written Assessment** *continued*

Use + or − to make the number sentence true.

8. 8 = 13 _____ 5

15 = 9 _____ 6

8 _____ 3 = 11

17 _____ 9 = 8

Unit

Fill in the missing numbers.

9.

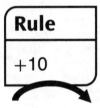

Rule
+10

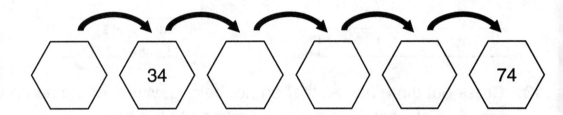

10.

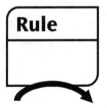

Rule

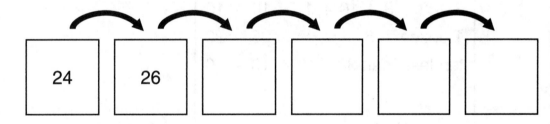

11. Write 2 things that you are sure *will not* happen.

_____

_____

LESSON 1·14 **Written Assessment** *continued*

Part B

12. Use the tally chart to complete the bar graph.

Number of Goals	Number of Children
0	///
1	‍卌 //
2	//
3	卌
4	///
5	/

Soccer Goals by Children

13. Cross out three names that do not belong. Write the name on the tag. Add at least 3 more correct names to the box.

	half of 40	10 twos
3 + 3 + 3 + 10 + 1		10 + 10
1 dozen + 6		25 − 20
ten less than 30		10 + 10 + 10

14. 14 − 3 = 8 + 3

Explain what the equal sign means in this number sentence.

_____

_____

_____

_____

150   *Assessment Handbook*

LESSON 1·14 | **Open Response**

Counting Coins

Imad collects quarters, dimes, nickels, and pennies. This morning, he took $1.80 from his collection. He counted the coins and found that he had **twice as many** nickels as dimes. What coins could Imad have?

Explain with words and pictures how you figured out your answer. Remember to show all of your work. You may use your tool-kit money to help you.

LESSON 2·10   Self Assessment

Check one box for each skill.

Skills	I can do this on my own and explain how to do it.	I can do this on my own.	I can do this if I get help or look at an example.
1. Solve extended facts like these: $4 + 8$ $40 + 80$ $400 + 800$			
2. Complete a "What's My Rule?" table.			
3. Use a number story diagram.			
4. Use the counting-up method.			
5. Use the trade-first method.			
6. Use the partial-sums method.			

LESSON 2·10 | **Written Assessment**

Part A

Fill in the unit box and the blanks.

Unit

1. 3 + _____ = 12

    30 + _____ = 120

    300 + _____ = 1,200

2. 17 = 8 + _____

    170 = 80 + _____

    1,700 = 800 + _____

Complete the tables. Write your own number pair in the last row of each table.

3.

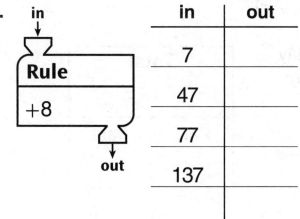

in	out
7	
47	
77	
137	

4.

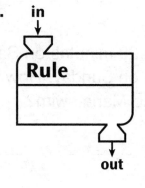

in	out
60	100
80	120
30	70
90	130

5. Use 3 of the cards below to write a name for the target number.
Remember to write each step separately.

[3] [7] [4] [2] [5]   [9] target number

_____

_____

_____

_____

Solve the following number stories. Use diagrams or pictures to help you.

6. One python clutch has 31 eggs. Another python clutch has 19 eggs. How many more eggs are in the first clutch?

Number model: _____

Answer the question: _____
(unit)

Quantity

Quantity

_____
Difference

7. Maria swam for 20 minutes on Saturday and 36 minutes on Sunday. How many minutes in all did Maria swim?

Number model: _____

Total	
Part	**Part**

Answer the question: _____
(unit)

Draw the hands to show the time.

8.

7:10

9.

3:35

Written Assessment *continued*

10. In the number 8,439,

the 4 means _____ .

the 9 means _____ .

the 3 means _____ .

the 8 means _____ .

Part B

Complete the tables. Write your own number pair in the last row.

11.

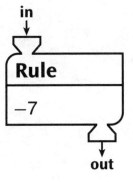

in	out
13	
	26
	86
	66

12.

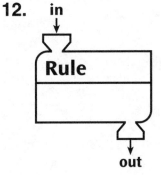

in	out
1,300	700
700	100
1,500	
	500

Write a number model for your ballpark estimate.
Use your favorite method to solve each problem.
Show your work.

Unit
miles

13. Ballpark estimate:

_____

   467
+394
_____

14. Ballpark estimate:

_____

   911
−812
_____

LESSON 2·10 | **Open Response**

A Birthday Dinner

Mr. Brown is cooking an 18-pound turkey for Keron's birthday dinner. The turkey must bake about 15 minutes for every pound.

For how long does the turkey need to bake? _____ hours _____ minutes

Show all of your work. Write an explanation of how you solved the problem.

Try This

At what time should the turkey go into the oven for dinner to be ready at 5 P.M.?

LESSON 3·10 | **Self Assessment**

Check one box for each skill.

Skills	I can do this on my own and can explain how to do it.	I can do this on my own.	I can do this if I get help or look at an example.
1. Make ballpark estimates.			
2. Solve number stories.			
3. Measure line segments.			
4. Make line plots.			
5. Find the perimeter of polygons.			
6. Find the area of rectangles.			

LESSON 3·10 | **Written Assessment**

Part A

Make a ballpark estimate for each problem. Write the number model.

1. $248 - 103 = ?$

Ballpark estimate:

_____

Unit

2. $169 + 28 = ?$

Ballpark estimate:

_____

Measure each line segment to the nearest $\frac{1}{2}$ inch.

3. _____ _____ in.

4. _____ _____ in.

Measure each line segment to the nearest $\frac{1}{2}$ centimeter.

5. _____ _____ cm

6. _____ _____ cm

7. Find the perimeter of the rectangle.

The perimeter is _____ cm.

7 cm

2 cm

LESSON 3·10 **Written Assessment** *continued*

8. Write one thing that you are certain *will* happen today.

_____

9. Write one thing that you are certain *will not* happen today.

_____

10. Carl earned $3.00. He spent $2.15 on a toy car. Use Ⓟ Ⓝ Ⓓ Ⓠ
to show how much money he had left.

Part B

11. a. Measure the sides of the
polygon in centimeters.

b. The perimeter is _____ cm.

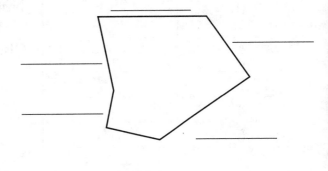

12. Draw a rectangle with an
area of 16 square centimeters.

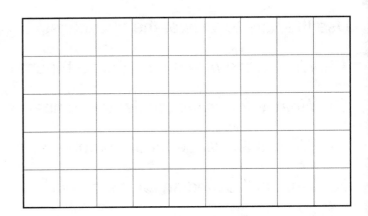

13. Fill in the blanks.

12 in. = _____ ft   _____ in. = 4 ft   6 ft = _____ yd

24 in. = _____ ft   _____ ft = 1 yd   12 ft = _____ yd

LESSON 3·10 | **Written Assessment** *continued*

14. Measure the line segment to the nearest $\frac{1}{2}$ inch.

_____   _____ in.

15. Measure the line segment to the nearest $\frac{1}{2}$ centimeter.

_____   _____ cm

16. Use the data from the tally chart to create a line plot. You may use your *Student Reference Book* to help you.

Number of Books Read	Number of Children
0	
1	
2	＃＃ /
3	＃＃
4	
5	///
6	
7	////

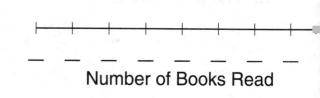

Number of Children

Number of Books Read

Use the data to answer the questions.

17. What is the *maximum* (greatest) number of books read?   _____ books

18. What is the *minimum* (least) number of books read?   _____ books

19. What is the range for the number of books read?   _____ books

20. What is the median for the number of books read by children?   _____ books

LESSON 3·10 | Open Response

Building a Fence

Gina has 24 feet of fence.

She wants to make the **largest rectangular area** possible for her rabbit to play in.

What length should she make each side of the rabbit pen?

Show all your work and explain how you found the **largest area.**

Self Assessment

LESSON
4·11

Check one box for each skill.

Skills	I can do this on my own and explain how to do it.	I can do this on my own.	I can do this if I get help or look at an example.
1. Know the first set of multiplication Fact Triangles.			
2. Write multiplication/ division fact families.			
3. Fill in pieces of the number grid.			
4. Solve multiplication and division number stories.			
5. Know which digit is in the hundreds place.			
6. Solve "What's My Rule?" problems.			

LESSON 4·11 | **Written Assessment** | Progress Check 4

Part A

Complete the fact families.

1. $2 \times 4 =$ _____

$4 \times 2 =$ _____

_____ $\div 2 = 4$

_____ $\div 4 = 2$

2. $7 \times 1 =$ _____

$1 \times 7 =$ _____

$7 \div 1 =$ _____

$7 \div 7 =$ _____

3. Write the number that is

100 more than 603. _____

100 more than 1,468. _____

100 less than 968. _____

100 less than 2,751. _____

4. Fill in the blanks. Use >, <, or =.

2×6 _____ 6×2

7×1 _____ 15×0

0×6 _____ 3×0

9×1 _____ 4×2

5×3 _____ 3×5

5×1 _____ 1×5

Reminder:

> means *is greater than*

< means *is less than*

= means *is the same as*

5. Find the area of each rectangle.

A = _____ sq cm

B = _____ sq cm

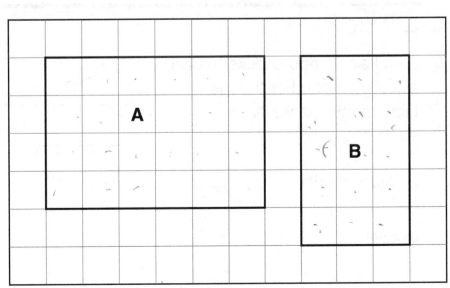

LESSON 4·11 | **Written Assessment** *continued*

6. Fill in the blanks.

in
↓
Rule
×2
↓
out

in	out
7	
4	
2	
0	

7. Fill in the missing numbers.

	950

For Problems 8 and 9, fill in a multiplication/division diagram. Then use counters, arrays, pictures, or whatever you need to find the answer. Record your answers with a unit. Write a number model.

8. The pet shop keeps 5 puppies in each pen. There are 3 pens. How many puppies in all?

pens	puppies per pen	puppies in all
3	5	15

Number model: _____

Answer: __15_____
(unit)

Part B

9. Ellie has 21 dog snacks to divide equally among her 3 dogs. How many snacks does each dog get?

dogs	snacks per dog	snacks in all

Number model: _____

Answer: _____
(unit)

Written Assessment *continued*

10. Fill in the blanks.

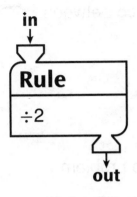

in	out
8	
	6
	5
14	
	2

11. Fill in the blanks.

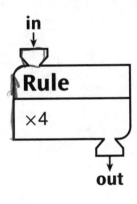

in	out
7	
	20
3	
	24
8	

12. Use the numbers 3, 7, and 21 to write a multiplication/division fact family.

_____   _____

_____   _____

LESSON 4·11 | # Open Response

A Multiplication Problem

Mrs. Sita told her class that they could calculate the **difference** between

$$25 \times 8$$
and
$$25 \times 9$$

without doing any multiplication.

Show or explain how Mrs. Sita's class might have solved the problem.

(Hint: They might use pictures, arrays, number models, diagrams, coins, or counters.)

Make sure to include the answer to the problem in your explanation.

LESSON 5·13 | Self Assessment

Check one box for each skill.

	I can do this on my own and can explain how to do it.	I can do this on my own.	I can do this if I get help or look at an example.
1. Read and write very large numbers.			
2. Read and write decimal numbers.			
3. Use base-10 blocks to work with decimals.			
4. Add and subtract 2-digit numbers.			
5. Use ballpark estimates to help check if my answer makes sense.			
6. Add and subtract extended facts.			

LESSON 5·13 **Written Assessment**

Part A

Write the number that matches the description.

1. 3 in the ten-thousands place

   0 in the hundreds place

   5 in the thousands place

   7 in the tens place

   6 in the ones place

   ___ ___, ___ ___ ___

2. 9 in the ones place

   4 in the hundreds place

   6 in the ten-thousands place

   5 in the tens place

   0 in the thousands place

   ___ ___, ___ ___ ___

Write >, <, or =.

3. 63,000 _____ 59,888

4. 46,526 _____ 40,999

Fill in the blanks.

Unit

5. 7,000 + 6,000 = _____

6. 11,000 − 3,000 = _____

Write the sums.

Unit

7. 13 + 7 + 9 + 11 = _____

8. 24 + 12 + 8 + 6 = _____

LESSON 5·13 | **Written Assessment** *continued*

Solve. Show your work. Use a ballpark estimate to check whether your answer makes sense. Write a number model for your estimate.

Unit
stars

9. Ballpark estimate: _____

$$49$$
$$+ \; 36$$

10. Ballpark estimate: _____

$$72$$
$$- \; 28$$

Find the perimeter and area of the rectangle.

Unit
cm

11. Perimeter = _____
                                (unit)

12. Area = _____
                        (unit)

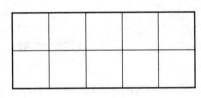

LESSON 5·13 **Written Assessment** *continued*

Part B

If each grid is ONE, then what part of each grid is shaded? Write the decimal and the fraction below each grid.

13.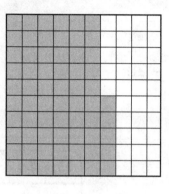

_____ = _____
decimal   fraction

14.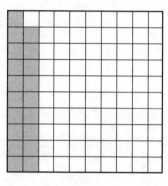

_____ = _____
decimal   fraction

15.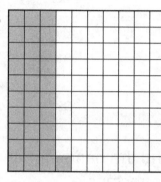

_____ = _____
decimal   fraction

Use the grids above to compare the decimals.

Which is more?

16. 0.65 or 0.31?   **17.** 0.19 or 0.65?   **18.** 0.31 or 0.19?

_____   _____   _____

Write the number that matches the description.

19. 5 in the tenths place

3 in the thousandths place

0 in the hundredths place

7 in the ones place

___.___ ___ ___

20. 5 in the hundredths place

3 in the tenths place

0 in the thousandths place

7 in the ones place

___.___ ___ ___

LESSON 5·13   # Open Response

Playing with Place Value

1. Janine was playing a game of *Number Top-It.* She had the cards shown.

Ten-Thousands	Thousands	Hundreds	Tens	Ones
		2		3

On her next turn, she drew a 7. Tell where you think the card should go. Explain how you would convince Janine that this is the best move.

2. When Janine finished the game, these are the cards she had.

Her teacher added a rule. Everyone gets to make one switch. (They move two cards, switching them with each other.)

Ten-Thousands	Thousands	Hundreds	Tens	Ones
4	7	2	7	3

Tell which cards you think she should switch. Use place value to explain your answer.

LESSON 6·13 — Self Assessment

Check one box for each skill.

Skills	I can do this on my own and can explain how to do it.	I can do this on my own.	I can do this if I get help or look at an example.
1. Name polygons.			
2. Name 3-D shapes.			
3. Draw line segments, rays, and lines.			
4. Identify right angles.			
5. Identify parallel and intersecting line segments.			
6. Find and draw lines of symmetry.			

LESSON 6·13   Written Assessment

Part A

1. Use a straightedge. Draw line segments to form a quadrangle.

2. Use the points to write one letter name for the quadrangle.

_____

• U

Q •

D •

• A

3. Which letter names the right angle?   Angle _____

4. Circle the pairs of line segments that are parallel.
   Underline the pairs of line segments that intersect.

   a. _____
   _____

   b.

   c.

   d.

5. Draw the line of symmetry for the trapezoid.

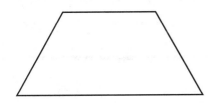

6. 36 books. 6 children.
   How many books per child?

children	books per child	books in all

Number model: _____

Answer: _____
             (unit)

LESSON 6·13 | **Written Assessment** *continued*

Fill in the ovals to identify each figure.

7.
- ○ prism
- ○ pyramid
- ○ cylinder

8.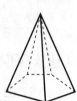
- ○ sphere
- ○ cone
- ○ cylinder

9.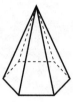
- ○ prism
- ○ pyramid
- ○ cylinder

10. The base of this figure is a

- ○ triangle
- ○ square
- ○ pentagon

11. Color 0.4 of the grid.   **12.** Color 0.04 of the grid.   **13.** Color 0.34 of the grid.

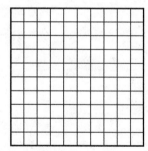 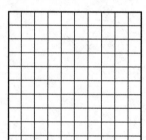 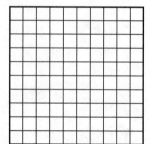

14. Write 0.4, 0.04, and 0.34 in order from smallest to largest. Use the grids to help.

_____ _____ _____

Part B

15. Draw the other half to make it a symmetric shape.

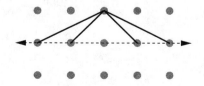

16. Draw as many lines of symmetry as you can.

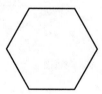

LESSON 6·13 **Written Assessment** *continued*

17. Draw a ray, $\overrightarrow{IJ}$, that is parallel to $\overrightarrow{KL}$.

18. Draw a line, $\overleftrightarrow{EF}$, that intersects $\overrightarrow{HG}$.

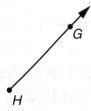

19. Draw a triangle with one right angle. Label the points. Use the right angle symbol to show the right angle.

20. This is a picture of a 3-D shape. It has

_____ faces

_____ base

_____ edges

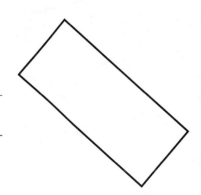

21. There are many names for this shape. Write some of them on the lines.

_____

_____

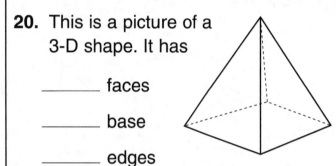

22. Draw a picture of each turn. Draw a curved arrow to show the direction of each turn. The vertex of the angle and one side have already been drawn for you.

a. $\frac{1}{2}$ turn clockwise

b. $\frac{1}{4}$ turn counterclockwise

LESSON
6·13 **Open Response**

Writing Directions

Carole drew this shape. Each side of her shape measures 1 inch.

Carole wants her friend to draw exactly the same
shape. Help her write directions for the shape
to send to her friend. Use words from the
Geometry Word Box to help you.

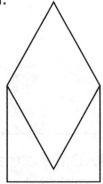

Geometry Word Box			
parallel	intersect	vertex	side
edge	right angle	clockwise	counterclockwise
line segment	rhombus	square	rectangle

LESSON 7·10   Self Assessment

Check one box for each skill.

Skills	I can do this on my own and explain how to do it.	I can do this on my own.	I can do this if I get help or look at an example.
1. Use arrays to help find answers.			
2. Know multiplication facts.			
3. Share things equally.			
4. Draw parallel and intersecting lines.			
5. Solve 3-digit addition problems.			
6. Make estimates to check problems.			

**LESSON
7·10**

Written Assessment

Part A

Fill in the missing factors and products.

1. 8 × 5 = ____

2. 10 × ____ = 30

3. 9 × 2 = ____

4. 7 × ____ = 70

5. 4 × 5 = ____

6. ____ × 8 = 16

7.   4
    × 7
   ▢

8.   3
    × 6
   ▢

9.   7
    × 3
   ▢

10.   4
    × 6
   ▢

Solve. Use diagrams, counters, arrays, pictures, or whatever you need to find the answer. Record your answer with a unit. Write a number model.

11. Linda has 32 crayons to put into boxes. 8 crayons fit into each box. How many boxes does she need?

boxes	crayons per box	crayons in all

Number model: _____

Answer: _____
          (unit)

12. 7 children picked 42 apples. If they share the apples equally, how many will each child get?

children	apples per child	apples in all

Number model: _____

Answer: _____
          (unit)

LESSON 7·10 | **Written Assessment** *continued*

Use a straightedge.

13. Draw $\overline{AB}$ parallel to $\overline{EF}$.

14. Draw $\overrightarrow{CD}$ intersecting $\overrightarrow{GH}$.

15. This is a picture of a rectangular prism. This shape has

_____ faces   _____ edges   _____ vertices

Make ballpark estimates for each problem. Write number models for your estimates. Then add or subtract. Use your estimates to check if your answers make sense.

Unit

16. a. ballpark estimate:

_____

b.   378
    $+\ 219$

17. a. ballpark estimate:

_____

b.   463
    $-\ 148$

LESSON 7·10 | **Written Assessment** *continued*

Part B

18. _____ = (30 ÷ 5) + 5

19. 9 + (3 × 5) = _____

20. 7 + (8 × 8) = _____

21. _____ = 12 − (12 ÷ 2)

Solve the multiplication/division puzzle. Fill in the blanks.

22.

×, ÷	40	600
8		
7		

Estimate to answer the question below.
Assume that there is no tax on the items.

23. Allen wants to buy a notebook for $3.89 and a pen
for $1.99. He has $5.00. Does he have enough money? _____

Explain your thinking: _____

_____

_____

Number model you used: _____

**LESSON
7·10** | **Open Response**

Button Dolls

Mr. Moore's third grade class is making button dolls for the school fair. They are called button dolls because the eyes are made from 2 buttons and there are always 3 buttons on the clothes of each doll.

The buttons are sold in packages of 12.

Mr. Moore wants to buy enough packages so that all of the buttons in the packages will be used without any left over.

How many packages could he buy?

How many dolls will that make?

Use words or pictures to tell how you solved the problem.

LESSON 8·9 | **Self Assessment** |

Check one box for each skill.

Skills	I can do this on my own and can explain how to do it.	I can do this on my own.	I can do this if I get help or look at an example.
1. Read and write fractions.			
2. Compare fractions to $\frac{1}{2}$.			
3. Find fractional parts of collections.			
4. Write fractions on a number line.			
5. Complete a symmetrical shape.			
6. Tell the value of each digit in a decimal.			

LESSON 8·9

Written Assessment

Progress Check 8

Part A

Use counters to help.

1. Circle $\frac{7}{8}$ of the marbles.

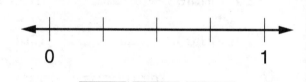

2. Shade $\frac{2}{3}$ of the squares.

3. Write at least 5 names in this name-collection box.

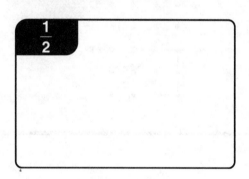

$\frac{1}{2}$

4. Write the missing fractions on the number line.

0 _____ 1

_____ _____ _____

5. Circle all the fractions below that are greater than $\frac{1}{2}$. Use your Fraction Cards to help.

$\frac{7}{8}$ $\frac{1}{3}$ $\frac{1}{4}$ $\frac{3}{8}$ $\frac{2}{4}$ $\frac{2}{3}$ $\frac{3}{4}$

6. In the number 28.47,

the 2 means _____.

the 8 means _____.

the 4 means _____.

the 7 means _____.

7. If I wanted an equal chance of taking out a sphere or a cube I would put in ___ spheres.

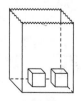

Assessment Masters   **183**

LESSON 8·9 | **Written Assessment** *continued*

Solve. Draw a picture to show what you did.

8. Four people share 8 pieces of candy.

   a. How many pieces does each person get? _____ pieces

   b. What fraction of the candy did each person get? _____

9. Fill in the blanks.

   60 minutes = _____ hour

   120 minutes = _____ hours

   30 minutes = _____ hour

   _____ minutes = $\frac{1}{4}$ hour

10. Use a straightedge. Draw the other half of the symmetric shape.

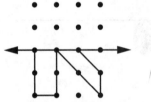

| **Part B** |

Shade the circles to match the mixed number or fraction.

11.

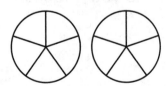

   $\frac{9}{5}$ Write another name for $\frac{9}{5}$. _____

12.

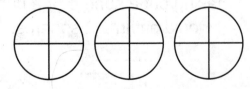

   $2\frac{3}{4}$ Write another name for $2\frac{3}{4}$. _____

LESSON 8·9 | **Written Assessment** *continued*

13. Cross out all the names that do not belong in this name-collection box. Then add one more name.

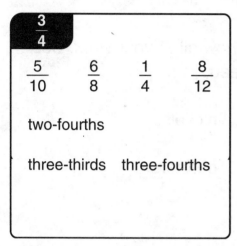

$\frac{3}{4}$

$\frac{5}{10}$ $\frac{6}{8}$ $\frac{1}{4}$ $\frac{8}{12}$

two-fourths

three-thirds   three-fourths

14. Fill in the blanks. Use a clock to help.

90 minutes = _____ hours

_____ minutes = $1\frac{1}{4}$ hours

_____ minutes = $\frac{1}{3}$ hour

_____ minute = $\frac{1}{60}$ hour

5 minutes = _____ hour

Solve. Use coins to help.

15. Lora's mom gave her $\frac{3}{4}$ of a dollar to buy a drink.

Greg's mom gave him $\frac{4}{5}$ of a dollar to buy a drink.

Who received more money? _____

Explain how you got your answer. _____

_____

_____

16. If I wanted to take out a sphere about half as often as a cube, I would put

in _____ spheres.

LESSON 8·9 | **Open Response**

Solving a Coin Problem

Robert found 24 coins. $\frac{1}{3}$ of them were pennies, $\frac{1}{4}$ of them were nickels, $\frac{1}{6}$ of them were dimes, and the rest were quarters.

1. Tell how many of each coin Robert found. Show all of your work. Use coins, pictures, counters, or whatever you need.

   Robert had _____ pennies, _____ nickels,

   _____ dimes, _____ quarters.

2. Explain how you found the number of dimes.

3. How much are his coins worth altogether? _____
   Show all of your work.

LESSON 9·14 | Self Assessment

Check one box for each skill.

Skills	I can do this on my own and can explain how to do it.	I can do this on my own.	I can do this if I get help or look at an example.
1. Solve multiplication number stories.			
2. Use partial products to solve multiplication problems.			
3. Use the lattice method to solve multiplication problems.			
4. Compare fractions using Fraction Cards.			
5. Find the area and perimeter of a shape.			
6. Estimate money amounts.			

LESSON
9·14 | **Written Assessment**

Part A

1. How much do four 40-pound beavers weigh? _____ pounds

Show your work.

Use partial products or the lattice method to solve.

2.   23
      × 4

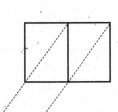

3.   49
      × 8

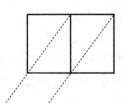

4. Put these fractions in order from smallest to largest. You may use
your Fraction Cards.

$$\frac{9}{9} \qquad \frac{2}{3} \qquad \frac{5}{6} \qquad \frac{4}{12} \qquad \frac{0}{2}$$

_____ _____ _____ _____ _____

↑   ↑
smallest   largest

LESSON 9·14 **Written Assessment** *continued*

Complete the number sentences.

5. $7 \times (8 - 8) =$ _____

6. _____ $= (7 \times 8) - 8$

7. $7 + (3 \times 9) =$ _____

8. _____ $= (7 + 3) \times 9$

9. Draw a rectangle with a perimeter of 24 centimeters.

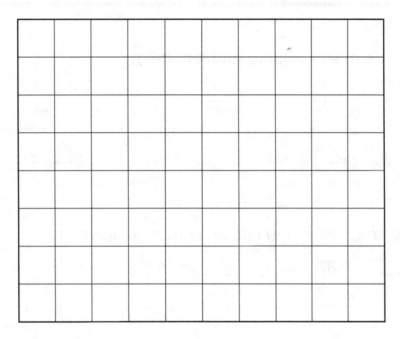

10. How do you know the perimeter is 24 cm?

_____

_____

11. What is the area of your rectangle? _____ sq cm

12. How did you find the area?

_____

_____

LESSON 9·14 **Written Assessment** *continued*

Mr. Stevens has $10.00 to buy as many packs of batteries as he can. 1 pack of batteries costs $3.59.

13. How many packs can he buy? _____

14. About how much money will he spend? _____

15. About how much change will he get back? _____

Part B

16. Explain Lora's mistake in the problem below.

```
    28
  × 60
 _____
   120
  + 48
 _____
   168
```

_____

_____

_____

17. Use partial products or the lattice method to solve.

```
    37
  × 28
  ____
```

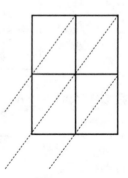

18. Marge is buying hamburger buns for the third grade picnic. She needs 90 buns. They come in packages of 8. How many packages should she buy? _____

Explain how you figured out your answer.

_____

_____

_____

_____

LESSON 9·14 | **Open Response**

Factor Patterns

1. Explore what happens to the product when you double a factor. For example, multiply 4 × 5. Then double the 4 and multiply 8 × 5; then double the 5 and multiply 4 × 10. Show your work.

2. Try doubling one of the factors in other multiplication facts. Show your work.
   Describe a pattern you see when you double factors.

3. Based on your work with doubling factors, predict what will happen when you triple a factor. Explain how you would convince someone that your prediction is true for all multiplication facts.

LESSON 10·11   Self Assessment

Check one box for each skill.

Skills	I can do this on my own and can explain how to do it.	I can do this on my own.	I can do this if I get help or look at an example.
1. Measure to the nearest $\frac{1}{2}$ inch and $\frac{1}{2}$ centimeter.			
2. Make a frequency table to show data.			
3. Make a line plot to show data.			
4. Find the median, mode, and mean for a set of data.			
5. Find fractional parts of collections.			
6. Multiply 3-digit numbers by 1-digit numbers.			

LESSON 10·11 | **Written Assessment**

Part A

1. Measure and label the sides of the polygon in centimeters.

2. The perimeter of the polygon is _____ cm.

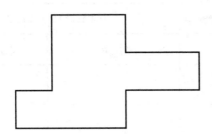

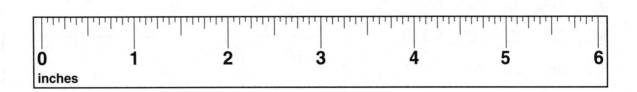

3. Make a dot at 2 inches. Label it with the letter A.

4. Make a dot at $4\frac{1}{2}$ inches. Label it with the letter B.

5. Make a dot at $5\frac{1}{2}$ inches. Label it with the letter C.

Solve. Show your work.

6.   286
     ×   4

7.   305
     ×   6

Written Assessment *continued*

8. Measure the line segment to the nearest $\frac{1}{2}$ inch.

_____

about _____ in.

9. The children in Mr. Barrie's class had the following scores on a spelling test. Show these scores in a frequency table.

Spelling Test Scores

85	95	90	100	70
95	100	75	85	85
90	75	95	100	90
85	95	85	90	100
95	75	85	95	95

Scores	Frequency	
	Tallies	**Number**
70		
75		
80		
85		
90		
95		
100		
	Total	

10. Make a line plot to show the spelling test data from the frequency table.

Spelling Test Scores in Mr. Barrie's Class

Number of Children

```
70   75   80   85   90   95   100
         Spelling Test Scores
```

11. The median test score is _____.

12. The mode of the test scores is _____.

LESSON 10·11 | **Written Assessment** *continued*

13. Fill in the blanks.

_____ inches = 4 feet $1\frac{1}{2}$ feet = _____ inches

2 yards = _____ feet   _____ inches = 2 yards

14. Color $\frac{1}{4}$ of the marbles blue. Color $\frac{2}{3}$ of the marbles green.

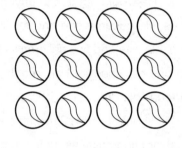

Write a fraction that shows
the number of marbles *not* colored. _____

Part B

15. Look at the Litter Sizes table. Figure out
the mean (average) number of puppies.
Use your calculator to help you.

The mean number of puppies is _____.

Litter Sizes	
Dog's Name	**Number of Puppies**
Fifi	6
Spot	3
Duchess	5
Honey	5
Rover	7
Daisy	4

Solve. Show your work.

16.   29
     × 34

17.   42
     × 56

LESSON 10·11 | **Open Response**

Writing about a Top Dog

The Daily News has an article about "Top Dogs" in the same space each week. Last week's article is at the right.

Jenny wanted to write an article about her "Top Dog" Magic. Jenny needed to know how many words she should write.

She did not want to count all of the words. She used the *mean* number of words from the first 3 lines of the article to make her estimate.

Use Jenny's strategy to make an estimate for the total number of words in all 15 lines.

Show all of your work.
Describe each step.

> **This Week's Top Dog—Leif the Lab**
>
> Jim was hurt badly when his car crashed 4 years ago. He could not walk and he lost his ability to remember many things. He would not talk to anyone, even family and friends. He became sad and felt like he had no future. Soon, his wife and two children were angry with him. Then one day, he met Leif, a golden Labrador, who changed his life. Leif became a constant companion. He is able to help Jim with over one hundred tasks that Jim finds difficult. Leif can get laundry out of the washing machine, call the elevator, pick up items in the supermarket, and even hand over the payment at the supermarket checkout. Leif has saved Jim's life many times, because he always reminds Jim to look before crossing the street. Since Leif came along, Jim is a new man!

Do you think that Jenny's strategy is a good one? Explain.

LESSON 11·6 Self Assessment

Check one box for each skill.

Skills	I can do this on my own and explain how to do it.	I can do this on my own.	I can do this if I get help or look at an example.
1. Read and write numbers up to 1,000,000.			
2. Know the value of each digit in 6-digit numbers.			
3. Tell and show time to the nearest minute on an analog clock.			
4. Use basic probability terms to describe a spinner.			
5. Make predictions about the outcomes of a spinner experiment.			
6. Use fractions to describe parts of a spinner.			

Written Assessment

Part A

1. Write the number that has
9 in the ten-thousands place,
3 in the ones place,
7 in the hundred-thousands place,
0 in the tens place,
6 in the thousands place, and
1 in the hundreds place.

796,103

2. Write the number that is 10,000
more than the number in
Problem 1.

997,214

3. Read the number below to yourself.
Circle the digit that means forty thousand.
Underline the digit that means four hundred.

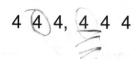

4 ④ 4, 4 4 4

4. Last night, Corey started reading at 7:12 P.M. He stopped reading
$\frac{1}{2}$ hour later. Draw hands on the clock face in Problem 4a to show
the time he started reading. Draw hands on the clock face in
Problem 4b to show the time he stopped reading.

a.

b.

LESSON 11·6 | **Written Assessment** *continued*

5. Shade the oval next to each statement that is true for the spinner.

   ⬭ You are equally likely
to get dots or black.

   ⬭ You are less likely to
get stripes than dots.

   ⬭ You are more likely to
get stripes than white.

   ⬭ You are certain to
get stripes.

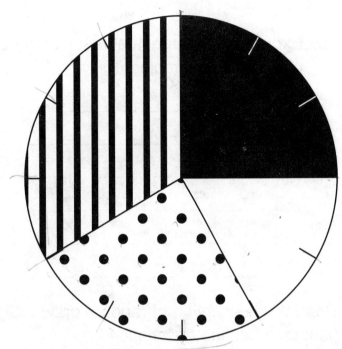

6. What fraction of the spinner in Problem 5 is covered with dots? _____

7. What fraction of the spinner in Problem 5 is covered with stripes? _____

8. Use the spinner from Problem 5. Predict the number of times a paper
clip might land on each section of the spinner if you spin 12 times.
Record your predictions in the second column of the table. Then take a
paper clip and actually spin 12 times. Record your results in the third
column of the table.

Section of the Spinner	Predicted Results for 12 Spins	Actual Results for 12 Spins
black	4	3
white	3	4
stripes	5	3
dots	4	

LESSON 11·6 | **Written Assessment** *continued*

Part B

9. Explain why your actual results may be different from your predictions in Problem 8.

_____

_____

_____

_____

_____

Read the description of random draws. Circle the picture of the jar that best matches the description.

10. From 100 random draws you get:

   a black marble ● 28 times.

   a white marble ○ 72 times.

10 marbles in a jar

10 marbles in a jar

11. From 50 random draws, you get:

   a black marble ● 27 times.

   a white marble ○ 23 times.

10 marbles in a jar

10 marbles in a jar

Open Response

Progress
Check 11

The Sandwich Spinner

At **Ellen's Sandwich Shop,** customers spin a spinner to win one of three free sandwiches.

1. Make a spinner so that the following statements are true:

   ◆ About $\frac{1}{2}$ the time, customers win a **turkey** sandwich.

   ◆ Customers win a **peanut butter** sandwich about *twice* as often as they win a **cheese** sandwich.

2. Each employee made a tally chart and recorded when a customer won a sandwich. At the end of the day, their tally charts did not match.

Spin to Win a Free Sandwich!

	Andy's
Turkey	~~HHT~~ ~~HHT~~ ~~HHT~~
Peanut Butter	~~HHT~~ ~~HHT~~ ////
Cheese	////

	Barb's
Turkey	~~HHT~~ ~~HHT~~ ~~HHT~~ //
Peanut Butter	~~HHT~~ ~~HHT~~ /
Cheese	~~HHT~~

	Jose's
Turkey	~~HHT~~ ~~HHT~~
Peanut Butter	~~HHT~~ ~~HHT~~ ////
Cheese	~~HHT~~ ////

Which employee's tally chart is most likely to be correct?
Explain how you found your answer.

Name Date Time

LESSON 1·14 **Written Assessment** Progress Check 1

Part A

1. Draw coins to show 58¢ two different ways. Use Ⓟ, Ⓝ, Ⓓ, and Ⓠ.
   Sample answers: ⓆⓆⓃⓅⓅⓅ; ⒹⒹⒹⒹⒹⓃⓅⓅⓅ

Use >, <, or =.

2. \$0.90 ___<___ ⓆⓆⓆⓆⓃ

3. ⓆⒹⒹⓃⓃⓅ ___<___ ⓆⓆⓆ

Draw the minute hand and hour hand to show the times.

4. 
2:15

5. 
3:30

6. 
9:45

Write seven names for the number 18 in the name-collection box.

7. **18** Sample answers:
   one and one half dozen   – 2 + 20
   20 – 2   1,018 – 1,000
   double 9   10 + 5 + 3
   2 + 2 + 2 + 2 + 2 + 2 + 2 + 2 + 2

Name Date Time

LESSON 1·14 **Written Assessment** *continued*

Use + or – to make the number sentence true.

8. 8 = 13 ___–___ 5
   15 = 9 ___+___ 6
   8 ___+___ 3 = 11
   17 ___–___ 9 = 8

Unit

Fill in the missing numbers.

9. Rule: +10

24 → 34 → 44 → 54 → 64 → 74

10. Rule: +2

24 → 26 → 28 → 30 → 32 → 34

11. Write 2 things that you are sure *will not* happen.
    Sample answers: I will sprout wings and fly; my dog will chirp like a bird.

Name Date Time

LESSON 1·14 **Written Assessment** *continued*

Part B

12. Use the tally chart to complete the bar graph.

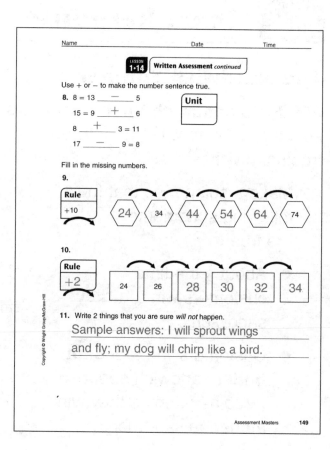

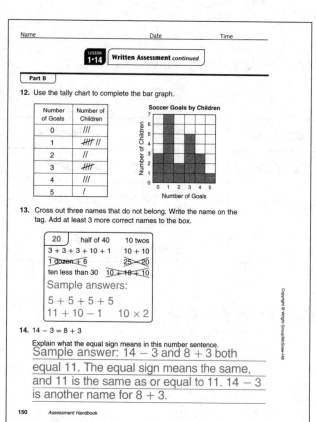

Number of Goals	Number of Children
0	///
1	~~////~~ //
2	//
3	~~////~~
4	///
5	/

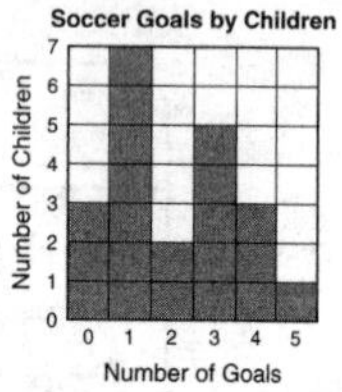

13. Cross out three names that do not belong. Write the name on the tag. Add at least 3 more correct names to the box.

   20   half of 40   10 twos
   3 + 3 + 3 + 10 + 1   10 + 10
   ~~1 dozen + 6~~   ~~25 – 20~~
   ten less than 30   ~~10 + 10 + 10~~
   Sample answers:
   5 + 5 + 5 + 5
   11 + 10 – 1   10 × 2

14. 14 – 3 = 8 + 3
    Explain what the equal sign means in this number sentence.
    Sample answer: 14 – 3 and 8 + 3 both equal 11. The equal sign means the same, and 11 is the same as or equal to 11. 14 – 3 is another name for 8 + 3.

Page 153

LESSON 2·10 Written Assessment

Progress Check 2

Part A

Fill in the unit box and the blanks.

Unit [ ]

1. $3 + \underline{9} = 12$
   $30 + \underline{90} = 120$
   $300 + \underline{900} = 1,200$

2. $17 = 8 + \underline{9}$
   $170 = 80 + \underline{90}$
   $1,700 = 800 + \underline{900}$

Complete the tables. Write your own number pair in the last row of each table.

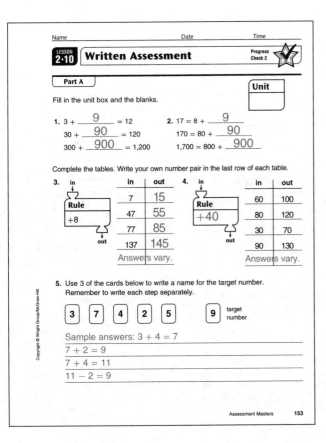

3. Rule +8

in	out
7	15
47	55
77	85
137	145

Answers vary.

4. Rule +40

in	out
60	100
80	120
30	70
90	130

Answers vary.

5. Use 3 of the cards below to write a name for the target number. Remember to write each step separately.

[3] [7] [4] [2] [5]   [9] target number

Sample answers: $3 + 4 = 7$
$7 + 2 = 9$
$7 + 4 = 11$
$11 - 2 = 9$

Page 154

LESSON 2·10 Written Assessment continued

Solve the following number stories. Use diagrams or pictures to help you.

6. One python clutch has 31 eggs. Another python clutch has 19 eggs. How many more eggs are in the first clutch?

   Number model: $19 + ? = 31$
   or $31 - 19 = ?$

   Answer the question: __12 eggs__
   (unit)

Quantity
31

Quantity
19

?
Difference

7. Maria swam for 20 minutes on Saturday and 36 minutes on Sunday. How many minutes in all did Maria swim?

   Number model: $20 + 36 = ?$

   Answer the question: __56 minutes__
   (unit)

Total
?

Part	Part
20	36

Draw the hands to show the time.

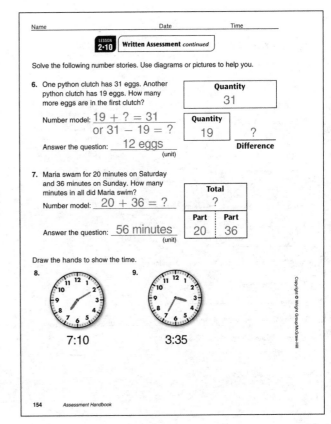

8.

7:10

9.

3:35

Page 155

LESSON 2·10 Written Assessment continued

10. In the number 8,439,
    the 4 means __400__.
    the 9 means __9__.
    the 3 means __30__.
    the 8 means __8,000__.

Part B

Complete the tables. Write your own number pair in the last row.

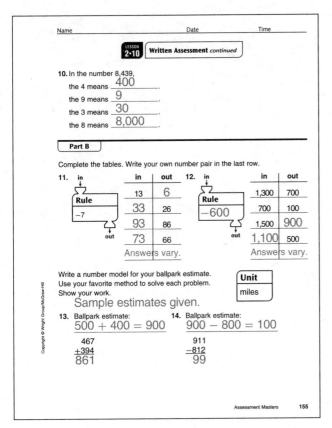

11. Rule −7

in	out
13	6
33	26
93	86
73	66

Answers vary.

12. Rule −600

in	out
1,300	700
700	100
1,500	900
1,100	500

Answers vary.

Write a number model for your ballpark estimate. Use your favorite method to solve each problem. Show your work.

Unit miles

Sample estimates given.

13. Ballpark estimate:
    $500 + 400 = 900$

    467
    +394
    861

14. Ballpark estimate:
    $900 - 800 = 100$

    911
    −812
    99

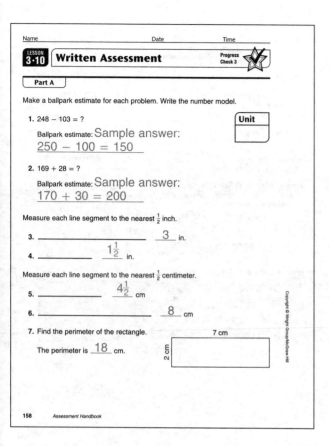

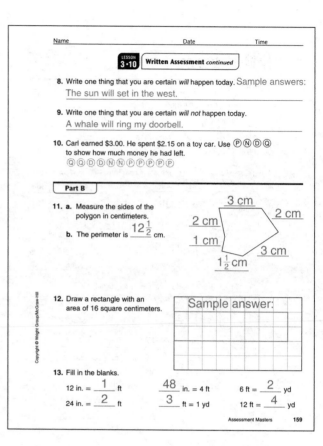

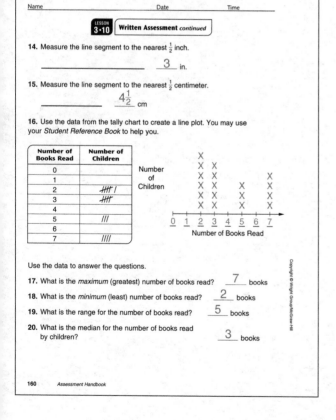

Panel 1 (page 158):

Name _____ Date _____ Time _____

LESSON 3·10 **Written Assessment** Progress Check 3

Part A

Make a ballpark estimate for each problem. Write the number model.

1. 248 − 103 = ?

Ballpark estimate: Sample answer:
250 − 100 = 150

Unit

2. 169 + 28 = ?

Ballpark estimate: Sample answer:
170 + 30 = 200

Measure each line segment to the nearest $\frac{1}{2}$ inch.

3. _____ __3__ in.

4. _____ $1\frac{1}{2}$ in.

Measure each line segment to the nearest $\frac{1}{2}$ centimeter.

5. _____ $4\frac{1}{2}$ cm

6. _____ __8__ cm

7. Find the perimeter of the rectangle.

The perimeter is __18__ cm.

7 cm / 2 cm

158   Assessment Handbook

Panel 2 (page 159):

Name _____ Date _____ Time _____

LESSON 3·10 **Written Assessment** *continued*

8. Write one thing that you are certain *will* happen today. Sample answers:
The sun will set in the west.

9. Write one thing that you are certain *will not* happen today.
A whale will ring my doorbell.

10. Carl earned $3.00. He spent $2.15 on a toy car. Use Ⓟ Ⓝ Ⓓ Ⓠ
to show how much money he had left.
Ⓠ Ⓓ Ⓓ Ⓝ Ⓝ Ⓟ Ⓟ Ⓟ Ⓟ Ⓟ

Part B

11. a. Measure the sides of the polygon in centimeters.
b. The perimeter is __$12\frac{1}{2}$__ cm.

3 cm / 2 cm / 1 cm / 2 cm / 3 cm / $1\frac{1}{2}$ cm

12. Draw a rectangle with an area of 16 square centimeters.

Sample answer:

13. Fill in the blanks.

12 in. = __1__ ft   __48__ in. = 4 ft   6 ft = __2__ yd
24 in. = __2__ ft   __3__ ft = 1 yd   12 ft = __4__ yd

Assessment Masters   159

Panel 3 (page 160):

Name _____ Date _____ Time _____

LESSON 3·10 **Written Assessment** *continued*

14. Measure the line segment to the nearest $\frac{1}{2}$ inch.

_____ __3__ in.

15. Measure the line segment to the nearest $\frac{1}{2}$ centimeter.

_____ $4\frac{1}{2}$ cm

16. Use the data from the tally chart to create a line plot. You may use your *Student Reference Book* to help you.

Number of Books Read	Number of Children
0	
1	
2	ЖЖ I
3	ЖЖ
4	
5	///
6	
7	////

Number of Children

```
              X
          X   X
          X   X        X
          X   X    X   X
          X   X    X   X
          X   X    X   X
        0 1 2 3 4 5 6 7
        Number of Books Read
```

Use the data to answer the questions.

17. What is the *maximum* (greatest) number of books read? __7__ books

18. What is the *minimum* (least) number of books read? __2__ books

19. What is the range for the number of books read? __5__ books

20. What is the median for the number of books read by children? __3__ books

160   Assessment Handbook

LESSON 4·11 | **Written Assessment**

Progress Check 4

Part A

Complete the fact families.

1. $2 \times 4 = \underline{8}$
   $4 \times 2 = \underline{8}$
   $\underline{8} \div 2 = 4$
   $\underline{8} \div 4 = 2$

2. $7 \times 1 = \underline{7}$
   $1 \times 7 = \underline{7}$
   $7 \div 1 = \underline{7}$
   $7 \div 7 = \underline{1}$

3. Write the number that is
   100 more than 603. $\underline{703}$
   100 more than 1,468. $\underline{1,568}$
   100 less than 968. $\underline{868}$
   100 less than 2,751. $\underline{2,651}$

4. Fill in the blanks. Use >, <, or =.

   $2 \times 6 \underline{\quad =\quad} 6 \times 2$
   $7 \times 1 \underline{\quad >\quad} 15 \times 0$
   $0 \times 6 \underline{\quad =\quad} 3 \times 0$
   $9 \times 1 \underline{\quad >\quad} 4 \times 2$
   $5 \times 3 \underline{\quad =\quad} 3 \times 5$
   $5 \times 1 \underline{\quad =\quad} 1 \times 5$

   Reminder:
   > means *is greater than*
   < means *is less than*
   = means *is the same as*

5. Find the area of each rectangle.
   A = $\underline{24}$ sq cm
   B = $\underline{15}$ sq cm

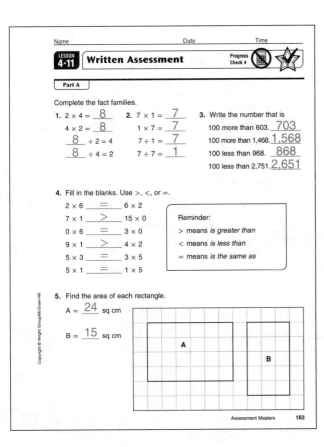

LESSON 4·11 | **Written Assessment** *continued*

6. Fill in the blanks.

   in
   Rule ×2
   out

in	out
7	14
4	8
2	4
0	0

   Answers vary.

7. Fill in the missing numbers.

929	930
	940
	950
	960
	970

For Problems 8 and 9, fill in a multiplication/division diagram. Then use counters, arrays, pictures, or whatever you need to find the answer. Record your answers with a unit. Write a number model.

8. The pet shop keeps 5 puppies in each pen. There are 3 pens. How many puppies in all?

pens	puppies per pen	puppies in all
3	5	?

   Number model: $5 \times 3 = ?$

   Answer: $\underline{15 \text{ puppies}}$
   (unit)

Part B

9. Ellie has 21 dog snacks to divide equally among her 3 dogs. How many snacks does each dog get?

dogs	snacks per dog	snacks in all
3	?	21

   Number model: $21 \div 3 = ?$

   Answer: $\underline{7 \text{ snacks}}$
   (unit)

LESSON 4·11 | **Written Assessment** *continued*

10. Fill in the blanks.

    in
    Rule ÷2
    out

in	out
8	4
12	6
10	5
14	7
4	2

11. Fill in the blanks.

    in
    Rule ×4
    out

in	out
7	28
5	20
3	12
6	24
8	32

12. Use the numbers 3, 7, and 21 to write a multiplication/division fact family.

    $3 \times 7 = 21$ $7 \times 3 = 21$
    $21 \div 3 = 7$ $21 \div 7 = 3$

LESSON 5·13 | **Written Assessment**   Progress Check 5

Part A

Write the number that matches the description.

1. 3 in the ten-thousands place
0 in the hundreds place
5 in the thousands place
7 in the tens place
6 in the ones place

3 5 , 0 7 6

2. 9 in the ones place
4 in the hundreds place
6 in the ten-thousands place
5 in the tens place
0 in the thousands place

6 0 , 4 5 9

Write >, <, or =.

3. 63,000 > 59,888

4. 46,526 > 40,999

Fill in the blanks.

5. 7,000 + 6,000 = 13,000   Unit

6. 11,000 − 3,000 = 8,000

Write the sums.   Unit

7. 13 + 7 + 9 + 11 = 40

8. 24 + 12 + 8 + 6 = 50

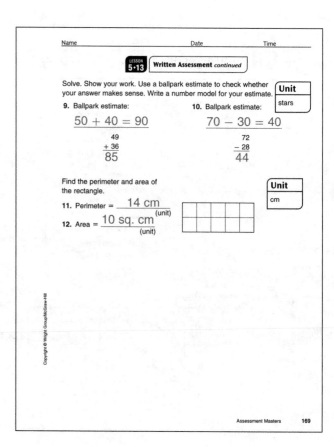

LESSON 5·13 | **Written Assessment** *continued*

Solve. Show your work. Use a ballpark estimate to check whether your answer makes sense. Write a number model for your estimate.   Unit | stars

9. Ballpark estimate:

$50 + 40 = 90$

$$\begin{array}{r} 49 \\ + 36 \\ \hline 85 \end{array}$$

10. Ballpark estimate:

$70 - 30 = 40$

$$\begin{array}{r} 72 \\ - 28 \\ \hline 44 \end{array}$$

Find the perimeter and area of the rectangle.   Unit | cm

11. Perimeter = 14 cm (unit)

12. Area = 10 sq. cm (unit)

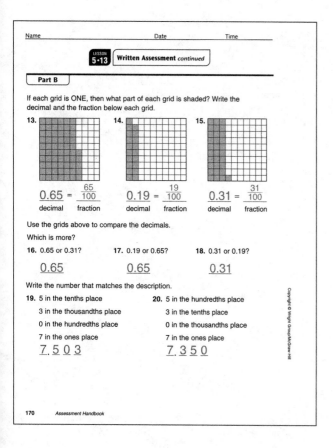

LESSON 5·13 | **Written Assessment** *continued*

Part B

If each grid is ONE, then what part of each grid is shaded? Write the decimal and the fraction below each grid.

13.

$0.65 = \frac{65}{100}$
decimal   fraction

14.

$0.19 = \frac{19}{100}$
decimal   fraction

15.

$0.31 = \frac{31}{100}$
decimal   fraction

Use the grids above to compare the decimals.

Which is more?

16. 0.65 or 0.31?

0.65

17. 0.19 or 0.65?

0.65

18. 0.31 or 0.19?

0.31

Write the number that matches the description.

19. 5 in the tenths place
3 in the thousandths place
0 in the hundredths place
7 in the ones place

7 . 5 0 3

20. 5 in the hundredths place
3 in the tenths place
0 in the thousandths place
7 in the ones place

7 . 3 5 0

Name _____ Date _____ Time _____

LESSON 6·13 Written Assessment

Progress Check 6

Part A

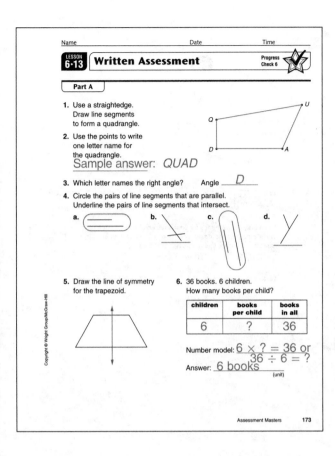

1. Use a straightedge. Draw line segments to form a quadrangle.

2. Use the points to write one letter name for the quadrangle.

Sample answer: *QUAD*

3. Which letter names the right angle? Angle ___D___

4. Circle the pairs of line segments that are parallel. Underline the pairs of line segments that intersect.

a. b. c. d.

5. Draw the line of symmetry for the trapezoid.

6. 36 books. 6 children. How many books per child?

children	books per child	books in all
6	?	36

Number model: $6 \times ? = 36$ or $36 \div 6 = ?$

Answer: 6 books (unit)

Assessment Masters 173

Name _____ Date _____ Time _____

LESSON 6·13 Written Assessment *continued*

Fill in the ovals to identify each figure.

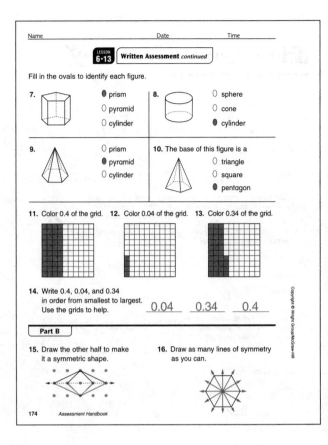

7. ● prism ○ pyramid ○ cylinder

8. ○ sphere ○ cone ● cylinder

9. ○ prism ● pyramid ○ cylinder

10. The base of this figure is a
○ triangle ○ square ● pentagon

11. Color 0.4 of the grid. 12. Color 0.04 of the grid. 13. Color 0.34 of the grid.

14. Write 0.4, 0.04, and 0.34 in order from smallest to largest. Use the grids to help. ___0.04___ ___0.34___ ___0.4___

Part B

15. Draw the other half to make it a symmetric shape.

16. Draw as many lines of symmetry as you can.

174 Assessment Handbook

Name _____ Date _____ Time _____

LESSON 6·13 Written Assessment *continued*

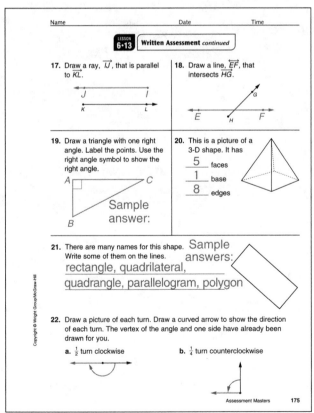

17. Draw a ray, $\overrightarrow{IJ}$, that is parallel to $\overleftrightarrow{KL}$.

18. Draw a line, $\overleftrightarrow{EF}$, that intersects $\overleftrightarrow{HG}$.

19. Draw a triangle with one right angle. Label the points. Use the right angle symbol to show the right angle.

Sample answer:

20. This is a picture of a 3-D shape. It has
___5___ faces
___1___ base
___8___ edges

21. There are many names for this shape. Write some of them on the lines.
Sample answers:
rectangle, quadrilateral, quadrangle, parallelogram, polygon

22. Draw a picture of each turn. Draw a curved arrow to show the direction of each turn. The vertex of the angle and one side have already been drawn for you.

a. $\frac{1}{2}$ turn clockwise

b. $\frac{1}{4}$ turn counterclockwise

Assessment Masters 175

LESSON 7·10 Written Assessment   Progress Check 7

Part A

Fill in the missing factors and products.

1. 8 × 5 = __40__   2. 10 × __3__ = 30   3. 9 × 2 = __18__
4. 7 × __10__ = 70   5. 4 × 5 = __20__   6. __2__ × 8 = 16

7. 4   8. 3   9. 7   10. 4
   × 7   × 6   × 3   × 6
   [28]   [18]   [21]   [24]

Solve. Use diagrams, counters, arrays, pictures, or whatever you need to find the answer. Record your answer with a unit. Write a number model.

11. Linda has 32 crayons to put into boxes. 8 crayons fit into each box. How many boxes does she need?

boxes	crayons per box	crayons in all
?	8	32

Number model: 32 ÷ 8 = ? or ? × 8 = 32

Answer: __4 boxes__
        (unit)

12. 7 children picked 42 apples. If they share the apples equally, how many will each child get?

children	apples per child	apples in all
7	?	42

Number model: 42 ÷ 7 = ? or 7 × ? = 42

Answer: __6 apples__
        (unit)

LESSON 7·10 Written Assessment *continued*

Use a straightedge.

13. Draw $\overleftrightarrow{AB}$ parallel to $\overleftrightarrow{EF}$.   14. Draw $\overrightarrow{CD}$ intersecting $\overleftrightarrow{GH}$.

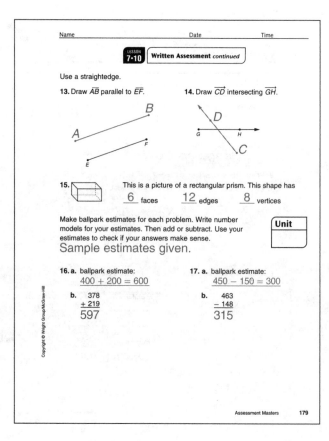

15. 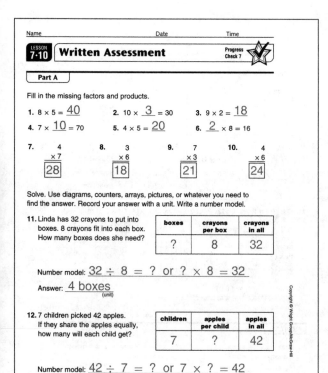 This is a picture of a rectangular prism. This shape has __6__ faces __12__ edges __8__ vertices

Make ballpark estimates for each problem. Write number models for your estimates. Then add or subtract. Use your estimates to check if your answers make sense.

Sample estimates given.

Unit

16. a. ballpark estimate:
       400 + 200 = 600
    b.   378
        + 219
        597

17. a. ballpark estimate:
       450 − 150 = 300
    b.   463
        − 148
        315

LESSON 7·10 Written Assessment *continued*

Part B

18. __11__ = (30 ÷ 5) + 5   19. 9 + (3 × 5) = __24__
20. 7 + (8 × 8) = __71__   21. __6__ = 12 − (12 ÷ 2)

Solve the multiplication/division puzzle. Fill in the blanks.

22.

×, ÷	40	600
8	320	4,800
7	280	4,200

Estimate to answer the question below. Assume that there is no tax on the items.

23. Allen wants to buy a notebook for $3.89 and a pen for $1.99. He has $5.00. Does he have enough money? __no__

Explain your thinking: Sample answer:
$1.99 is almost $2.00, and $3.89 is almost $4.00. That is almost $6.00.

Number model you used: $2.00 + $4.00 = $6.00

LESSON 8·9 Written Assessment

Progress Check 8

Part A

Use counters to help.

1. Circle $\frac{7}{8}$ of the marbles.

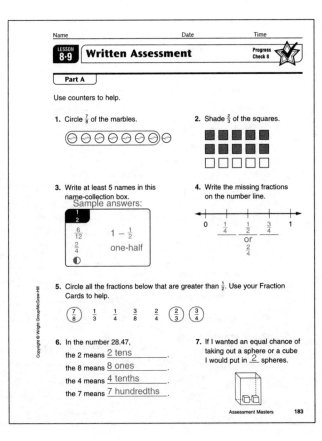

2. Shade $\frac{2}{3}$ of the squares.

3. Write at least 5 names in this name-collection box.

Sample answers:

$\frac{1}{2}$

$\frac{6}{12}$ $1 - \frac{1}{2}$

$\frac{2}{4}$ one-half

◑

4. Write the missing fractions on the number line.

0    $\frac{1}{4}$ $\frac{1}{2}$ $\frac{3}{4}$ 1

or $\frac{2}{4}$

5. Circle all the fractions below that are greater than $\frac{1}{2}$. Use your Fraction Cards to help.

⑦⁄₈ $\frac{1}{3}$ $\frac{1}{4}$ $\frac{3}{8}$ $\frac{2}{4}$ ②⁄₃   ③⁄₄

6. In the number 28.47,

the 2 means _2 tens_ .

the 8 means _8 ones_ .

the 4 means _4 tenths_ .

the 7 means _7 hundredths_ .

7. If I wanted an equal chance of taking out a sphere or a cube I would put in _2_ spheres.

LESSON 8·9 Written Assessment continued

Solve. Draw a picture to show what you did.

8. Four people share 8 pieces of candy.

a. How many pieces does each person get? _2_ pieces

b. What fraction of the candy did each person get? $\frac{1}{4}$ or $\frac{2}{8}$

9. Fill in the blanks.

60 minutes = _1_ hour

120 minutes = _2_ hours

30 minutes = _$\frac{1}{2}$_ hour

_15_ minutes = $\frac{1}{4}$ hour

10. Use a straightedge. Draw the other half of the symmetric shape.

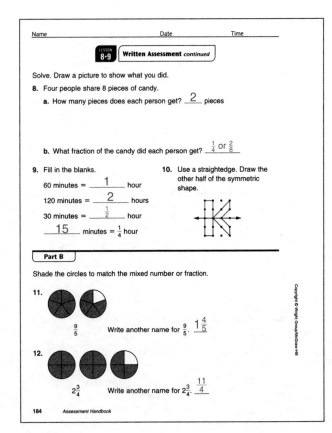

Part B

Shade the circles to match the mixed number or fraction.

11.

$\frac{9}{5}$ Write another name for $\frac{9}{5}$. $1\frac{4}{5}$

12.

$2\frac{3}{4}$ Write another name for $2\frac{3}{4}$. $\frac{11}{4}$

LESSON 8·9 Written Assessment continued

13. Cross out all the names that do not belong in this name-collection box. Then add one more name.

$\frac{3}{4}$

Sample answer:

~~$\frac{5}{10}$~~ $\frac{6}{8}$ ~~$\frac{1}{4}$~~   ~~$\frac{8}{12}$~~

~~two-fourths~~

~~three-thirds~~   three-fourths

14. Fill in the blanks. Use a clock to help.

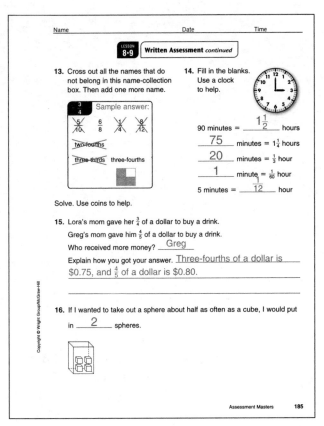

90 minutes = _$1\frac{1}{2}$_ hours

_75_ minutes = $1\frac{1}{4}$ hours

_20_ minutes = $\frac{1}{3}$ hour

_1_ minute = $\frac{1}{60}$ hour

5 minutes = _$\frac{1}{12}$_ hour

Solve. Use coins to help.

15. Lora's mom gave her $\frac{3}{4}$ of a dollar to buy a drink.

Greg's mom gave him $\frac{4}{5}$ of a dollar to buy a drink.

Who received more money? _Greg_

Explain how you got your answer. _Three-fourths of a dollar is $0.75, and $\frac{4}{5}$ of a dollar is $0.80._

16. If I wanted to take out a sphere about half as often as a cube, I would put in _2_ spheres.

Page 1 (top left)

Name _____ Date _____ Time _____

LESSON 9·14 **Written Assessment**

Progress Check 9

Part A

1. How much do four 40-pound beavers weigh? __160__ pounds

   Show your work.

Use partial products or the lattice method to solve.

2.
```
   23
 × 4
 ─────
  80
+12
 ─────
  92
```

3.
```
   49
 × 8
 ─────
 320
+72
 ─────
 392
```

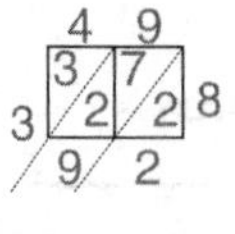

4. Put these fractions in order from smallest to largest. You may use your Fraction Cards.

$\frac{9}{9}$ $\frac{2}{3}$ $\frac{5}{6}$ $\frac{4}{12}$ $\frac{0}{2}$

$\frac{0}{2}$ $\frac{4}{12}$ $\frac{2}{3}$ $\frac{5}{6}$ $\frac{9}{9}$

↑ smallest   ↑ largest

188 Assessment Handbook

Page 2 (top right)

Name _____ Date _____ Time _____

LESSON 9·14 **Written Assessment** *continued*

Complete the number sentences.

5. $7 \times (8 - 8) =$ __0__   6. __48__ $= (7 \times 8) - 8$

7. $7 + (3 \times 9) =$ __34__   8. __90__ $= (7 + 3) \times 9$

9. Draw a rectangle with a perimeter of 24 centimeters.

Sample answers for Problems 9–12:

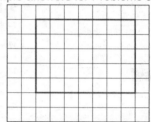

10. How do you know the perimeter is 24 cm?
    My rectangle is 7 cm long and 5 cm wide. I added the
    lengths of the 4 sides. 7 + 7 + 5 + 5 = 24.

11. What is the area of your rectangle? __35__ sq cm

12. How did you find the area?
    I counted the square centimeters; I multiplied the length of
    the rectangle by the width of the rectangle.

Assessment Masters 189

Page 3 (bottom left)

Name _____ Date _____ Time _____

LESSON 9·14 **Written Assessment** *continued*

Mr. Stevens has $10.00 to buy as many packs of batteries as he can.
1 pack of batteries costs $3.59. Sample answers:

13. How many packs can he buy? __2__

14. About how much money will he spend? About $7.00

15. About how much change will he get back? About $3.00

Part B

16. Explain Lora's mistake in the problem below.

```
   28
 × 60
 ─────
 120
+ 48
 ─────
 168
```
Lora multiplied 60 times 2 instead of 60 times
20. She also multiplied 8 by 6 instead of 8
times 60.

17. Use partial products or the lattice method to solve.

```
   37
 × 28
 ─────
1,036
```

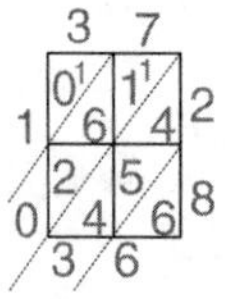

18. Marge is buying hamburger buns for the third grade picnic. She needs
    90 buns. They come in packages of 8. How many packages should
    she buy? __12 packages__

    Explain how you figured out your answer.
    80 buns come in 10 packages because 8 × 10 = 80.
    2 more packages would make 96 buns. Marge needs 12
    packages to get 90 buns. 6 buns would be left over.

190 Assessment Handbook

---

210   *Assessment Handbook*

LESSON 10·11 **Written Assessment**   Progress Check 10

Part A

1. Measure and label the sides of the polygon in centimeters.

2. The perimeter of the polygon is __16__ cm.

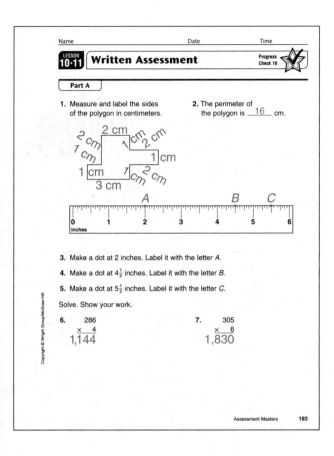

3. Make a dot at 2 inches. Label it with the letter *A*.

4. Make a dot at 4½ inches. Label it with the letter *B*.

5. Make a dot at 5½ inches. Label it with the letter *C*.

Solve. Show your work.

6.
```
   286
 ×   4
 1,144
```

7.
```
   305
 ×   6
 1,830
```

LESSON 10·11 **Written Assessment** *continued*

8. Measure the line segment to the nearest ½ inch.

about __5__ in.

9. The children in Mr. Barrie's class had the following scores on a spelling test. Show these scores in a frequency table.

Spelling Test Scores

85	95	90	100	70
95	100	75	85	85
90	75	95	100	90
85	95	85	90	100
95	75	85	95	95

Scores	Frequency	
	Tallies	Number
70	/	1
75	///	3
80		0
85	~~HHH~~ /	6
90	////	4
95	~~HHH~~ //	7
100	////	4
	Total	25

10. Make a line plot to show the spelling test data from the frequency table.

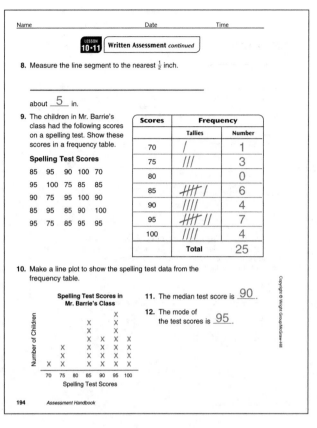

Spelling Test Scores in Mr. Barrie's Class

11. The median test score is __90__.

12. The mode of the test scores is __95__.

LESSON 10·11 **Written Assessment** *continued*

13. Fill in the blanks.

__48__ inches = 4 feet   1½ feet = __18__ inches

2 yards = __6__ feet   __72__ inches = 2 yards

14. Color ¼ of the marbles blue. Color ⅔ of the marbles green.

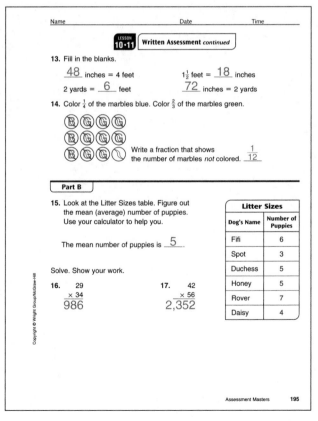

Write a fraction that shows the number of marbles *not* colored. __1/12__

Part B

15. Look at the Litter Sizes table. Figure out the mean (average) number of puppies. Use your calculator to help you.

The mean number of puppies is __5__.

Litter Sizes	
Dog's Name	Number of Puppies
Fifi	6
Spot	3
Duchess	5
Honey	5
Rover	7
Daisy	4

Solve. Show your work.

16.
```
   29
 × 34
  986
```

17.
```
   42
 × 56
 2,352
```

LESSON 11·6 **Written Assessment**

Part A

1. Write the number that has
   9 in the ten-thousands place,
   3 in the ones place,
   7 in the hundred-thousands place,
   0 in the tens place,
   6 in the thousands place, and
   1 in the hundreds place.

   7 9 6 , 1 0 3

2. Write the number that is 10,000 more than the number in Problem 1.

   8 0 6 , 1 0 3

3. Read the number below to yourself.
   Circle the digit that means forty thousand.
   Underline the digit that means four hundred.

   4 ④ 4 , 4 4 4

4. Last night, Corey started reading at 7:12 P.M. He stopped reading $\frac{1}{2}$ hour later. Draw hands on the clock face in Problem 4a to show the time he started reading. Draw hands on the clock face in Problem 4b to show the time he stopped reading.

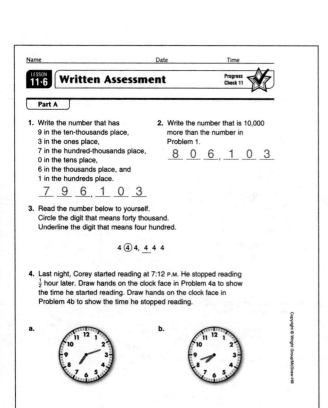

a.   b.

LESSON 11·6 **Written Assessment** *continued*

5. Shade the oval next to each statement that is true for the spinner.

   ⬭ You are equally likely to get dots or black.

   ⬭ You are less likely to get stripes than dots.

   ⬭ You are more likely to get stripes than white.

   ⬭ You are certain to get stripes.

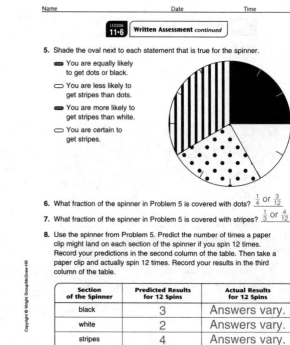

6. What fraction of the spinner in Problem 5 is covered with dots? $\frac{1}{4}$ or $\frac{3}{12}$

7. What fraction of the spinner in Problem 5 is covered with stripes? $\frac{1}{3}$ or $\frac{4}{12}$

8. Use the spinner from Problem 5. Predict the number of times a paper clip might land on each section of the spinner if you spin 12 times. Record your predictions in the second column of the table. Then take a paper clip and actually spin 12 times. Record your results in the third column of the table.

Section of the Spinner	Predicted Results for 12 Spins	Actual Results for 12 Spins
black	3	Answers vary.
white	2	Answers vary.
stripes	4	Answers vary.
dots	3	Answers vary.

LESSON 11·6 **Written Assessment** *continued*

Part B

9. Explain why your actual results may be different from your predictions in Problem 8.

   Sample answer: My predictions are based on the fraction of the spinner that is covered with black, white, dots, or stripes. My actual results are based on where the paper clip pointed after each spin. If I spin lots of times, the actual results will probably come closer to my predictions.

Read the description of random draws. Circle the picture of the jar that best matches the description.

10. From 100 random draws you get:

    a black marble ● 28 times.
    a white marble ○ 72 times.

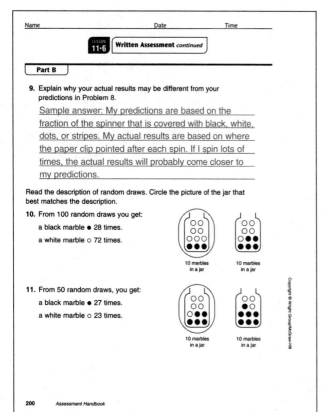

    10 marbles in a jar   10 marbles in a jar

11. From 50 random draws, you get:

    a black marble ● 27 times.
    a white marble ○ 23 times.

    10 marbles in a jar   10 marbles in a jar

Beginning-of-Year Assessment

1. Solve.

Unit
apples

a. _____ = 4 + 6 **b.** 10 − 3 = _____ **c.** _____ = 9 − 1

d. $\begin{array}{r} 2 \\ + 8 \\ \hline \end{array}$ **e.** $\begin{array}{r} 10 \\ - 5 \\ \hline \end{array}$ **f.** $\begin{array}{r} 6 \\ + 6 \\ \hline \end{array}$

2. Solve.

Unit
pennies

a. 4 + 3 = 7 **b.** 6 = 11 − 5 **c.** 5 = 8 − 3

40 + 30 = _____ _____ = 110 − 50 _____ = 80 − 30

3. Solve.

Unit
third graders

a. $\begin{array}{r} 75 \\ + 36 \\ \hline \end{array}$ **b.** $\begin{array}{r} 82 \\ - 47 \\ \hline \end{array}$

4. Find the area of the shape below.

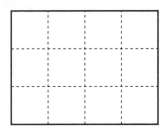

☐ = 1 square unit

Area = _____ square units

Beginning-of-Year Assessment *cont.*

5. Circle the best answer.

   a. A desk is about

      3 inches high.

      3 feet high.

      3 miles high.

   b. An ant is about

      1 centimeter long.

      1 meter long.

      1 kilometer long.

6. Fill in the missing numbers.

   a. 342, 344, 346, _____, _____, _____, _____, _____, _____

   b. Write about a pattern that you see in the numbers.

_____

_____

7. a. Write your own number pattern.

_____, _____, _____, _____, _____, _____, _____, _____, _____

   b. Write about your pattern.

_____

_____

Beginning-of-Year Assessment *cont.*

8. Solve. If needed, you may use the diagrams to help.

a. Erin played basketball for 25 minutes during gym class and for 40 minutes after school. How many minutes did she play basketball in all? Show your work.

Total	
Part	**Part**

Erin played basketball for _____ minutes.

b. Jorge had 24 crayons. Serena had 14 crayons. How many more crayons did Jorge have than Serena? Show your work.

Quantity

Quantity

_____
Difference

Jorge had _____ more crayons.

LESSON 6·13 | Mid-Year Assessment

1. Fill in the unit box. Complete each fact.

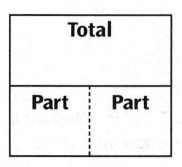

Unit

a. $7 + 8 =$ _____

b. $11 - 5 =$ _____

c. $6 + 7 =$ _____

d. $9 = 15 -$ _____

e. $3 +$ _____ $= 10$

f. _____ $= 13 - 8$

2. Fill in the diagram if needed. Solve.
Show your work.

The second grade collected 67 cans. The third grade collected 122 cans. How many cans were collected in all?

Answer: _____ cans were collected in all.

Total	
Part	**Part**

3. Follow the directions for each clock.

a. Write the time.

_____

b. Write the time.

_____

c. Draw the hands.

3:35

LESSON 6·13 **Mid-Year Assessment** *continued*

4. Fill in the unit box. Add or subtract. Show your work.

a. 682
      − 236
      _____

b. 427
      + 339
      _____

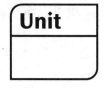

Unit

5. Fill in the diagram if needed. Solve. Show your work.

Rashida has 87 stickers. Justin has 45 stickers. How many more stickers does Rashida have than Justin?

Rashida has _____ more stickers than Justin.

Quantity

Quantity

_____
Difference

6. Use your ruler. Measure each line segment below to the nearest $\frac{1}{2}$ inch and to the nearest $\frac{1}{2}$ centimeter.

_____

a. about _____ inches

b. about _____ centimeters

_____

c. about _____ inches

d. about _____ centimeters

LESSON 6·13 **Mid-Year Assessment** *continued*

7. Use the tally chart to complete the bar graph.

Total Wins	
Teams	**Number of Wins**
Team A	~~HHf~~ ////
Team B	~~HHf~~ /
Team C	~~HHf~~
Team D	~~HHf~~ ~~HHf~~

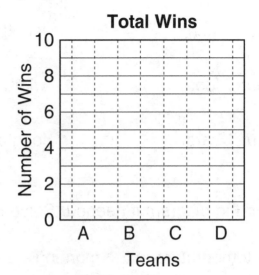

Total Wins

8. Fill in the diagram if needed. Solve.
Show your work.

Colin had $65. He spent $33 at the store.
How much money did Colin have left?

$ _____

| **Start** | **Change** | **End** |

9. Fill in the unit box. Solve.

Unit

a. 5 − 3 = _____

e. 8 + 4 = _____

b. 50 − 30 = _____

f. 800 + 400 = _____

c. _____ = 6 + 2

g. _____ = 9 − 6

d. _____ = 60 + 20

h. _____ = 900 − 600

10. Match.

About 1 inch   length of your math journal

About 1 foot   width of a door

About 1 yard   length of a paperclip

11. Fill in the diagram if needed. Solve. Show your work.

The temperature in the morning was 55°F.
The temperature in the afternoon was 78°F.
How much warmer was the temperature in
the afternoon than in the morning?

Change

Start		End

_____ °F

12. Which of the following is about 1 centimeter? Circle the best answer.

Thickness of a pattern block

Length of a pair of scissors

Length of your arm

LESSON 11·6 | # End-of-Year Assessment

1. Write the number that matches the description.

   9 in the ones place

   3 in the tenths place

   4 in the tens place

   6 in the hundredths place

   _____ _____ . _____ _____

2. In the number 547,698,

   the 6 means _____.

   the 4 means _____.

   the 5 means _____.

   the 9 means _____.

3. Solve.

   a. _____ = 3 + 8

   _____ = 30 + 80

   b. 14 – 9 = _____

   140 – 90 = _____

   c. _____ = 7 + 8

   _____ = 70 + 80

   d. 12 – 8 = _____

   1,200 – 800 = _____

   e. 6 + 7 = _____

   600 + 700 = _____

   f. _____ = 16 – 7

   _____ = 1,600 – 700

4. Ezra has 356 pennies in a jar. Jenna has 142 pennies in a box. How many more pennies does Ezra have than Jenna? You may draw a diagram to help. Show your work.

   a. Number model: _____

   b. Answer: _____

LESSON 11·6 | **End-of-Year Assessment** *continued*

5. Solve.

   a. 138 × _____ = 138

   b. 25 × 3 = 3 × _____

   c. 3 + 5 + 7 = 7 + 3 + _____

6. Write six multiples of 5.

   _____ _____ _____ _____ _____ _____

7. Draw the other half of the symmetric shape below.

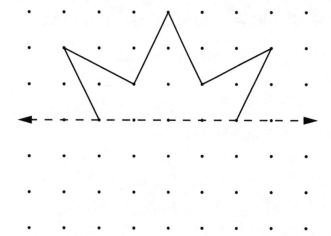

8. Use your fraction cards to compare the fractions below.
   Which is more?

   a. $\frac{2}{3}$ or $\frac{2}{6}$?   **b.** $\frac{5}{6}$ or $\frac{4}{4}$?   **c.** $\frac{3}{4}$ or $\frac{4}{8}$?

   _____   _____   _____

9. Write the letter for the best description of each event.

   _____ It will rain at least once this year.   **a.** certain

   _____ The sun will rise tomorrow.   **b.** likely

   _____ A bird will fly into your house.   **c.** unlikely

LESSON 11·6 | **End-of-Year Assessment** *continued*

10. Find the area and perimeter of this figure.

    a. area: _____ sq cm

    b. perimeter: _____ cm

    c. Explain how you found the perimeter.

_____

_____

6 cm

2 cm

11. a. Make a ballpark estimate for 600 − 158.

_____

    b. How did you get your estimate?

_____

_____

    c. Are there closer estimates? _____
        Why or why not?

_____

_____

12. Follow the directions for each clock.

    a. Draw the hands.   **b.** Draw the hands.   **c.** Write the time.

      6:55   2:42   _____

LESSON 11·6 **End-of-Year Assessment** *continued*

13. Solve.

    a. $2 \times 9 =$ _____

    b. $3 \times 9 =$ _____

    c. $4 \times 9 =$ _____

    d. $5 \times 8 =$ _____

    e. $6 \times 8 =$ _____

    f. $7 \times 8 =$ _____

14. Write at least 2 names for $\frac{2}{3}$. You may use your fraction cards to help.

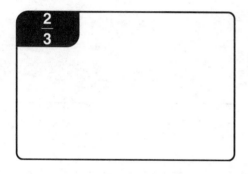

15. Circle $\frac{3}{5}$ of the stars.

16. You may draw an array or use counters to solve. 24 children were in gym class. Ms. Dublin asked $\frac{1}{4}$ of the children to get jump ropes. How many children did Ms. Dublin ask to get jump ropes?

_____ children

17. Circle the angle that shows a $\frac{1}{4}$ turn. Underline the angle that shows more than a $\frac{1}{2}$ turn but less than a $\frac{3}{4}$ turn.

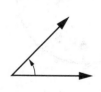  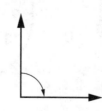 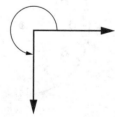

End-of-Year Assessment *continued*

18. There are 2 red cubes and 5 blue cubes in the bag. Without looking inside the bag, Renee's chances of pulling out a blue cube are

_____ out of _____.

19. The picture shows a 3-D shape. Fill in all of the ovals that describe the shape.

⬭ pyramid   ⬭ exactly 6 faces

⬭ cube   ⬭ exactly 6 edges

⬭ prism   ⬭ rectangular bases

20. Solve. You may use coins and bills to help.

$3.62 + $2.23 = $ _____._____

21. Complete the "What's My Rule?" tables and write the rules.

a.

Rule

in	out
7	21
	24
30	90
25	

b.

Rule

in	out
82	
43	33
	65
15	5

c.

Rule

in	out
	48
9	54
10	60
70	

LESSON 11·6 | **End-of-Year Assessment** *continued*

22. Use your favorite multiplication method to solve. Show your work.

a. 74
　　×6
　　───

b. 406
　　× 5
　　───

23. Julia bought 7 boxes of pencils. There were 8 pencils in each box. How many pencils did she buy altogether? You may draw an array or diagram to help. Show your work.

a. Number model: _____

b. Answer: _____

24. Sam's turtle crawled 3 feet. Mary's turtle crawled 2 feet 7 inches. How much further did Sam's turtle crawl than Mary's turtle?

_____

25. Aliya read her book for 120 minutes.
How many hours did Aliya read? _____

26. While on vacation, Steve's family rode on a train for 48 hours. How many days did they spend on the train? _____

LESSON 11·6 End-of-Year Assessment *continued*

27. Add or subtract. Show your work.

a. $\begin{array}{r} 682 \\ -\ 236 \\ \hline \end{array}$

b. $\begin{array}{r} 427 \\ +\ 339 \\ \hline \end{array}$

Unit
books

28. The children in the Garden Club picked 21 flowers to give to their teachers. They gave 3 flowers to each teacher. How many teachers received flowers? You may draw an array or diagram to help. Show your work.

a. Number model: _____

b. _____ teachers received flowers.

29. Write >, <, or =.

a. $3 + 7$ _____ 5×2

b. $18 - 9$ _____ $18 + 9$

c. 4×7 _____ $34 - 7$

d. 5×5 _____ $100 - 75$

30. Solve.

a. $3 \times (4 + 6) =$ _____

b. $(3 \times 4) + 6 =$ _____

c. _____ $= 6 \times (2 + 7)$

d. _____ $= (6 \times 2) + 7$

31. Write the name of each shape. Use the word box to help.

square, hexagon, rhombus, trapezoid, octagon, rectangle, triangle, pentagon

a.

b.

c.

d.

_____ _____ _____ _____

End-of-Year Assessment *continued*

32. Circle the right angle.

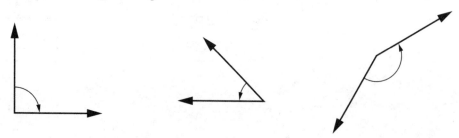

33. Write these numbers in order from smallest to largest.

374,589   473,859   437,895   347,598

_____   _____   _____   _____

smallest   largest

34. Each grid is ONE.

    a. What part of each grid is shaded? Write the decimal below
    each grid.

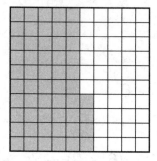 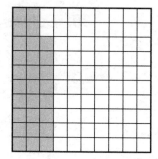 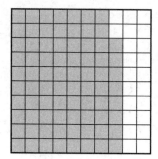

_____   _____   _____

35. Write the decimals from Problem 30 in order from smallest to
largest. You may use the grids to help.

_____   _____   _____

smallest   largest

LESSON 11·6 **End-of-Year Assessment** *continued*

36. Write 6 different names for 24.

> **24**

37. Use the data from the tally chart to create a line plot.

Sisters of Children in Room 312

Number of Sisters	Number of Children
0	///
1	HHT //
2	////
3	//
4	/
5	
6	/

Sisters of Children in Room 312

Number of Children

_____

— — — — — — — — — —

Number of Sisters

38. Use the line plot from Problem 37 to answer these questions.

   a. What is the maximum number of sisters? _____

   b. What is the minimum number of sisters? _____

   c. What is the range for the number of sisters? _____

   d. What is the mode for the number of sisters? _____

   e. What is the median for the number of sisters? _____

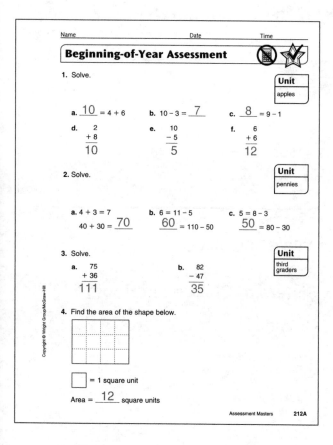

Beginning-of-Year Assessment

1. Solve.

Unit: apples

a. $\underline{10} = 4 + 6$
b. $10 - 3 = \underline{7}$
c. $\underline{8} = 9 - 1$

d.
```
  2
+ 8
───
 10
```
e.
```
 10
- 5
───
  5
```
f.
```
  6
+ 6
───
 12
```

2. Solve.

Unit: pennies

a. $4 + 3 = 7$
   $40 + 30 = \underline{70}$
b. $6 = 11 - 5$
   $\underline{60} = 110 - 50$
c. $5 = 8 - 3$
   $\underline{50} = 80 - 30$

3. Solve.

Unit: third graders

a.
```
  75
+ 36
────
 111
```
b.
```
  82
- 47
────
  35
```

4. Find the area of the shape below.

☐ = 1 square unit

Area = $\underline{12}$ square units

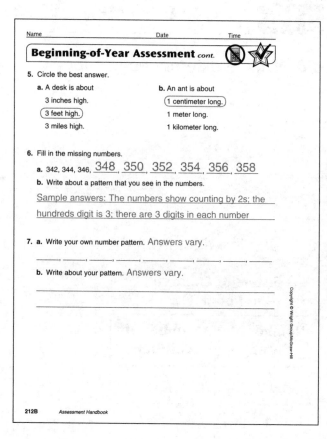

Beginning-of-Year Assessment *cont.*

5. Circle the best answer.

a. A desk is about
   3 inches high.
   (3 feet high.)
   3 miles high.

b. An ant is about
   (1 centimeter long.)
   1 meter long.
   1 kilometer long.

6. Fill in the missing numbers.

a. 342, 344, 346, $\underline{348}$, $\underline{350}$, $\underline{352}$, $\underline{354}$, $\underline{356}$, $\underline{358}$

b. Write about a pattern that you see in the numbers.

Sample answers: The numbers show counting by 2s; the hundreds digit is 3; there are 3 digits in each number

7. a. Write your own number pattern. Answers vary.

_____ _____ _____ _____ _____ _____

b. Write about your pattern. Answers vary.

_____

_____

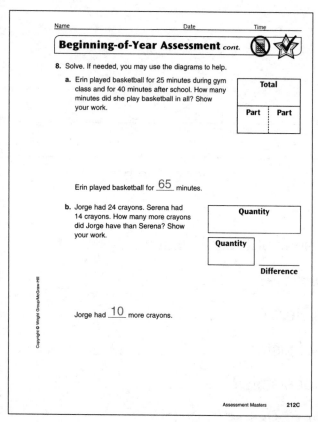

Beginning-of-Year Assessment *cont.*

8. Solve. If needed, you may use the diagrams to help.

a. Erin played basketball for 25 minutes during gym class and for 40 minutes after school. How many minutes did she play basketball in all? Show your work.

Total	
Part	Part

Erin played basketball for $\underline{65}$ minutes.

b. Jorge had 24 crayons. Serena had 14 crayons. How many more crayons did Jorge have than Serena? Show your work.

Quantity

Quantity

Difference

Jorge had $\underline{10}$ more crayons.

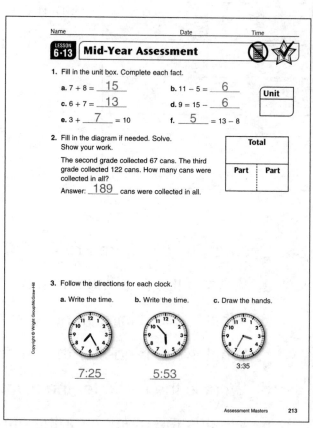

6·13 Mid-Year Assessment

1. Fill in the unit box. Complete each fact.

a. $7 + 8 = \underline{15}$
b. $11 - 5 = \underline{6}$
c. $6 + 7 = \underline{13}$
d. $9 = 15 - \underline{6}$
e. $3 + \underline{7} = 10$
f. $\underline{5} = 13 - 8$

Unit

2. Fill in the diagram if needed. Solve. Show your work.

The second grade collected 67 cans. The third grade collected 122 cans. How many cans were collected in all?

Answer: $\underline{189}$ cans were collected in all.

Total	
Part	Part

3. Follow the directions for each clock.

a. Write the time.

7:25

b. Write the time.

5:53

c. Draw the hands.

3:35

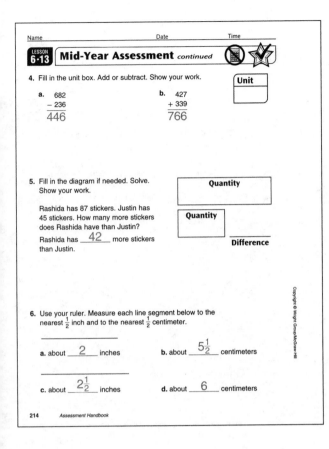

LESSON 6·13 Mid-Year Assessment *continued*

4. Fill in the unit box. Add or subtract. Show your work.

Unit

a. 682
   − 236
   ―――
   446

b. 427
   + 339
   ―――
   766

5. Fill in the diagram if needed. Solve.
   Show your work.

Quantity	

Rashida has 87 stickers. Justin has
45 stickers. How many more stickers
does Rashida have than Justin?

Quantity	

Difference

Rashida has __42__ more stickers
than Justin.

6. Use your ruler. Measure each line segment below to the
nearest $\frac{1}{2}$ inch and to the nearest $\frac{1}{2}$ centimeter.

a. about __2__ inches

b. about __$5\frac{1}{2}$__ centimeters

c. about __$2\frac{1}{2}$__ inches

d. about __6__ centimeters

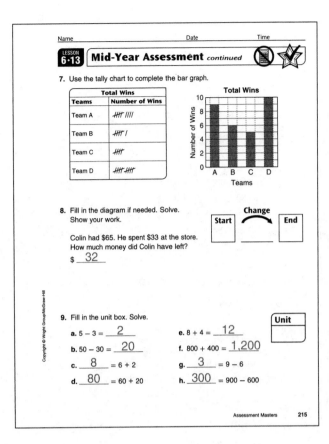

LESSON 6·13 Mid-Year Assessment *continued*

7. Use the tally chart to complete the bar graph.

Total Wins

Teams	Number of Wins
Team A	‖‖‖ ‖‖‖
Team B	‖‖‖	
Team C	‖‖‖
Team D	‖‖‖ ‖‖‖

8. Fill in the diagram if needed. Solve.
   Show your work.

Start **Change** **End**

Colin had $65. He spent $33 at the store.
How much money did Colin have left?

$ __32__

9. Fill in the unit box. Solve.

Unit

a. 5 − 3 = __2__

b. 50 − 30 = __20__

c. __8__ = 6 + 2

d. __80__ = 60 + 20

e. 8 + 4 = __12__

f. 800 + 400 = __1,200__

g. __3__ = 9 − 6

h. __300__ = 900 − 600

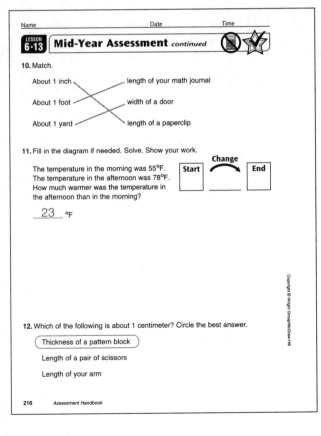

LESSON 6·13 Mid-Year Assessment *continued*

10. Match.

About 1 inch — length of your math journal

About 1 foot — width of a door

About 1 yard — length of a paperclip

11. Fill in the diagram if needed. Solve. Show your work.

Start **Change** **End**

The temperature in the morning was 55°F.
The temperature in the afternoon was 78°F.
How much warmer was the temperature in
the afternoon than in the morning?

__23__ °F

12. Which of the following is about 1 centimeter? Circle the best answer.

(Thickness of a pattern block)

Length of a pair of scissors

Length of your arm

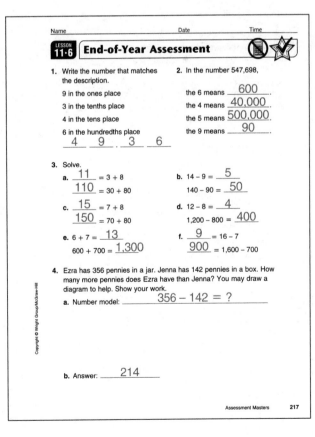

LESSON 11·6 End-of-Year Assessment

1. Write the number that matches
   the description.

   9 in the ones place
   3 in the tenths place
   4 in the tens place
   6 in the hundredths place

   __4__ __9__ . __3__ __6__

2. In the number 547,698,

   the 6 means __600__
   the 4 means __40,000__
   the 5 means __500,000__
   the 9 means __90__

3. Solve.

a. __11__ = 3 + 8
   __110__ = 30 + 80

b. 14 − 9 = __5__
   140 − 90 = __50__

c. __15__ = 7 + 8
   __150__ = 70 + 80

d. 12 − 8 = __4__
   1,200 − 800 = __400__

e. 6 + 7 = __13__
   600 + 700 = __1,300__

f. __9__ = 16 − 7
   __900__ = 1,600 − 700

4. Ezra has 356 pennies in a jar. Jenna has 142 pennies in a box. How
   many more pennies does Ezra have than Jenna? You may draw a
   diagram to help. Show your work.

a. Number model: __356 − 142 = ?__

b. Answer: __214__

LESSON 11·6 | End-of-Year Assessment *continued*

5. Solve.

a. 138 × __1__ = 138

b. 25 × 3 = 3 × __25__

c. 3 + 5 + 7 = 7 + 3 + __5__

6. Write six multiples of 5.

__Answers vary, but must be multiples of 5.__

7. Draw the other half of the symmetric shape below.

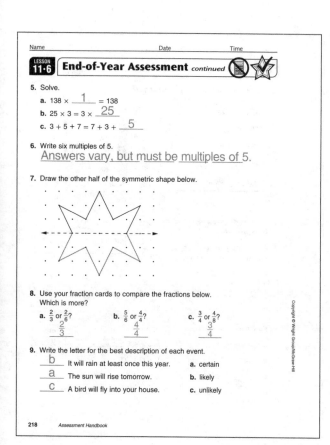

8. Use your fraction cards to compare the fractions below. Which is more?

a. $\frac{2}{3}$ or $\frac{2}{6}$?　__$\frac{2}{3}$__

b. $\frac{5}{6}$ or $\frac{4}{4}$?　__$\frac{4}{4}$__

c. $\frac{3}{4}$ or $\frac{4}{8}$?　__$\frac{3}{4}$__

9. Write the letter for the best description of each event.

__b__ It will rain at least once this year.　　a. certain

__a__ The sun will rise tomorrow.　　b. likely

__c__ A bird will fly into your house.　　c. unlikely

LESSON 11·6 | End-of-Year Assessment *continued*

10. Find the area and perimeter of this figure.

a. area: __12__ sq cm

b. perimeter: __16__ cm

c. Explain how you found the perimeter.

__Sample answer: I counted the measures for each side and added them; 6 + 2 + 6 + 2 = 16.__

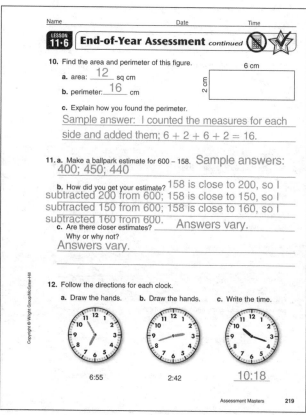

6 cm, 2 cm

11. a. Make a ballpark estimate for 600 – 158. __Sample answers: 400; 450; 440__

b. How did you get your estimate? __158 is close to 200, so I subtracted 200 from 600; 158 is close to 150, so I subtracted 150 from 600; 158 is close to 160, so I subtracted 160 from 600.__

c. Are there closer estimates? __Answers vary.__ Why or why not? __Answers vary.__

12. Follow the directions for each clock.

a. Draw the hands.　b. Draw the hands.　c. Write the time.

6:55　　2:42　　__10:18__

LESSON 11·6 | End-of-Year Assessment *continued*

13. Solve.

a. 2 × 9 = __18__　　d. 5 × 8 = __40__

b. 3 × 9 = __27__　　e. 6 × 8 = __48__

c. 4 × 9 = __36__　　f. 7 × 8 = __56__

14. Write at least 2 names for $\frac{2}{3}$. You may use your fraction cards to help. __Answers vary but must be equivalent to $\frac{2}{3}$.__

O$\frac{2}{3}$

15. Circle $\frac{3}{5}$ of the stars.

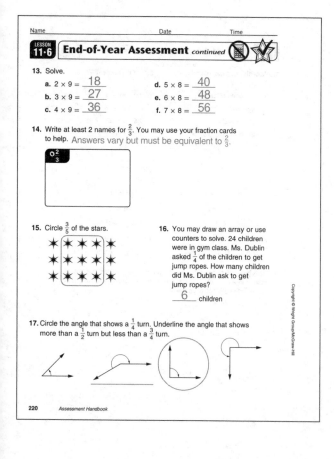

16. You may draw an array or use counters to solve. 24 children were in gym class. Ms. Dublin asked $\frac{1}{4}$ of the children to get jump ropes. How many children did Ms. Dublin ask to get jump ropes?

__6__ children

17. Circle the angle that shows a $\frac{1}{4}$ turn. Underline the angle that shows more than a $\frac{1}{2}$ turn but less than a $\frac{3}{4}$ turn.

LESSON 11·6 | End-of-Year Assessment *continued*

18. There are 2 red cubes and 5 blue cubes in the bag. Without looking inside the bag, Renee's chances of pulling out a blue cube are

__5__ out of __7__.

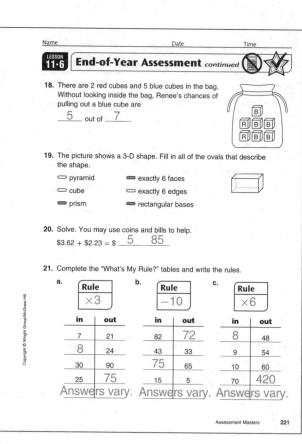

19. The picture shows a 3-D shape. Fill in all of the ovals that describe the shape.

- ○ pyramid　　● exactly 6 faces
- ○ cube　　○ exactly 6 edges
- ● prism　　● rectangular bases

20. Solve. You may use coins and bills to help.

$3.62 + $2.23 = $ __5 85__

21. Complete the "What's My Rule?" tables and write the rules.

a.

Rule ×3	
in	out
7	21
8	24
30	90
25	75

Answers vary.

b.

Rule −10	
in	out
82	72
43	33
75	65
15	5

Answers vary.

c.

Rule ×6	
in	out
8	48
9	54
10	60
70	420

Answers vary.

LESSON 11·6 **End-of-Year Assessment** *continued*

22. Use your favorite multiplication method to solve. Show your work.

a. 74
×6
444

b. 406
× 5
2,030

23. Julia bought 7 boxes of pencils. There were 8 pencils in each box. How many pencils did she buy altogether? You may draw an array or diagram to help. Show your work.

a. Number model: _____ $7 \times 8 = ?$

b. Answer: _____ **56**

24. Sam's turtle crawled 3 feet. Mary's turtle crawled 2 feet 7 inches. How much further did Sam's turtle crawl than Mary's turtle?
5 inches

25. Aliya read her book for 120 minutes. How many hours did Aliya read? **2 hours**

26. While on vacation, Steve's family rode on a train for 48 hours. How many days did they spend on the train? **2 days**

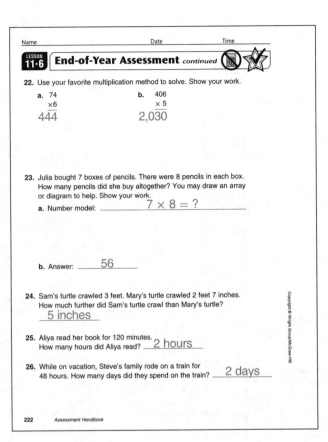

Copyright © Wright Group/McGraw-Hill

LESSON 11·6 **End-of-Year Assessment** *continued*

27. Add or subtract. Show your work.

Unit
books

a. 682
− 236
446

b. 427
+ 339
766

28. The children in the Garden Club picked 21 flowers to give to their teachers. They gave 3 flowers to each teacher. How many teachers received flowers? You may draw an array or diagram to help. Show your work.

a. Number model: _____ $21 \div 3 = ?$ or $3 \times ? = 21$

b. _____ **7** teachers received flowers.

29. Write >, <, or =.

a. $3 + 7$ **=** 5×2
b. $18 - 9$ **<** $18 + 9$
c. 4×7 **>** $34 - 7$
d. 5×5 **=** $100 - 75$

30. Solve.

a. $3 \times (4 + 6) =$ **30**
b. $(3 \times 4) + 6 =$ **18**
c. **54** $= 6 \times (2 + 7)$
d. **19** $= (6 \times 2) + 7$

31. Write the name of each shape. Use the word box to help.

square, hexagon, rhombus, trapezoid, octagon, rectangle, triangle, pentagon

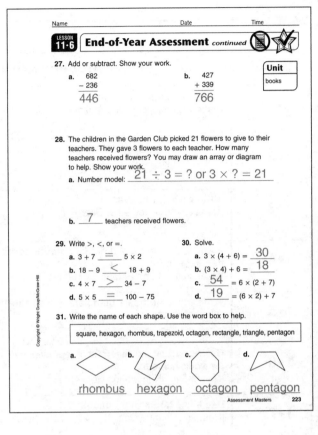

a. rhombus **b.** hexagon **c.** octagon **d.** pentagon

Copyright © Wright Group/McGraw-Hill

LESSON 11·6 **End-of-Year Assessment** *continued*

32. Circle the right angle.

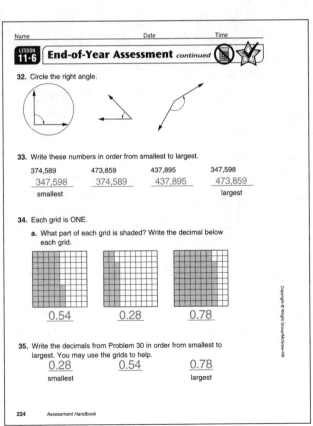

33. Write these numbers in order from smallest to largest.

374,589   473,859   437,895   347,598

347,598   **374,589**   **437,895**   **473,859**
smallest   largest

34. Each grid is ONE.

a. What part of each grid is shaded? Write the decimal below each grid.

0.54   **0.28**   **0.78**

35. Write the decimals from Problem 30 in order from smallest to largest. You may use the grids to help.

0.28   **0.54**   **0.78**
smallest   largest

Copyright © Wright Group/McGraw-Hill

LESSON 11·6 **End-of-Year Assessment** *continued*

36. Write 6 different names for 24.
Answers vary but must be equivalent to 24.

24

37. Use the data from the tally chart to create a line plot.

Sisters of Children in Room 312

Number of Sisters	Number of Children
0	///
1	₥₥ //
2	////
3	//
4	/
5	
6	/

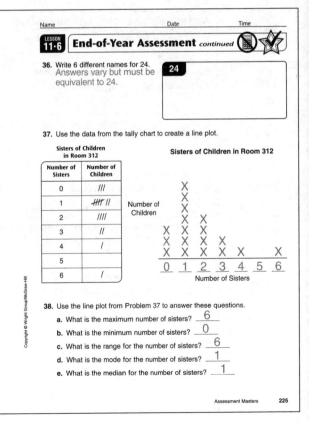

Sisters of Children in Room 312

38. Use the line plot from Problem 37 to answer these questions.

a. What is the maximum number of sisters? **6**

b. What is the minimum number of sisters? **0**

c. What is the range for the number of sisters? **6**

d. What is the mode for the number of sisters? **1**

e. What is the median for the number of sisters? **1**

Copyright © Wright Group/McGraw-Hill

Individual Profile of Progress

Name _____   Date _____

Lesson	Recognizing Student Achievement	A.P.*	Comments
1•1	**Extend numerical patterns.** [Patterns, Functions, and Algebra Goal 1]		
1•2	**Describe and extend numerical patterns.** [Patterns, Functions, and Algebra Goal 1]		
1•3	**Write whole numbers.** [Number and Numeration Goal 1]		
1•4	**Show and write time in digital notation to the nearest minute.** [Measurement and Reference Frames Goal 4]		
1•5	**Write whole numbers using standard base-10 notation.** [Number and Numeration Goal 1]		
1•6	**Use numerical expressions to represent equivalent names for whole numbers.** [Number and Numeration Goal 4]		
1•7	**Use basic terms of probability.** [Data and Chance Goal 3]		
1•8	**Add and subtract multidigit numbers.** [Operations and Computation Goal 2]		
1•9	**Solve addition and subtraction problems.** [Operations and Computation Goal 2]		
1•10	**Compare values of coin and bill combinations.** [Number and Numeration Goal 6]		
1•11	**Order whole numbers.** [Number and Numeration Goal 6]		
1•12	**Solve problems involving number patterns.** [Patterns, Functions, and Algebra Goal 1]		
1•13	**Solve basic subtraction facts.** [Operations and Computation Goal 1]		

*Assess Progress: **A** = adequate progress   **N** = not adequate progress   **N/A** = not assessed

Individual Profile of Progress

Name _____ Date _____

Problem(s)	Progress Check 1	A.P.*	Comments
Oral/Slate Assessment			
1	**Start at 60, 185, 418, and 973 to count up and back by 10s.** [Patterns, Functions, and Algebra Goal 1]		
2	**Start at $0, at $2.25, and at $5.50 to count by quarters.** [Operations and Computation Goal 2]		
3–4	**Record times shown on demonstration clock.** [Measurement and Reference Frames Goal 4]		
Written Assessment Part A			
1	**Draw coins to show money amounts.** [Operations and Computation Goal 2]		
2, 3	**Calculate and compare money amounts.** [Operations and Computation Goal 2; Patterns, Functions, and Algebra Goal 2]		
4–6	**Draw minute and hour hands to show times.** [Measurement and Reference Frames Goal 4]		
7	**Fill in a name-collection box.** [Number and Numeration Goal 4]		
8	**Use + or − to make a number sentence true.** [Patterns, Functions, and Algebra Goal 2; Operations and Computation Goal 1]		
9, 10	**Fill in Frames and Arrows.** [Patterns, Functions, and Algebra Goal 1]		
11	**Use the language of probability.** [Data and Chance Goal 3]		
Written Assessment Part B			
12	**Complete a bar graph.** [Data and Chance Goal 1]		
13	**Fill in a name-collection box.** [Number and Numeration Goal 4]		
14	**Explain number sentences.** [Patterns, Functions, and Algebra Goal 2]		

*Assess Progress: **A** = adequate progress **N** = not adequate progress **N/A** = not assessed **Formative Assessments**

Class Checklist:
Recognizing Student Achievement

Class _____

Date _____

Names	Extend numerical patterns. [Patterns, Functions, and Algebra Goal 1] 1•1	Describe and extend numerical patterns. [Patterns, Functions, and Algebra Goal 1] 1•2	Write whole numbers. [Number and Numeration Goal 1] 1•3	Show and write time in digital notation to the nearest minute. [Measurement and Reference Frames Goal 4] 1•4	Write whole numbers using standard base-10 notation. [Number and Numeration Goal 1] 1•5	Use numerical expressions to represent equivalent names for whole numbers. [Number and Numeration Goal 4] 1•6	Use basic terms of probability. [Data and Chance Goal 3] 1•7	Add and subtract multidigit numbers. [Operations and Computation Goal 2] 1•8	Solve addition and subtraction problems. [Operations and Computation Goal 2] 1•9	Compare values of coin and bill combinations. [Number and Numeration Goal 6] 1•10	Order whole numbers. [Number and Numeration Goal 6] 1•11	Solve problems involving number patterns. [Patterns, Functions, and Algebra Goal 1] 1•12	Solve basic subtraction facts. [Operations and Computation Goal 1] 1•13
1.													
2.													
3.													
4.													
5.													
6.													
7.													
8.													
9.													
10.													
11.													
12.													
13.													
14.													
15.													
16.													
17.													
18.													
19.													
20.													
21.													
22.													
23.													
24.													
25.													

Assess Progress: 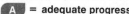 **A** = adequate progress 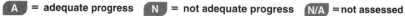 **N** = not adequate progress **N/A** = not assessed

Go to *www.everydaymathonline.com* for digital checklists.

Class _____

Date _____

Names	Oral/Slate			Written Part A									Part B		
	1. Start at 60, 185, 418, and 973 to count up and back by 10s. [Patterns, Functions, and Algebra Goal 1]	2. Start at $0, at $2.25, and at $5.50 to count by quarters. [Operations and Computation Goal 2]	3–4. Record times shown on demonstration clock. [Measurement and Reference Frames Goal 4]	1. Draw coins to show money amounts. [Operations and Computation Goal 2]	2, 3. Calculate and compare money amounts. [Operations and Computation Goal 2; Patterns, Functions, and Algebra Goal 2]	4–6. Draw minute and hour hands to show times. [Measurement and Reference Frames Goal 4]	7. Fill in a name-collection box. [Number and Numeration Goal 4]	8. Use + or − to make a number sentence true. [Patterns, Functions, and Algebra Goal 2; Operations and Computation Goal 1]	9, 10. Fill in Frames and Arrows. [Patterns, Functions, and Algebra Goal 1]	11. Use the language of probability. [Data and Chance Goal 3]	12. Complete a bar graph. [Data and Chance Goal 1]	13. Fill in a name-collection box. [Number and Numeration Goal 4]	14. Explain number sentences. [Patterns, Functions, and Algebra Goal 2]
1.													
2.													
3.													
4.													
5.													
6.													
7.													
8.													
9.													
10.													
11.													
12.													
13.													
14.													
15.													
16.													
17.													
18.													
19.													
20.													
21.													
22.													
23.													
24.													
25.													

Assess Progress: **A** = adequate progress **N** = not adequate progress **N/A** = not assessed **Formative Assessments**

Individual Profile of Progress

Name _____   Date _____

Lesson	Recognizing Student Achievement	A.P.*	Comments
2•1	**Write whole numbers.** [Number and Numeration Goal 1]		
2•2	**Solve basic facts and write fact families.** [Operations and Computation Goal 1]		
2•3	**Solve "What's My Rule?" tables.** [Patterns, Functions, and Algebra Goal 1]		
2•4	**Write number models.** [Patterns, Functions, and Algebra Goal 2]		
2•5	**Determine the value of digits in a given number.** [Number and Numeration Goal 1]		
2•6	**Write number stories.** [Operations and Computation Goal 6]		
2•7	**Solve multidigit addition problems.** [Operations and Computation Goal 2]		
2•8	**Understand multidigit subtraction problems.** [Operations and Computation Goal 2]		
2•9	**Write equivalent names for numbers.** [Number and Numeration Goal 4]		

*Assess Progress:  = adequate progress    = not adequate progress   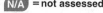 = not assessed

Individual Profile of Progress

Name _____ Date _____

Problem(s)	Progress Check 2	A.P.*	Comments
Oral/Slate Assessment			
1	**Practice easy basic addition and subtraction facts.** [Operations and Computation Goal 1]		
2	**Practice harder basic addition and subtraction facts.** [Operations and Computation Goal 1]		
3	**Practice addition involving multiples of 10.** [Operations and Computation Goal 1]		
4	**Practice addition involving complements of 10 and 100.** [Operations and Computation Goal 1]		
Written Assessment Part A			
1, 2	**Use basic facts to compute extended facts.** [Operations and Computation Goal 1]		
3, 4	**Complete "What's My Rule?" problems.** [Operations and Computation Goal 1; Patterns, Functions, and Algebra Goal 1]		
5	**Write equivalent names for whole numbers.** [Number and Numeration Goal 4]		
6, 7	**Solve number stories and write number models.** [Operations and Computation Goals 2 and 6]		
8, 9	**Show time on analog clocks.** [Measurement and Reference Frames Goal 4]		
10	**Identify place values for multidigit whole numbers.** [Number and Numeration Goal 1]		
Written Assessment Part B			
11, 12	**Complete "What's My Rule?" problems.** [Operations and Computation Goal 1; Patterns, Functions, and Algebra Goal 1]		
13, 14	**Make ballpark estimates for and solve multidigit addition and subtraction problems.** [Operations and Computation Goals 2 and 5]		

*Assess Progress: **A** = adequate progress **N** = not adequate progress **N/A** = not assessed **Formative Assessments**

Class Checklist:
Recognizing Student Achievement

Class _____

Date _____

Names	Write whole numbers. [Number and Numeration Goal 1] 2·1	Solve basic facts and write fact families. [Operations and Computation Goal 1] 2·2	Solve "What's My Rule?" tables. [Patterns, Functions, and Algebra Goal 1] 2·3	Write number models. [Patterns, Functions, and Algebra Goal 2] 2·4	Determine the value of digits in a given number. [Number and Numeration Goal 1] 2·5	Write number stories. [Operations and Computation Goal 6] 2·6	Solve multidigit addition problems. [Operations and Computation Goal 2] 2·7	Understand multidigit subtraction problems. [Operations and Computation Goal 2] 2·8	Write equivalent names for numbers. [Number and Numeration Goal 4] 2·9
1.									
2.									
3.									
4.									
5.									
6.									
7.									
8.									
9.									
10.									
11.									
12.									
13.									
14.									
15.									
16.									
17.									
18.									
19.									
20.									
21.									
22.									
23.									
24.									
25.									

Assess Progress:  **A** = adequate progress **N** = not adequate progress **N/A** = not assessed

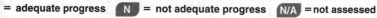

Class Checklist:
Progress Check 2

Class _____

Date _____

Names	Oral/Slate				Written — Part A							Written — Part B	
	1. Practice easy basic addition and subtraction facts. [Operations and Computation Goal 1]	2. Practice harder basic addition and subtraction facts. [Operations and Computation Goal 1]	3. Practice addition involving multiples of 10. [Operations and Computation Goal 1]	4. Practice addition involving complements of 10 and 100. [Operations and Computation Goal 1]	1, 2. Use basic facts to compute extended facts. [Operations and Computation Goal 1]	3, 4. Complete "What's My Rule?" problems. [Operations and Computation Goal 1; Patterns, Functions, and Algebra Goal 1]	5. Write equivalent names for whole numbers. [Number and Numeration Goal 4]	6, 7. Solve number stories and write number models. [Operations and Computation Goals 2 and 6]	8, 9. Show time on analog clocks. [Measurement and Reference Frames Goal 4]	10. Identify place values for multidigit whole numbers. [Number and Numeration Goal 1]	11, 12. Complete "What's My Rule?" problems. [Operations and Computation Goal 1; Patterns, Functions, and Algebra Goal 1]	13, 14. Make ballpark estimates for and solve multidigit addition and subtraction problems. [Operations and Computation Goals 2 and 5]	
1.													
2.													
3.													
4.													
5.													
6.													
7.													
8.													
9.													
10.													
11.													
12.													
13.													
14.													
15.													
16.													
17.													
18.													
19.													
20.													
21.													
22.													
23.													
24.													
25.													

Assess Progress: 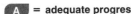 **A** = adequate progress **N** = not adequate progress **N/A** = not assessed  **Formative Assessments**

Individual Profile of Progress

Name _____ Date _____

Lesson	Recognizing Student Achievement	A.P.*	Comments
3◆1	**Explain the need for standard units of measure.** [Measurement and Reference Frames Goal 1]		
3◆2	**Measure line segments to the nearest $\frac{1}{2}$ inch.** [Measurement and Reference Frames Goal 1]		
3◆3	**Make ballpark estimates and record number models.** [Operations and Computation Goal 5]		
3◆4	**Measure to the nearest centimeter.** [Measurement and Reference Frames Goal 1]		
3◆5	**Use the Commutative and Associative Properties of Addition for 3- and 4-addend problems.** [Patterns, Functions, and Algebra Goal 4]		
3◆6	**Tell time to the nearest five minutes.** [Measurement and Reference Frames Goal 4]		
3◆7	**Demonstrate knowledge of basic subtraction facts.** [Operations and Computation Goal 1]		
3◆8	**Calculate the area of rectangles.** [Measurement and Reference Frames Goal 2]		
3◆9	**Find the area of rectangular shapes.** [Measurement and Reference Frames Goal 2]		

*Assess Progress: **A** = adequate progress **N** = not adequate progress **N/A** = not assessed

Individual Profile of Progress

Name _____ Date _____

Problem(s)	Progress Check 3	A.P.*	Comments
Oral/Slate Assessment			
1	**Solve U.S. standard units of length equivalency problems.** [Measurement and Reference Frames Goal 3]		
2	**Solve metric units of length equivalency problems.** [Measurement and Reference Frames Goal 3]		
3	**Model ballpark estimates involving 2- and 3-digit numbers.** [Operations and Computation Goal 5]		
4	**Model ballpark estimates involving 3-digit numbers.** [Operations and Computation Goal 5]		
Written Assessment Part A			
1, 2	**Estimate a difference and a sum.** [Operations and Computation Goal 5]		
3–6	**Measure line segments to the nearest $\frac{1}{2}$ inch and $\frac{1}{2}$ centimeter.** [Measurement and Reference Frames Goal 1]		
7	**Find the perimeter.** [Measurement and Reference Frames Goal 2]		
8, 9	**Use basic probability terms.** [Data and Chance Goal 3]		
10	**Solve a number story involving money.** [Operations and Computation Goal 2]		
Written Assessment Part B			
11	**Measure the sides of a polygon and find the perimeter.** [Measurement and Reference Frames Goals 1 and 2]		
12	**Draw a rectangle with a given area.** [Measurement and Reference Frames Goal 2]		
13	**Compare units of length.** [Measurement and Reference Frames Goal 3]		
14, 15	**Measure line segments to the nearest $\frac{1}{2}$ inch and $\frac{1}{2}$ centimeter.** [Measurement and Reference Frames Goal 1]		
16	**Create a line plot.** [Data and Chance Goal 1]		
17–20	**Find data landmarks for a set of data.** [Data and Chance Goal 2]		

*Assess Progress: **A** = adequate progress   **N** = not adequate progress   **N/A** = not assessed   **Formative Assessments**

Class Checklist:
Recognizing Student Achievement

Class _____

Date _____

Names	Explain the need for standard units of measure. [Measurement and Reference Frames Goal 1] 3·1	Measure line segments to the nearest $\frac{1}{2}$ inch. [Measurement and Reference Frames Goal 1] 3·2	Make ballpark estimates and record number models. [Operations and Computation Goal 5] 3·3	Measure to the nearest centimeter. [Measurement and Reference Frames Goal 1] 3·4	Use the Commutative and Associative Properties of Addition for 3- and 4-addend problems. [Patterns, Functions, and Algebra Goal 4] 3·5	Tell time to the nearest five minutes. [Measurement and Reference Frames Goal 4] 3·6	Demonstrate knowledge of basic subtraction facts. [Operations and Computation Goal 1] 3·7	Calculate the area of rectangles. [Measurement and Reference Frames Goal 2] 3·8	Find the area of rectangular shapes. [Measurement and Reference Frames Goal 2] 3·9
1.									
2.									
3.									
4.									
5.									
6.									
7.									
8.									
9.									
10.									
11.									
12.									
13.									
14.									
15.									
16.									
17.									
18.									
19.									
20.									
21.									
22.									
23.									
24.									
25.									

Assess Progress: **A** = adequate progress   **N** = not adequate progress   **N/A** = not assessed

Class Checklist:
Progress Check 3

Class _____

Date _____

	Oral/Slate				Written											
					Part A					Part B						
Names	1. Solve U.S. standard units of length equivalency problems. [Measurement and Reference Frames Goal 3]	2. Solve metric units of length equivalency problems. [Measurement and Reference Frames Goal 3]	3. Model ballpark estimates involving 2- and 3-digit numbers. [Operations and Computation Goal 5]	4. Model ballpark estimates involving 3-digit numbers. [Operations and Computation Goal 5]	1, 2. Estimate a difference and a sum. [Operations and Computation Goal 5]	3–6. Measure line segments to the nearest $\frac{1}{2}$ inch and $\frac{1}{2}$ centimeter. [Measurement and Reference Frames Goal 1]	7. Find the perimeter. [Measurement and Reference Frames Goal 2]	8, 9. Use basic probability terms. [Data and Chance Goal 3]	10. Solve a number story involving money. [Operations and Computation Goal 2]	11. Measure the sides of a polygon and find the perimeter. [Measurement and Reference Frames Goals 1 and 2]	12. Draw a rectangle with a given area. [Measurement and Reference Frames Goal 2]	13. Compare units of length. [Measurement and Reference Frames Goal 3]	14, 15. Measure line segments to the nearest $\frac{1}{2}$ inch and $\frac{1}{2}$ centimeter. [Measurement and Reference Frames Goal 1]	16. Create a line plot. [Data and Chance Goal 1]	17–20. Find data landmarks for a set of data. [Data and Chance Goal 2]
1.															
2.															
3.															
4.															
5.															
6.															
7.															
8.															
9.															
10.															
11.															
12.															
13.															
14.															
15.															
16.															
17.															
18.															
19.															
20.															
21.															
22.															
23.															
24.															
25.															

Assess Progress: **A** = adequate progress **N** = not adequate progress **N/A** = not assessed **Formative Assessments**

Individual Profile of Progress

Name _____ Date _____

Lesson	Recognizing Student Achievement	A.P.*	Comments
4•1	**Solve multiplication facts.** [Operations and Computation Goal 3]		
4•2	**Use arrays and multiples of equal groups to demonstrate the meaning of multiplication.** [Operations and Computation Goal 6]		
4•3	**Tell time to nearest minute and write time in digital notation.** [Measurement and Reference Frames Goal 4]		
4•4	**Use equal sharing to demonstrate the meaning of division.** [Operations and Computation Goal 6]		
4•5	**Find the area of rectangular shapes.** [Measurement and Reference Frames Goal 2]		
4•6	**Use the +, −, and = symbols.** [Patterns, Functions, and Algebra Goal 2]		
4•7	**Use equal sharing and equal grouping to demonstrate the meaning of division.** [Operations and Computation Goal 6]		
4•8	**Solve multiplication facts.** [Operations and Computation Goal 3]		
4•9	**Use number lines to order whole numbers and fractions.** [Number and Numeration Goal 6]		
4•10	**Collect and organize data.** [Data and Chance Goal 1]		

*Assess Progress:  **A** = adequate progress  **N** = not adequate progress 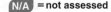 **N/A** = not assessed

Individual Profile of Progress

Name _____ Date _____

Problem(s)	Progress Check 4	A.P.*	Comments
Oral/Slate Assessment			
1	**Count up by 2s, 5s, and 10s.** [Operations and Computation Goal 3]		
2	**Count back by 2s, 5s, and 10s.** [Operations and Computation Goal 3]		
3–5	**Solve an equal-sharing and equal-grouping number story.** [Operations and Computation Goal 6]		
4	**Solve an equal-sharing number story.** [Operations and Computation Goal 6]		
Written Assessment Part A			
1, 2	**Complete fact families.** [Operations and Computation Goal 3]		
3	**Write the number that is 100 more.** [Number and Numeration Goal 1]		
4	**Use the Commutative Property of Multiplication and the Multiplicative Identity.** [Patterns, Functions, and Algebra Goal 4]		
5	**Find areas of rectangles.** [Measurement and Reference Frames Goal 2]		
6	**Use a rule to solve multiplication problems.** [Patterns, Functions, and Algebra Goal 1]		
7	**Extend numerical patterns.** [Patterns, Functions, and Algebra Goal 1]		
8	**Solve a multiplication number story.** [Operations and Computation Goal 6]		
Written Assessment Part B			
9	**Solve a division number story.** [Operations and Computation Goal 6]		
10, 11	**Use rules to solve multiplication and division problems.** [Operations and Computation Goal 3; Patterns, Functions, and Algebra Goal 1]		
12	**Write a multiplication/division fact family.** [Operations and Computation Goal 3; Patterns, Functions, and Algebra Goal 2]		

*Assess Progress: **A** = adequate progress   **N** = not adequate progress   **N/A** = not assessed   **Formative Assessments**

Class _____

Date _____

Names	4·1	4·2	4·3	4·4	4·5	4·6	4·7	4·8	4·9	4·10
	Solve multiplication facts. [Operations and Computation Goal 3]	**Use arrays and multiples of equal groups to demonstrate the meaning of multiplication.** [Operations and Computation Goal 6]	**Tell time to nearest minute and write time in digital notation.** [Measurement and Reference Frames Goal 4]	**Use equal sharing to demonstrate the meaning of division.** [Operations and Computation Goal 6]	**Find the area of rectangular shapes.** [Measurement and Reference Frames Goal 2]	**Use the +, –, and = symbols.** [Patterns, Functions, and Algebra Goal 2]	**Use equal sharing and equal grouping to demonstrate the meaning of division.** [Operations and Computation Goal 6]	**Solve multiplication facts.** [Operations and Computation Goal 3]	**Use number lines to order whole numbers and fractions.** [Number and Numeration Goal 6]	**Collect and organize data.** [Data and Chance Goal 1]
1.										
2.										
3.										
4.										
5.										
6.										
7.										
8.										
9.										
10.										
11.										
12.										
13.										
14.										
15.										
16.										
17.										
18.										
19.										
20.										
21.										
22.										
23.										
24.										
25.										

Assess Progress: **A** = adequate progress   **N** = not adequate progress   **N/A** = not assessed

Class Checklist:
Progress Check 4

Class _____

Date _____

	Oral/Slate				Written										
					Part A								Part B		
Names	1. Count up by 2s, 5s, and 10s. [Operations and Computation Goal 3]	2. Count back by 2s, 5s, and 10s. [Operations and Computation Goal 3]	3–5. Solve an equal-sharing and equal-grouping number story. [Operations and Computation Goal 6]	4. Solve an equal-sharing number story. [Operations and Computation Goal 6]	1, 2. Complete fact families. [Operations and Computation Goal 3]	3. Write the number that is 100 more. [Number and Numeration Goal 1]	4. Use the Commutative Property of Multiplication and the Multiplicative Identity. [Patterns, Functions, and Algebra Goal 4]	5. Find areas of rectangles. [Measurement and Reference Frames Goal 2]	6. Use a rule to solve multiplication problems. [Patterns, Functions, and Algebra Goal 1]	7. Extend numerical patterns. [Patterns, Functions, and Algebra Goal 1]	8. Solve a multiplication number story. [Operations and Computation Goal 6]	9. Solve a division number story. [Operations and Computation Goal 6]	10, 11. Use rules to solve multiplication and division problems. [Operations and Computation Goal 3; Patterns, Functions, and Algebra Goal 1]	12. Write a multiplication/division fact family. [Operations and Computation Goal 3; Patterns, Functions, and Algebra Goal 2]
1.														
2.														
3.														
4.														
5.														
6.														
7.														
8.														
9.														
10.														
11.														
12.														
13.														
14.														
15.														
16.														
17.														
18.														
19.														
20.														
21.														
22.														
23.														
24.														
25.														

Assess Progress: **A** = adequate progress **N** = not adequate progress **N/A** = not assessed **Formative Assessments**

Name _____   Date _____

Lesson	Recognizing Student Achievement	A.P.*	Comments
5◆1	**Write whole numbers up to five digits.** [Number and Numeration Goal 1]		
5◆2	**Find the maximum, minimum, and range of a data set.** [Data and Chance Goal 2]		
5◆3	**Compare numbers.** [Number and Numeration Goal 6]		
5◆4	**Compare numbers.** [Number and Numeration Goal 6]		
5◆5	**Use basic facts to compute extended facts.** [Operations and Computation Goal 1]		
5◆6	**Use multiples of 10 to count base-10 blocks.** [Number and Numeration Goal 3]		
5◆7	**Read and write money totals in decimal notation.** [Number and Numeration Goal 1]		
5◆8	**Describe relationships between units of time.** [Measurement and Reference Frames Goal 3]		
5◆9	**Compare decimals.** [Number and Numeration Goal 6]		
5◆10	**Compare decimals.** [Number and Numeration Goal 6]		
5◆11	**Determine the values of digits in decimal numbers.** [Number and Numeration Goal 1]		
5◆12	**Solve multiplication facts up to 10 × 10.** [Operations and Computation Goal 3]		

*Assess Progress: **A** = adequate progress   **N** = not adequate progress   **N/A** = not assessed

Individual Profile of Progress

Name _____ Date _____

Problem(s)	Progress Check 5	A.P.*	Comments
Oral/Slate Assessment			
1	**Read and compare 4- and 5-digit whole numbers.** [Number and Numeration Goals 1 and 6]		
2	**Read and compare 6-digit whole numbers.** [Number and Numeration Goals 1 and 6]		
3	**Read 1-place decimals.** [Number and Numeration Goal 1]		
4	**Read 2- and 3-place decimals.** [Number and Numeration Goal 1]		
5	**Write 1-place decimals.** [Number and Numeration Goal 1]		
6	**Write 2- and 3-place decimals.** [Number and Numeration Goal 1]		
Written Assessment Part A			
1, 2	**Write 5-digit numbers.** [Number and Numeration Goal 1]		
3, 4	**Compare 5-digit numbers.** [Number and Numeration Goal 6]		
5, 6	**Use basic facts to compute extended facts.** [Operations and Computation Goal 1]		
7, 8	**Find the sum of 4 addends.** [Patterns, Functions, and Algebra Goal 4]		
9, 10	**Use strategies to solve problems involving the addition and subtraction of multidigit whole numbers. Make ballpark estimates.** [Operations and Computation Goals 2 and 5]		
11, 12	**Find the perimeter and area of a rectangle.** [Measurement and Reference Frames Goal 2]		
Written Assessment Part B			
13–15	**Write the decimal and fraction that represent a shaded grid when the grid is ONE.** [Number and Numeration Goals 1 and 5]		
16–18	**Compare decimals.** [Number and Numeration Goal 6]		
19, 20	**Write decimal numbers.** [Number and Numeration Goal 1]		

*Assess Progress: **A** = adequate progress **N** = not adequate progress **N/A** = not assessed **Formative Assessments**

Class Checklist:
Recognizing Student Achievement

Class _____

Date _____

Names	5·1 Write whole numbers up to five digits. [Number and Numeration Goal 1]	5·2 Find the maximum, minimum, and range of a data set. [Data and Chance Goal 2]	5·3 Compare numbers. [Number and Numeration Goal 6]	5·4 Compare numbers. [Number and Numeration Goal 6]	5·5 Use basic facts to compute extended facts. [Operations and Computation Goal 1]	5·6 Use multiples of 10 to count base-10 blocks. [Number and Numeration Goal 3]	5·7 Read and write money totals in decimal notation. [Number and Numeration Goal 1]	5·8 Describe relationships between units of time. [Measurement and Reference Frames Goal 3]	5·9 Compare decimals. [Number and Numeration Goal 6]	5·10 Compare decimals. [Number and Numeration Goal 6]	5·11 Determine the values of digits in decimal numbers. [Number and Numeration Goal 1]	5·12 Solve multiplication facts up to 10 × 10. [Operations and Computation Goal 3]
1.												
2.												
3.												
4.												
5.												
6.												
7.												
8.												
9.												
10.												
11.												
12.												
13.												
14.												
15.												
16.												
17.												
18.												
19.												
20.												
21.												
22.												
23.												
24.												
25.												

Assess Progress: **A** = adequate progress **N** = not adequate progress **N/A** = not assessed

Class Checklist:
Progress Check 5

Class _____

Date _____

Names	Oral/Slate						Written Part A							Part B		
	1. Read and compare 4- and 5-digit whole numbers. [Number and Numeration Goals 1 and 6]	2. Read and compare 6-digit whole numbers. [Number and Numeration Goals 1 and 6]	3. Read 1-place decimals. [Number and Numeration Goal 1]	4. Read 2- and 3-place decimals. [Number and Numeration Goal 1]	5. Write 1-place decimals. [Number and Numeration Goal 1]	6. Write 2- and 3-place decimals. [Number and Numeration Goal 1]	1, 2. Write 5-digit numbers. [Number and Numeration Goal 1]	3, 4. Compare 5-digit numbers. [Number and Numeration Goal 6]	5, 6. Use basic facts to compute extended facts. [Operations and Computation Goal 1]	7, 8. Find the sum of 4 addends. [Patterns, Functions, and Algebra Goal 4]	9, 10. Use strategies to solve problems involving the addition and subtraction of multidigit whole numbers. Make ballpark estimates. [Operations and Computation Goals 2 and 5]	11, 12. Find the perimeter and area of a rectangle. [Measurement and Reference Frames Goal 2]	13–15. Write the decimal and fraction that represent a shaded grid when the grid is ONE. [Number and Numeration Goals 1 and 5]	16–18. Compare decimals. [Number and Numeration Goal 6]	19, 20. Write decimal numbers. [Number and Numeration Goal 1]
1.															
2.															
3.															
4.															
5.															
6.															
7.															
8.															
9.															
10.															
11.															
12.															
13.															
14.															
15.															
16.															
17.															
18.															
19.															
20.															
21.															
22.															
23.															
24.															
25.															

Assess Progress: **A** = adequate progress **N** = not adequate progress **N/A** = not assessed **Formative Assessments**

Individual Profile of Progress

Name _____   Date _____

Lesson	Recognizing Student Achievement	A.P.*	Comments
6◆1	**Draw line segments.** [Geometry Goal 1]		
6◆2	**Identify parallel and intersecting lines and segments.** [Geometry Goal 1]		
6◆3	**Read decimal numbers.** [Number and Numeration Goal 1]		
6◆4	**Draw line segments, rays, and lines.** [Geometry Goal 1]		
6◆5	**Identify points and draw line segments to form a quadrangle.** [Geometry Goal 1]		
6◆6	**Measure line segments to the nearest $\frac{1}{2}$ centimeter.** [Measurement and Reference Frames Goal 1]		
6◆7	**Demonstrate automaticity with multiplication facts.** [Operations and Computation Goal 3]		
6◆8	**Recognize a right angle.** [Geometry Goal 1]		
6◆9	**Complete symmetric shapes.** [Geometry Goal 3]		
6◆10	**Model decimals with base-10 blocks and shaded grids, and write the decimal represented by the base-10 blocks.** [Number and Numeration Goal 1]		
6◆11	**Identify properties of solid figures—pyramids and prisms.** [Geometry Goal 2]		
6◆12	**Demonstrate automaticity with multiplication facts.** [Operations and Computation Goal 3]		

*Assess Progress: **A** = adequate progress   **N** = not adequate progress   **N/A** = not assessed

Go to *www.everydaymathonline.com* for digital checklists.

Individual Profile of Progress

Name _____   Date _____

Problem(s)	Progress Check 6	A.P.*	Comments
Oral/Slate Assessment			
1	**Identify 2-dimensional and 3-dimensional shapes.** [Geometry Goal 2]		
2	**Describe the characteristics of 2-dimensional and 3-dimensional shapes.** [Geometry Goal 2]		
3	**Draw: quadrangle, pentagon, triangle, trapezoid; rectangle that is not a square; triangle with three equal sides; triangle with two equal sides.** [Geometry Goal 2]		
4	**Draw: angle greater than a right angle, angle smaller than a right angle, right angle.** [Geometry Goal 1; Measurement and Reference Frames Goal 1]		
Written Assessment Part A			
1, 3	**Draw line segments to form a quadrangle. Identify a right triangle.** [Geometry Goal 1]		
2	**Use letters to name a quadrangle.** [Geometry Goal 2]		
4	**Identify parallel and intersecting line segments.** [Geometry Goal 1]		
5	**Draw a line of symmetry.** [Geometry Goal 3]		
6	**Solve an equal-sharing problem.** [Operations and Computation Goal 6]		
7–10	**Identify and describe plane and solid figures.** [Geometry Goal 2]		
11–13	**Model decimals through hundredths.** [Number and Numeration Goal 1]		
14	**Order decimals through hundredths.** [Number and Numeration Goal 6]		
Written Assessment Part B			
15–16	**Complete a symmetrical design and draw lines of symmetry.** [Geometry Goal 3]		
17–19	**Draw parallel rays and an intersecting line and ray. Draw a right triangle.** [Geometry Goals 1 and 2]		
20	**Identify the faces, base, and edges of a pyramid.** [Geometry Goal 2]		
21	**Describe a rectangle.** [Geometry Goal 2]		
22	**Describe angle rotations.** [Measurement and Reference Frames Goal 1]		

*Assess Progress: **A** = adequate progress   **N** = not adequate progress   **N/A** = not assessed   Formative Assessments

Class Checklist:
Recognizing Student Achievement

Class _____

Date _____

Names	6·1	6·2	6·3	6·4	6·5	6·6	6·7	6·8	6·9	6·10	6·11	6·12
	Draw line segments. [Geometry Goal 1]	Identify parallel and intersecting lines and segments. [Geometry Goal 1]	Read decimal numbers. [Number and Numeration Goal 1]	Draw line segments, rays, and lines. [Geometry Goal 1]	Identify points and draw line segments to form a quadrangle. [Geometry Goal 1]	Measure line segments to the nearest $\frac{1}{2}$ centimeter. [Measurement and Reference Frames Goal 1]	Demonstrate automaticity with multiplication facts. [Operations and Computation Goal 3]	Recognize a right angle. [Geometry Goal 1]	Complete symmetric shapes. [Geometry Goal 3]	Model decimals with base-10 blocks and shaded grids, and write the decimal represented by the base-10 blocks. [Number and Numeration Goal 1]	Identify properties of solid figures—pyramids and prisms. [Geometry Goal 2]	Demonstrate automaticity with multiplication facts. [Operations and Computation Goal 3]
1.												
2.												
3.												
4.												
5.												
6.												
7.												
8.												
9.												
10.												
11.												
12.												
13.												
14.												
15.												
16.												
17.												
18.												
19.												
20.												
21.												
22.												
23.												
24.												
25.												

Assess Progress: **A** = adequate progress   **N** = not adequate progress   **N/A** = not assessed

Class Checklist:
Progress Check 6

Class

Date

| | Oral/Slate | | | | Written | | | | | | | | | | | |
| | | | | | Part A | | | | | | | | Part B | | | |
Names	1. Identify 2-dimensional and 3-dimensional shapes. [Geometry Goal 2]	2. Describe the characteristics of 2-dimensional and 3-dimensional shapes. [Geometry Goal 2]	3. Draw: quadrangle, pentagon, triangle, trapezoid; rectangle that is not a square; triangle with three equal sides; triangle with two equal sides. [Geometry Goal 2]	4. Draw: angle greater than a right angle, angle smaller than a right angle, right angle. [Geometry Goal 1; Measurement and Reference Frames Goal 1]	1, 3. Draw line segments to form a quadrangle. Identify a right triangle. [Geometry Goal 1]	2. Use letters to name a quadrangle. [Geometry Goal 2]	4. Identify parallel and intersecting line segments. [Geometry Goal 1]	5. Draw a line of symmetry. [Geometry Goal 3]	6. Solve an equal-sharing problem. [Operations and Computation Goal 6]	7–10. Identify and describe plane and solid figures. [Geometry Goal 2]	11–13. Model decimals through hundredths. [Number and Numeration Goal 1]	14. Order decimals through hundredths. [Number and Numeration Goal 6]	15, 16. Complete a symmetrical design and draw lines of symmetry. [Geometry Goal 3]	17–19. Draw parallel rays and an intersecting line and ray. Draw a right triangle. [Geometry Goals 1 and 2]	20. Identify the faces, base, and edges of a pyramid. [Geometry Goal 2]	21. Describe a rectangle. [Geometry Goal 2]	22. Describe angle rotations. [Measurement and Reference Frames Goal 1]
1.																	
2.																	
3.																	
4.																	
5.																	
6.																	
7.																	
8.																	
9.																	
10.																	
11.																	
12.																	
13.																	
14.																	
15.																	
16.																	
17.																	
18.																	
19.																	
20.																	
21.																	
22.																	
23.																	
24.																	
25.																	

Assess Progress: A = adequate progress N = not adequate progress N/A = not assessed **Formative Assessments**

Go to *www.everydaymathonline.com* for digital checklists.

Lesson	Recognizing Student Achievement	A.P.*	Comments
7◆1	**Compute multiplication facts.** [Operations and Computation Goal 3]		
7◆2	**Use arrays to model multiplication.** [Operations and Computation Goal 6]		
7◆3	**Find and use rules to solve multiplication and division problems.** [Patterns, Functions, and Algebra Goal 1]		
7◆4	**Show that parentheses affect the order of operations.** [Patterns, Functions, and Algebra Goal 3]		
7◆5	**Show that the operation inside the parentheses is carried out first.** [Patterns, Functions, and Algebra Goal 3]		
7◆6	**Use relationships between units of time to solve number stories.** [Measurement and Reference Frames Goal 3]		
7◆7	**Explain how an estimate is obtained.** [Operations and Computation Goal 5]		
7◆8	**Multiply 2-digit numbers by a 1-digit number.** [Operations and Computation Goal 4]		
7◆9	**Identify and describe solid figures.** [Geometry Goal 2]		

*Assess Progress: **A** = adequate progress **N** = not adequate progress **N/A** = not assessed

Individual Profile of Progress

Name _____ Date _____

Problem(s)	Progress Check 7	A.P.*	Comments
Oral/Slate Assessment			
1	**Conduct choral fact practice with the first set of Fact Triangles.** [Operations and Computation Goal 3]		
2	**Conduct choral fact practice with the second set of Fact Triangles.** [Operations and Computation Goal 3]		
3	**Solve multiplication number stories using counters, arrays, and diagrams.** [Operations and Computation Goal 6]		
4	**Solve division number stories using counters, arrays, and diagrams.** [Operations and Computation Goal 6]		
Written Assessment Part A			
1–10	**Fill in missing factors and products.** [Operations and Computation Goal 3]		
11, 12	**Solve equal-groups and equal-shares number stories.** [Operations and Computation Goal 6]		
13, 14	**Draw parallel and intersecting line segments and rays.** [Geometry Goal 1]		
15	**Identify faces, vertices, and edges.** [Geometry Goal 2]		
16a, 17a	**Make ballpark estimates.** [Operations and Computation Goal 5]		
16b, 17b	**Solve multidigit addition and subtraction problems.** [Operations and Computation Goal 2]		
Written Assessment Part B			
18–21	**Use parentheses in number sentences.** [Patterns, Functions, and Algebra Goal 3]		
22	**Solve an extended facts multiplication puzzle.** [Operations and Computation Goal 3]		
23	**Estimate the answer to a number story involving money.** [Operations and Computation Goal 5]		

*Assess Progress: **A** = adequate progress **N** = not adequate progress **N/A** = not assessed **Formative Assessments**

Class Checklist:
Recognizing Student Achievement

Class _____

Date _____

Names	Compute multiplication facts. [Operations and Computation Goal 3] 7·1	Use arrays to model multiplication. [Operations and Computation Goal 6] 7·2	Find and use rules to solve multiplication and division problems. [Patterns, Functions, and Algebra Goal 1] 7·3	Show that parentheses affect the order of operations. [Patterns, Functions, and Algebra Goal 3] 7·4	Show that the operation inside the parentheses is carried out first. [Patterns, Functions, and Algebra Goal 3] 7·5	Use relationships between units of time to solve number stories. [Measurement and Reference Frames Goal 3] 7·6	Explain how an estimate is obtained. [Operations and Computation Goal 5] 7·7	Multiply 2-digit numbers by a 1-digit number. [Operations and Computation Goal 4] 7·8	Identify and describe solid figures. [Geometry Goal 2] 7·9
1.									
2.									
3.									
4.									
5.									
6.									
7.									
8.									
9.									
10.									
11.									
12.									
13.									
14.									
15.									
16.									
17.									
18.									
19.									
20.									
21.									
22.									
23.									
24.									
25.									

Assess Progress: **A** = adequate progress   **N** = not adequate progress   **N/A** = not assessed

Go to *www.everydaymathonline.com* for digital checklists.

Class _____

Date _____

Names	Oral/Slate				Written Part A						Part B		
	1. Conduct choral fact practice with the first set of Fact Triangles. [Operations and Computation Goal 3]	2. Conduct choral fact practice with the second set of Fact Triangles. [Operations and Computation Goal 3]	3. Solve multiplication number stories using counters, arrays, and diagrams. [Operations and Computation Goal 6]	4. Solve division number stories using counters, arrays, and diagrams. [Operations and Computation Goal 6]	1–10. Fill in missing factors and products. [Operations and Computation Goal 3]	11, 12. Solve equal-groups and equal-shares number stories. [Operations and Computation Goal 6]	13, 14. Draw parallel and intersecting line segments and rays. [Geometry Goal 1]	15. Identify faces, vertices, and edges. [Geometry Goal 2]	16a, 17a. Make ballpark estimates. [Operations and Computation Goal 5]	16b, 17b. Solve multidigit addition and subtraction problems. [Operations and Computation Goal 2]	18–21. Use parentheses in number sentences. [Patterns, Functions, and Algebra Goal 3]	22. Solve an extended facts multiplication puzzle. [Operations and Computation Goal 3]	23. Estimate the answer to a number story involving money. [Operations and Computation Goal 5]
1.													
2.													
3.													
4.													
5.													
6.													
7.													
8.													
9.													
10.													
11.													
12.													
13.													
14.													
15.													
16.													
17.													
18.													
19.													
20.													
21.													
22.													
23.													
24.													
25.													

Assess Progress:  **A** = adequate progress **N** = not adequate progress **N/A** = not assessed **Formative Assessments**

Individual Profile of Progress

Name _____   Date _____

Lesson	Recognizing Student Achievement	A.P.*	Comments
8•1	**Identify and write fractions that name regions.** [Number and Numeration Goal 2]		
8•2	**Describe events using basic probability terms.** [Data and Chance Goal 3]		
8•3	**Demonstrate how parentheses affect the order of operations.** [Patterns, Functions, and Algebra Goal 3]		
8•4	**Identify the value of digits in numbers through hundred-thousands.** [Number and Numeration Goal 1]		
8•5	**Make and test predictions for simple experiments.** [Data and Chance Goal 4]		
8•6	**Describe relationships between equivalent units of time.** [Measurement and Reference Frames Goal 3]		
8•7	**Use Fraction Cards to find equivalent fractions.** [Number and Numeration Goal 5]		
8•8	**Solve problems involving fractional parts of a collection.** [Number and Numeration Goal 2]		

*Assess Progress:  **A** = adequate progress **N** = not adequate progress **N/A** = not assessed

Go to *www.everydaymathonline.com* for digital checklists.

Individual Profile of Progress

Name _____ Date _____

Problem(s)	Progress Check 8	A.P.*	Comments
Oral/Slate Assessment			
1	Identify fractions greater than $\frac{1}{2}$, less than $\frac{1}{2}$, or equal to $\frac{1}{2}$. [Number and Numeration Goal 6]		
2	**Identify the value of digits in 3-place decimals.** [Number and Numeration Goal 1]		
3	**Model fractions.** [Number and Numeration Goal 2]		
4	**Solve fraction number stories using counters, arrays, or diagrams.** [Number and Numeration Goal 2]		
Written Assessment Part A			
1, 2, 8b	**Find fractional parts of sets.** [Number and Numeration Goal 2]		
3	**Write equivalent names for $\frac{1}{2}$.** [Number and Numeration Goal 5]		
4	**Write fractions in order.** [Number and Numeration Goal 6]		
5	**Compare fractions to $\frac{1}{2}$.** [Number and Numeration Goal 6]		
6	**Identify the value of digits in decimals.** [Number and Numeration Goal 1]		
7	**Predict outcomes of simple experiments.** [Data and Chance Goal 4]		
8a	**Use equal sharing to demonstrate the meaning of division.** [Operations and Computation Goal 6]		
9	**Describe relationships among units of time.** [Measurement and Reference Frames Goal 3]		
10	**Complete a 2-dimensional symmetric design.** [Geometry Goal 3]		
Written Assessment Part B			
11, 12	**Shade circles to match mixed numbers or fractions.** [Number and Numeration Goals 2 and 5]		
13	**Find equivalent names.** [Number and Numeration Goal 5]		
14	**Describe relationships among units of time.** [Measurement and Reference Frames Goal 3]		
15	**Solve a problem involving fractional parts of collections.** [Number and Numeration Goal 2]		
16	**Predict outcomes of an experiment.** [Data and Chance Goal 4]		

*Assess Progress: **A** = adequate progress   **N** = not adequate progress   **N/A** = not assessed   **Formative Assessments**

Go to *www.everydaymathonline.com* for digital checklists.   Individual Profile of Progress   **257**

Class _____

Date _____

Names	Identify and write fractions that name regions. [Number and Numeration Goal 2]	Describe events using basic probability terms. [Data and Chance Goal 3]	Demonstrate how parentheses affect the order of operations. [Patterns, Functions, and Algebra Goal 3]	Identify the value of digits in numbers through hundred-thousands. [Number and Numeration Goal 1]	Make and test predictions for simple experiments. [Data and Chance Goal 4]	Describe relationships between equivalent units of time. [Measurement and Reference Frames Goal 3]	Use Fraction Cards to find equivalent fractions. [Number and Numeration Goal 5]	Solve problems involving fractional parts of a collection. [Number and Numeration Goal 2]
	8•1	8•2	8•3	8•4	8•5	8•6	8•7	8•8
1.								
2.								
3.								
4.								
5.								
6.								
7.								
8.								
9.								
10.								
11.								
12.								
13.								
14.								
15.								
16.								
17.								
18.								
19.								
20.								
21.								
22.								
23.								
24.								
25.								

Assess Progress:  **A** = adequate progress   **N** = not adequate progress   **N/A** = not assessed

Class Checklist:
Progress Check 8

Class _____

Date _____

Names	Oral/Slate				Written Part A									Part B				
	1. Identify fractions greater than ½, less than ½, or equal to ½. [Number and Numeration Goal 6]	2. Identify the value of digits in 3-place decimals. [Number and Numeration Goal 1]	3. Model fractions. [Number and Numeration Goal 2]	4. Solve fraction number stories using counters, arrays, or diagrams. [Number and Numeration Goal 2]	1, 2, 8b. Find fractional parts of sets. [Number and Numeration Goal 2]	3. Write equivalent names for ½. [Number and Numeration Goal 5]	4. Write fractions in order. [Number and Numeration Goal 6]	5. Compare fractions to ½. [Number and Numeration Goal 6]	6. Identify the value of digits in decimals. [Number and Numeration Goal 1]	7. Predict outcomes of simple experiments. [Data and Chance Goal 4]	8a. Use equal sharing to demonstrate the meaning of division. [Operations and Computation Goal 6]	9. Describe relationships among units of time. [Measurement and Reference Frames Goal 3]	10. Complete a 2-dimensional symmetric design. [Geometry Goal 3]	11, 12. Shade circles to match mixed numbers or fractions. [Number and Numeration Goals 2 and 5]	13. Find equivalent names. [Number and Numeration Goal 5]	14. Describe relationships among units of time. [Measurement and Reference Frames Goal 3]	15. Solve a problem involving fractional parts of collections. [Number and Numeration Goal 2]	16. Predict outcomes of an experiment. [Data and Chance Goal 4]
1.																		
2.																		
3.																		
4.																		
5.																		
6.																		
7.																		
8.																		
9.																		
10.																		
11.																		
12.																		
13.																		
14.																		
15.																		
16.																		
17.																		
18.																		
19.																		
20.																		
21.																		
22.																		
23.																		
24.																		
25.																		

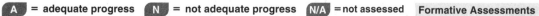

Assess Progress: **A** = adequate progress **N** = not adequate progress **N/A** = not assessed **Formative Assessments**

Individual Profile of Progress

Name _____   Date _____

Lesson	Recognizing Student Achievement	A.P.*	Comments
9◆1	**Solve problems involving multiples of 10, 100, and 1,000.** [Number and Numeration Goal 3]		
9◆2	**Use strategies to solve 1-digit by 2-digit multiplication problems.** [Operations and Computation Goal 4]		
9◆3	**Predict the outcome of an experiment.** [Data and Chance Goal 4]		
9◆4	**Solve multiplication problems.** [Operations and Computation Goal 4]		
9◆5	**Compare fractions.** [Number and Numeration Goal 6]		
9◆6	**Use concrete materials to model common fractions.** [Number and Numeration Goal 2]		
9◆7	**Solve problems involving fractional parts of a region.** [Number and Numeration Goal 2]		
9◆8	**Demonstrate that parentheses affect the order of operations.** [Patterns, Functions, and Algebra Goal 3]		
9◆9	**Identify and describe polygons.** [Geometry Goal 2]		
9◆10	**Describe angle rotations.** [Measurement and Reference Frames Goal 1]		
9◆11	**Describe angle rotations.** [Measurement and Reference Frames Goal 1]		
9◆12	**Demonstrate automaticity with multiplication facts.** [Operations and Computation Goal 3]		
9◆13	**Find the areas of rectangular shapes.** [Measurement and Reference Frames Goal 2]		

*Assess Progress: **A** = adequate progress   **N** = not adequate progress   **N/A** = not assessed

Individual Profile of Progress

Name   Date

Problem(s)	Progress Check 9	A.P.*	Comments
Oral/Slate Assessment			
1	**Estimate the sums and differences of multidigit addition and subtraction problems.** [Operations and Computation Goal 5]		
2	**Compare fractions.** [Number and Numeration Goal 6]		
3	**Solve multiplication number stories using counters, arrays, or pictures.** [Operations and Computation Goals 3 and 6]		
4	**Solve division number stories using counters, arrays, or pictures.** [Operations and Computation Goals 3 and 6]		
Written Assessment Part A			
1	**Solve a multidigit multiplication number story.** [Operations and Computation Goal 4]		
2, 3	**Use the lattice or partial-products method to solve multidigit multiplication problems.** [Operations and Computation Goals 3 and 4]		
4	**Use area models to order fractions.** [Number and Numeration Goal 6]		
5–8	**Solve problems involving parentheses.** [Patterns, Functions, and Algebra Goal 3]		
9–12	**Describe and use strategies for calculating the perimeter and the area of a shape.** [Measurement and Reference Frames Goal 2]		
13–15	**Make reasonable estimates.** [Operations and Computation Goal 5]		
Written Assessment Part B			
16	**Describe the strategy used to solve a multidigit multiplication problem.** [Operations and Computation Goals 3 and 4]		
17	**Solve a multidigit multiplication problem.** [Operations and Computation Goal 4]		
18	**Use equal grouping to model division.** [Operations and Computation Goal 6]		

*Assess Progress: **A** = adequate progress   **N** = not adequate progress   **N/A** = not assessed   **Formative Assessments**

Class Checklist:
Recognizing Student Achievement

Class _____

Date _____

Names	9·1 Solve problems involving multiples of 10, 100, and 1,000. [Number and Numeration Goal 3]	9·2 Use strategies to solve 1-digit by 2-digit multiplication problems. [Operations and Computation Goal 4]	9·3 Predict the outcome of an experiment. [Data and Chance Goal 4]	9·4 Solve multiplication problems. [Operations and Computation Goal 4]	9·5 Compare fractions. [Number and Numeration Goal 6]	9·6 Use concrete materials to model common fractions. [Number and Numeration Goal 2]	9·7 Solve problems involving fractional parts of a region. [Number and Numeration Goal 2]	9·8 Demonstrate that parentheses affect the order of operations. [Patterns, Functions, and Algebra Goal 3]	9·9 Identify and describe polygons. [Geometry Goal 2]	9·10 Describe angle rotations. [Measurement and Reference Frames Goal 1]	9·11 Describe angle rotations. [Measurement and Reference Frames Goal 1]	9·12 Demonstrate automaticity with multiplication facts. [Operations and Computation Goal 3]	9·13 Find the areas of rectangular shapes. [Measurement and Reference Frames Goal 2]
1.													
2.													
3.													
4.													
5.													
6.													
7.													
8.													
9.													
10.													
11.													
12.													
13.													
14.													
15.													
16.													
17.													
18.													
19.													
20.													
21.													
22.													
23.													
24.													
25.													

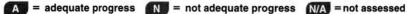

Assess Progress: **A** = adequate progress **N** = not adequate progress **N/A** = not assessed

Class Checklist:
Progress Check 9

Class _____

Date _____

| | Oral/Slate | | | | Written | | | | | | | | | |
| | | | | | Part A | | | | | | | Part B | | |
Names	1. Estimate the sums and differences of multidigit addition and subtraction problems. [Operations and Computation Goal 5]	2. Compare fractions. [Number and Numeration Goal 6]	3. Solve multiplication number stories using counters, arrays, or pictures. [Operations and Computation Goals 3 and 6]	4. Solve division number stories using counters, arrays, or pictures. [Operations and Computation Goals 3 and 6]	1. Solve multidigit multiplication number story. [Operations and Computation Goal 4]	2, 3. Use the lattice or partial-products method to solve multidigit multiplication problems. [Operations and Computation Goals 3 and 4]	4. Use area models to order fractions. [Number and Numeration Goal 6]	5–8. Solve problems involving parentheses. [Patterns, Functions, and Algebra Goal 3]	9–12. Describe and use strategies for calculating the perimeter and the area of a shape. [Measurement and Reference Frames Goal 2]	13–15. Make reasonable estimates. [Operations and Computation Goal 5]	16. Describe the strategy used to solve a multidigit multiplication problem. [Operations and Computation Goals 3 and 4]	17. Solve a multidigit multiplication problem. [Operations and Computation Goal 4]	18. Use equal grouping to model division. [Operations and Computation Goal 6]
1.													
2.													
3.													
4.													
5.													
6.													
7.													
8.													
9.													
10.													
11.													
12.													
13.													
14.													
15.													
16.													
17.													
18.													
19.													
20.													
21.													
22.													
23.													
24.													
25.													

Assess Progress: **A** = adequate progress **N** = not adequate progress **N/A** = not assessed **Formative Assessments**

Go to *www.everydaymathonline.com* for digital checklists.

Individual Profile of Progress

Name _____   Date _____

Lesson	Recognizing Student Achievement	A.P.*	Comments
10◆1	**Measure to the nearest $\frac{1}{2}$ inch and $\frac{1}{2}$ cm.** [Measurement and Reference Frames Goal 1]		
10◆2	**Write decimal numbers and identify the value of the digits.** [Number and Numeration Goal 1]		
10◆3	**Demonstrate automaticity with multiplication facts through 10 × 10.** [Operations and Computation Goal 3]		
10◆4	**Demonstrate automaticity with multiplication facts through 10 × 10.** [Operations and Computation Goal 3]		
10◆5	**Draw conclusions about data representations.** [Data and Chance Goal 2]		
10◆6	**Complete a bar graph.** [Data and Chance Goal 1]		
10◆7	**Explain what *median* means.** [Data and Chance Goal 2]		
10◆8	**Predict the outcome of an experiment.** [Data and Chance Goal 4]		
10◆9	**Solve problems involving fractional parts of sets.** [Number and Numeration Goal 2]		
10◆10	**Find the median of a data set.** [Data and Chance Goal 2]		

*Assess Progress: **A** = adequate progress   **N** = not adequate progress   **N/A** = not assessed

Individual Profile of Progress

Name _____   Date _____

Problem(s)	Progress Check 10	A.P.*	Comments
Oral/Slate Assessment			
1	**Solve multiplication facts with factors of 0, 1, 2, 5, and 10.** [Operations and Computation Goal 3]		
2	**Solve multiplication facts with extensions.** [Operations and Computation Goal 3]		
3	**Solve problems involving fractional parts of a collection.** [Number and Numeration Goal 2]		
4	**Solve fraction stories.** [Number and Numeration Goal 2]		
Written Assessment Part A			
1	**Measure the sides of a rectangle in centimeters.** [Measurement and Reference Frames Goal 1]		
2	**Calculate the perimeter of a shape.** [Measurement and Reference Frames Goal 2]		
3–5	**Label points on a ruler.** [Measurement and Reference Frames Goal 1]		
6, 7	**Use strategies to solve problems involving the multiplication of 3-digit numbers by 1-digit numbers.** [Operations and Computation Goal 4]		
8	**Measure a line segment to the nearest $\frac{1}{2}$ inch.** [Measurement and Reference Frames Goal 1]		
9, 10	**Use data to complete a frequency table and create a line plot.** [Data and Chance Goal 1]		
11, 12	**Find the median and mode of a data set.** [Data and Chance Goal 2]		
13	**Describe the relationships among units of length.** [Measurement and Reference Frames Goal 3]		
14	**Solve problems involving fractional parts of a collection.** [Number and Numeration Goal 2]		
Written Assessment Part B			
15	**Find the mean of a data set.** [Data and Chance Goal 2]		
16, 17	**Use strategies to solve problems involving the multiplication of 2-digit numbers by 2-digit numbers.** [Operations and Computation Goal 4]		

*Assess Progress: **A** = adequate progress   **N** = not adequate progress   **N/A** = not assessed   **Formative Assessments**

Class Checklist:
Recognizing Student Achievement

Class _____

Date _____

Names	Measure to the nearest ½ inch and ½ cm. [Measurement and Reference Frames Goal 1] 10·1	Write decimal numbers and identify the value of the digits. [Number and Numeration Goal 1] 10·2	Demonstrate automaticity with multiplication facts through 10 × 10. [Operations and Computation Goal 3] 10·3	Demonstrate automaticity with multiplication facts through 10 × 10. [Operations and Computation Goal 3] 10·4	Draw conclusions about data representations. [Data and Chance Goal 2] 10·5	Complete a bar graph. [Data and Chance Goal 1] 10·6	Explain what median means. [Data and Chance Goal 2] 10·7	Predict the outcome of an experiment. [Data and Chance Goal 4] 10·8	Solve problems involving fractional parts of sets. [Number and Numeration Goal 2] 10·9	Find the median of a data set. [Data and Chance Goal 2] 10·10
1.										
2.										
3.										
4.										
5.										
6.										
7.										
8.										
9.										
10.										
11.										
12.										
13.										
14.										
15.										
16.										
17.										
18.										
19.										
20.										
21.										
22.										
23.										
24.										
25.										

Assess Progress:  = adequate progress 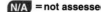 = not adequate progress  = not assessed

Class _____

Date _____

Names	Oral/Slate				Written Part A										Part B	
	1. Solve multiplication facts with factors of 0, 1, 2, 5, and 10. [Operations and Computation Goal 3]	2. Solve multiplication facts with extensions. [Operations and Computation Goal 3]	3. Solve problems involving fractional parts of a collection. [Number and Numeration Goal 2]	4. Solve fraction stories. [Number and Numeration Goal 2]	1. Measure the sides of a rectangle in centimeters. [Measurement and Reference Frames Goal 1]	2. Calculate the perimeter of a shape. [Measurement and Reference Frames Goal 2]	3–5. Label points on a ruler. [Measurement and Reference Frames Goal 1]	6, 7. Use strategies to solve problems involving the multiplication of 3-digit numbers by 1-digit numbers. [Operations and Computation Goal 4]	8. Measure a line segment to the nearest $\frac{1}{2}$ inch. [Measurement and Reference Frames Goal 1]	9, 10. Use data to complete a frequency table and create a line plot. [Data and Chance Goal 1]	11, 12. Find the median and mode of a data set. [Data and Chance Goal 2]	13. Describe the relationships among units of length. [Measurement and Reference Frames Goal 3]	14. Solve problems involving fractional parts of a collection. [Number and Numeration Goal 2]	15. Find the mean of a data set. [Data and Chance Goal 2]	16, 17. Use strategies to solve problems involving the multiplication of 2-digit numbers by 2-digit numbers. [Operations and Computation Goal 4]
1.															
2.															
3.															
4.															
5.															
6.															
7.															
8.															
9.															
10.															
11.															
12.															
13.															
14.															
15.															
16.															
17.															
18.															
19.															
20.															
21.															
22.															
23.															
24.															
25.															

Assess Progress: 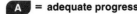 **A** = adequate progress **N** = not adequate progress **N/A** = not assessed **Formative Assessments**

Individual Profile of Progress

Name _____ Date _____

Lesson	Recognizing Student Achievement	A.P.*	Comments
11◆1	**Demonstrate automaticity with multiplication facts through 10 × 10.** [Operations and Computation Goal 3]		
11◆2	**Tell and write time to the nearest minute on an analog clock.** [Measurement and Reference Frames Goal 4]		
11◆3	**Collect and organize data.** [Data and Chance Goal 1]		
11◆4	**Interpret the language of probability to make a spinner.** [Data and Chance Goal 3]		
11◆5	**Draw conclusions based on data representations.** [Data and Chance Goal 2]		

*Assess Progress: **A** = adequate progress **N** = not adequate progress **N/A** = not assessed

Go to *www.everydaymathonline.com* for digital checklists.

Individual Profile of Progress

Name _____   Date _____

Problem(s)	Progress Check 11	A.P.*	Comments
Oral/Slate Assessment			
1	**Estimate total costs.** [Operations and Computation Goal 5]		
2	**Read 6-digit numbers aloud.** [Number and Numeration Goal 1]		
3	**Write a dictated number and identify digits in specified places.** [Number and Numeration Goal 1]		
4	**Solve fraction-of problems.** [Number and Numeration Goal 2]		
Written Assessment Part A			
1–3	**Write whole numbers. Identify the value of digits in whole numbers.** [Number and Numeration Goal 1]		
4a	**Show and tell time on an analog clock.** [Measurement and Reference Frames Goal 4]		
4b	**Describe relationships between units of time.** [Measurement and Reference Frames Goals 3 and 4]		
5	**Describe spinner outcomes using basic probability terms.** [Data and Chance Goal 3]		
6, 7	**Use fractions to describe parts of a spinner.** [Number and Numeration Goal 2]		
8	**Predict and test the outcome of a spinner experiment.** [Data and Chance Goal 4]		
Written Assessment Part B			
9	**Explain a prediction for the outcome of an experiment.** [Data and Chance Goal 4]		
10, 11	**Predict the outcomes of random-draw experiments.** [Data and Chance Goal 4]		

Assess Progress: **A** = adequate progress   **N** = not adequate progress   **N/A** = not assessed   **Formative Assessments**

Class Checklist:
Recognizing Student Achievement

Class _____

Date _____

Names	Demonstrate automaticity with multiplication facts through 10×10. [Operations and Computation Goal 3] 11·1	Tell and write time to the nearest minute on an analog clock. [Measurement and Reference Frames Goal 4] 11·2	Collect and organize data. [Data and Chance Goal 1] 11·3	Interpret the language of probability to make a spinner. [Data and Chance Goal 3] 11·4	Draw conclusions based on data representations. [Data and Chance Goal 2] 11·5
1.					
2.					
3.					
4.					
5.					
6.					
7.					
8.					
9.					
10.					
11.					
12.					
13.					
14.					
15.					
16.					
17.					
18.					
19.					
20.					
21.					
22.					
23.					
24.					
25.					

Assess Progress: 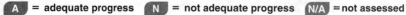 **A** = adequate progress **N** = not adequate progress **N/A** = not assessed

Go to *www.everydaymathonline.com* for digital checklists.

Names	Oral/Slate				Written Part A							Part B	
	1. Estimate total costs. [Operations and Computation Goal 5]	2. Read 6-digit numbers aloud. [Number and Numeration Goal 1]	3. Write a dictated number and identify digits in specified places. [Number and Numeration Goal 1]	4. Solve fraction-of problems. [Number and Numeration Goal 2]	1–3. Write whole numbers. Identify the value of digits in whole numbers. [Number and Numeration Goal 1]	4a. Show and tell time on an analog clock. [Measurement and Reference Frames Goal 4]	4b. Describe relationships between units of time. [Measurement and Reference Frames Goals 3 and 4]	5. Describe spinner outcomes using basic probability terms. [Data and Chance Goal 3]	6, 7. Use fractions to describe parts of a spinner. [Number and Numeration Goal 2]	8. Predict and test the outcome of a spinner experiment. [Data and Chance Goal 4]		9. Explain a prediction for the outcome of an experiment. [Data and Chance Goal 4]	10, 11. Predict the outcomes of random-draw experiments. [Data and Chance Goal 4]
1.													
2.													
3.													
4.													
5.													
6.													
7.													
8.													
9.													
10.													
11.													
12.													
13.													
14.													
15.													
16.													
17.													
18.													
19.													
20.													
21.													
22.													
23.													
24.													
25.													

Class _____

Date _____

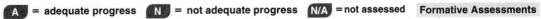

Assess Progress: **A** = adequate progress   **N** = not adequate progress   **N/A** = not assessed   **Formative Assessments**

Quarterly Checklist: Quarter 1

Names	Goal	1	1	4	6	6	1	1	4	2	2	1	1	6	2	2	5	1	3
	Number and Numeration									**Operations and Computation**									**Data and Chance**
	Lesson	1·3	1·5	1·6	1·10	1·11	2·1	2·5	2·9	1·8	1·9	1·13	2·2	2·6	2·7	2·8	3·3	3·7	1·7
	Date																		
1.																			
2.																			
3.																			
4.																			
5.																			
6.																			
7.																			
8.																			
9.																			
10.																			
11.																			
12.																			
13.																			
14.																			
15.																			
16.																			
17.																			
18.																			
19.																			
20.																			
21.																			
22.																			

Quarterly Checklist: Quarter 1

Names	Measurement and Reference Frames							Geometry			Patterns, Functions, and Algebra					
Goal	4	1	1	1	4	2	2				1	1	1	1	2	4
Lesson	1·4	3·1	3·2	3·4	3·6	3·8	3·9				1·1	1·2	1·12	2·3	2·4	3·5
Date																
1.																
2.																
3.																
4.																
5.																
6.																
7.																
8.																
9.																
10.																
11.																
12.																
13.																
14.																
15.																
16.																
17.																
18.																
19.																
20.																
21.																
22.																

Quarterly Checklist: Quarter 2

Names		Number and Numeration											Operations and Computation								
Goal		6	1	6	6	1	1	6	6	1	1	1	3	6	6	6	3	1	3	3	3
Lesson		4·9	5·1	5·3	5·4	5·6	5·7	5·9	5·10	5·11	6·3	6·10	4·1	4·2	4·4	4·7	4·8	5·5	5·12	6·7	6·12
Date																					
1.																					
2.																					
3.																					
4.																					
5.																					
6.																					
7.																					
8.																					
9.																					
10.																					
11.																					
12.																					
13.																					
14.																					
15.																					
16.																					
17.																					
18.																					
19.																					
20.																					
21.																					
22.																					

Quarterly Checklist: Quarter 2

Names	Data and Chance		Measurement and Reference Frames				Geometry							Patterns, Functions, and Algebra
Goal	1	2	4	2	3	1	1	1	1	1	3	2	2
Lesson	4•10	5•2	4•3	4•5	5•8	6•6	6•1	6•2	6•4	6•5	6•8	6•9	6•11	4•6
Date														
1.														
2.														
3.														
4.														
5.														
6.														
7.														
8.														
9.														
10.														
11.														
12.														
13.														
14.														
15.														
16.														
17.														
18.														
19.														
20.														
21.														
22.														

Quarterly Checklist: Quarter 3

Names	Number and Numeration							Operations and Computation							
Goal	2	1	5	2	3	6	2	2	3	6	5	4	4	4	3
Lesson	8•1	8•4	8•7	8•8	9•1	9•5	9•6	9•7	7•1	7•2	7•7	7•8	9•2	9•4	9•12
Date															
1.															
2.															
3.															
4.															
5.															
6.															
7.															
8.															
9.															
10.															
11.															
12.															
13.															
14.															
15.															
16.															
17.															
18.															
19.															
20.															
21.															
22.															

Quarterly Checklist: Quarter 3

Names	Data and Chance			Measurement and Reference Frames					Geometry		Patterns, Functions, and Algebra				
Goal	3	4	4	3	3	1	1	2	2	2	1	3	3	3	3
Lesson	8·2	8·5	9·3	7·6	8·6	9·10	9·11	9·13	7·9	9·9	7·3	7·4	7·5	8·3	9·8
Date															
1.															
2.															
3.															
4.															
5.															
6.															
7.															
8.															
9.															
10.															
11.															
12.															
13.															
14.															
15.															
16.															
17.															
18.															
19.															
20.															
21.															
22.															

Quarterly Checklist: Quarter 4

Names	Number and Numeration			Operations and Computation			Data and Chance							
Goal	1	2		3	3	3	2	1	2	4	2	1	3	2
Lesson	10·2	10·9		10·3	10·4	11·1	10·5	10·6	10·7	10·8	10·10	11·3	11·4	11·5
Date														
1.														
2.														
3.														
4.														
5.														
6.														
7.														
8.														
9.														
10.														
11.														
12.														
13.														
14.														
15.														
16.														
17.														
18.														
19.														
20.														
21.														
22.														

Quarterly Checklist: Quarter 4

Names	Measurement and Reference Frames			Geometry			Patterns, Functions, and Algebra		
Goal	1	4							
Lesson	10·1	11·2							
Date									
1.									
2.									
3.									
4.									
5.									
6.									
7.									
8.									
9.									
10.									
11.									
12.									
13.									
14.									
15.									
16.									
17.									
18.									
19.									
20.									
21.									
22.									

Individual Profile of Progress

Name _____ Date _____

Lesson	Recognizing Student Achievement	A.P.*	Comments

*Assess Progress:  = adequate progress 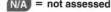 = not adequate progress  = not assessed

280   *Assessment Handbook*

Class Checklist:
Recognizing Student Achievement

Class _____

Date _____

Names							
1.							
2.							
3.							
4.							
5.							
6.							
7.							
8.							
9.							
10.							
11.							
12.							
13.							
14.							
15.							
16.							
17.							
18.							
19.							
20.							
21.							
22.							
23.							
24.							
25.							

Assess Progress: A = adequate progress N = not adequate progress N/A = not assessed

Parent Reflections

Use some of the following questions (or your own) and tell us how you see your child progressing in mathematics.

Do you see evidence of your child using mathematics at home?

What do you think are your child's strengths and challenges in mathematics?

Does your child demonstrate responsibility for completing Home Links?

What thoughts do you have about your child's progress in mathematics?

_____

_____

_____

_____

_____

_____

_____

_____

_____

_____

_____

_____

_____

_____

_____

_____

_____

_____

My Exit Slip

My Exit Slip

About My Math Class A

Draw a face or write the words that show how you feel.

Good   OK   Not so good

1. This is how I feel about math:	**2.** This is how I feel about working with a partner or in a group:	**3.** This is how I feel about working by myself:
4. This is how I feel about solving number stories:	**5.** This is how I feel about doing Home Links with my family:	**6.** This is how I feel about finding new ways to solve problems:

Circle **yes, sometimes,** or **no.**

7. I like to figure things out. I am curious.

     yes   **sometimes**   **no**

8. I keep trying even when I don't understand something right away.

     yes   **sometimes**   **no**

About My Math Class B

Circle the word that best describes how you feel.

1. I enjoy mathematics class.   **yes**   **sometimes**   **no**

2. I like to work with a partner or in a group.   **yes**   **sometimes**   **no**

3. I like to work by myself.   **yes**   **sometimes**   **no**

4. I like to solve problems in mathematics.   **yes**   **sometimes**   **no**

5. I enjoy doing Home Links with my family.   **yes**   **sometimes**   **no**

6. In mathematics, I am good at _____

_____

_____

7. One thing I like about mathematics is _____

_____

_____

8. One thing I find difficult in mathematics is _____

_____

_____

Math Log A

What did you learn in mathematics this week?

_____

- -

_____

- -

_____

- -

_____

- -

_____

- -

_____

- -

_____

- -

_____

- -

_____

Math Log B

Question:

Math Log C

Work Box	Tell how you solved this problem.
	_____
	_____
	_____
	_____
	_____

288

Math Log C

Work Box	Tell how you solved this problem.
	_____
	_____
	_____
	_____
	_____

Good Work!

🙂 I have chosen this work for my portfolio because

_____

_____

_____

_____

_____

_____

_____

_____

_____

_____

_____

_____

_____

_____

_____

_____

_____

_____

_____

_____

_____

_____

My Work

This work shows that I can _____

_____

_____

I am still learning to _____

_____

_____

_____

290

- ✄

My Work

This work shows that I can _____

_____

_____

I am still learning to _____

_____

_____

_____

Name-Collection Boxes

1.

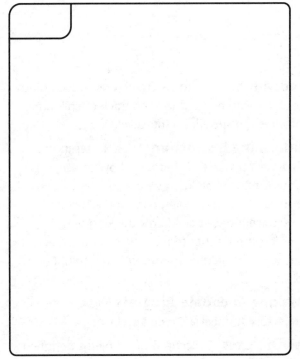

2.

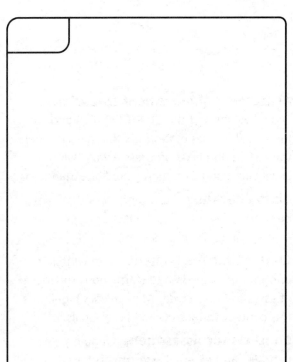

3.

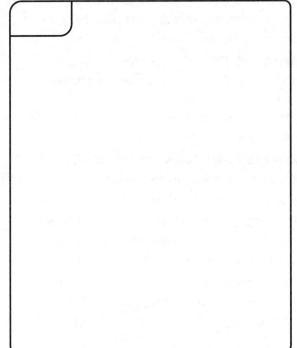

4.

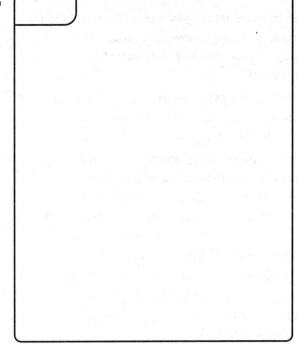

Glossary

Assessment Management Spreadsheets Digital versions of the Class Checklists and Individual Profiles of Progress that help teachers track child and class progress toward Grade-Level Goals and Common Core State Standards.

Class Checklists Recording tools that can be used to keep track of a class's progress on specific Grade-Level Goals.

Content for Assessment Material that is important for children to learn and is the focus of assessment. *Everyday Mathematics* highlights this content through Grade-Level Goals.

Contexts for Assessment Ongoing, periodic, and external assessments based on products or observations.

Enrichment Activities Optional activities that apply or deepen children's understanding.

Evidence from Assessment Information about children's knowledge, skills, and dispositions collected from observations or products.

External Assessments Assessments that are independent of the curriculum, for example, standardized tests.

Formative Assessments Assessments that provide information about children's current knowledge and abilities so that teachers can plan future instruction more effectively and so that children can identify their own areas of weakness or strength.

Grade-Level Goals Mathematical goals organized by content strand and articulated across grade levels from Pre-Kindergarten through Grade 6.

Individual Profile of Progress A recording tool that can be used to keep track of children's progress on specific Grade-Level Goals.

Informing Instruction These notes in the *Teacher's Lesson Guide* suggest how to use observations of children's work to adapt instruction by describing common errors and misconceptions in children's thinking and alerting the teacher to multiple solution strategies or unique insights children might offer.

Making Adequate Progress On a trajectory to meet a Grade-Level Goal.

Math Boxes Collections of problems designed to provide distributed practice. Math Boxes revisit content from prior units to build and maintain important concepts and skills. One or two problems on each page preview content from the next unit.

Mental Math and Reflexes Exercises at three levels of difficulty that prepare children for the lesson, build mental-arithmetic skills, and help teachers quickly assess individual strengths and weaknesses.

Observational Assessments Assessments based on observing children during daily activities or periodic assessments.

Ongoing Assessments Assessments based on children's everyday work during regular classroom instruction.

Open Response An extended response assessment included in the Progress Check lesson of each unit.

Periodic Assessments Formal assessments that are built into a curriculum such as the end-of-unit Progress Checks.

Portfolios Collections of student products and observations that provide opportunities for children to reflect on their mathematical growth and for teachers to understand and document that growth.

Product Assessments Assessments based on children's work from daily activities or from periodic assessments.

Program Evaluation Assessment intended to reveal how well a program of instruction is working. A school district, for example, might carry out program evaluation to identify schools with strong mathematics programs so that their success can be replicated.

Program Goals The fifteen cross-grade goals in *Everyday Mathematics* that weave the program together across grade levels. They form an organizing framework that supports both curriculum and assessment. Every Grade-Level Goal is linked to a Program Goal.

Progress Check The last lesson in every unit. Progress Check lessons include a student Self Assessment, an Oral and Slate Assessment, a Written Assessment, and an Open Response task.

Purposes of Assessment The reasons for assessment, which include providing information that can be used to plan future instruction, identifying what students have achieved during a period of time, and evaluating the quality of the mathematics program.

Readiness Activities Optional activities in many lessons that preview lesson content or provide alternative routes of access for learning concepts and skills.

Recognizing Student Achievement A feature in many lessons that highlights specific tasks used to monitor children's progress toward Grade-Level Goals. The notes identify the expectations for a child who is making adequate progress and point to skills or strategies that some children might be able to demonstrate.

Rubric A set of suggested guidelines for scoring assessment activities.

Student Self Assessment The individual reflection included in the Progress Check lesson of each unit.

Summative Assessments Assessments that aim to measure children's growth and achievement, for example, an assessment to determine whether children have learned certain material by the end of a fixed period of study such as a semester or a course.

Writing/Reasoning Prompt A question linked to a specific Math Boxes problem. Writing/Reasoning Prompts provide children with opportunities to respond to questions that extend and deepen their mathematical thinking.

Written Progress Check The Written Assessment included in the Progress Check lesson of each unit.

Index

Making adequate progress
    based on a rubric, 27
    definition of, 12, 27, 32–33
    in Recognizing Student Achievement notes, 10–14, 27,
        32–33
    in Written Assessments, 19
Math Boxes, 4, 8, 10, 12, 15, 24, 33
Math Logs 15, 17, 286–288
Mental Math and Reflexes, 4, 8, 10–11, 20
Mid-Year Assessment Answers, 226–227
Mid-Year Assessment Goals, 101
Mid-Year Assessment masters, 213–216
Mid-Year written assessment, 4, 18, 23, 28

Observations, 4, 8, 18, 26, 28
Ongoing Assessment, 3–4, 8–17, 25–26, 28
    by unit, Unit 1: 52, Unit 2: 60, Unit 3: 68, Unit 4: 76,
        Unit 5: 84, Unit 6: 92, Unit 7: 102, Unit 8: 110,
        Unit 9: 118, Unit 10: 126, Unit 11: 134
Open Response tasks, 4, 18, 21–22, 24, 28
    assessment masters, 151, 156, 161, 166, 171, 176,
        181, 186, 191, 196, 201
    by unit, Unit 1: 55–59, Unit 2: 63–67, Unit 3: 71–75,
        Unit 4: 79–83, Unit 5: 87–91, Unit 6: 95–99,
        Unit 7: 105–109, Unit 8: 113–117,
        Unit 9: 121–125, Unit 10: 129–133,
        Unit 11: 137–141
Oral and Slate Assessments, 20
Outside tests, 24

Parent Reflections 17, 282
Performance-based assessments, 24, 32–33
Periodic Assessment, 3–4, 8, 18–23, 25–26
    by unit: Unit 1: 54–59, Unit 2: 62–67, Unit 3: 70–75,
        Unit 4: 78–83, Unit 5: 86–91, Unit 6: 94–99,
        Unit 7: 104–109, Unit 8: 112–117,
        Unit 9: 120–125, Unit 10: 128–133,
        Unit 11: 136–141
Planning tips, 7
Portfolios, 4, 8, 15, 16–17, 26
Product Assessment, 16–17, 26
Products 4, 8, 18
Program Goals, 5–6, 28, 32, 37–50
    definition of, 5–6
    table list, 37–50
        Data and Chance, 5, 44–45
        Geometry, 5, 48
        Measurement and Reference Frames, 5, 46–47
        Number and Numeration, 5, 37–39
        Operations and Computation, 5, 40–43
        Patterns, Functions, and Algebra, 5, 49–50
    track progress toward, 32
Program Evaluation, 2
Progress Check Oral/Slate Assessments, 4, 18, 20, 28
Progress Check Written Assessments, 4, 18, 19, 20, 28,
    147–201, 202–212
Purposes of Assessment, 2

Readiness activities, 12–13, 21
Recognizing Student Achievement notes, 4, 8, 10–13, 19,
    25–28, 32–34
Record Keeping, 25–29, 34
    Assessment Management Speadsheets, 28–29
    options for recording data on checklists, 27
Rubrics, 22–23, 27, 29

Self Assessment masters, 21, 147, 152, 157, 162, 167, 172,
    177, 182, 187, 192, 197
Student Self Assessment, 4, 21
Sources of Evidence for Assessment, 4
Summative Assessment, 2, 7, 19–20

Written Assessments, 4, 18, 19–20
    masters, 148–150, 153–155, 158–160, 163–165,
        168–170, 173–175, 178–180, 183–185, 188–190,
        193–195, 198–200
Writing/Reasoning Prompts for Math Boxes, 4, 8, 15